MW00810111

HOW TO DESIGN AND BUILD
AUDIO AMPLIFIERS,
including digital circuits –2nd Edition

Other TAB books by the author

No. 680   *How To Troubleshoot and Repair Electronic Test Equipment*

HOW TO DESIGN AND BUILD

AUDIO AMPLIFIERS,
including digital circuits –2nd Edition
by MANNIE HOROWITZ

TAB BOOKS

BLUE RIDGE SUMMIT, PA. 17214

FIRST EDITION

SECOND PRINTING

DECEMBER 1980

Library of Congress Cataloging in Publication Data

Horowitz, Mannie.
    How to design and build audio amplifiers, including digital circuits.
    First ed. published in 1972 under title: How to build solid-state audio circuits.
    Includes index.
    1. Transistor audio amplifiers.   2. Electronic circuit design.   I. Title.
TK7871.58.A9H67   1980   621.3815.35   79.25411
ISBN 0-8306-9729-2
ISBN 0-8306-1206-8 pbk.

Preface

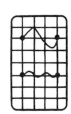

Scientists perform experiments and then generate theories in an attempt to explain their observations. Some of these theories are supported by evidence gathered over the years; others are simply disproved and discarded as so much nonsense.

This is what happened in the engineering field regarding transistors and transistor circuits. Many engineers have tried to explain the various phenomena they observed, especially in the case of audio power amplifiers. Many of these explanations held up well while others had to be disposed of as invalid. To one degree or another every engineer was guilty of this weakness. I was no exception. In this book I made every attempt to avoid theory unless it was required to do actual practical design work. It is my goal here to provide the tools necessary to design solid-state audio circuits successfully. As you proceed through the book, you will find some sections covering elementary topics. I am certain that most readers know the information covered. But the basic facts are included primarily to help anyone who is not too familiar with the topic discussed and secondarily to present a complete discussion of organized knowledge.

Circuit design is a science based primarily on fact, and to an even greater degree, on trial and error. Before reaching the trial-and-error stage, a circuit should be designed on paper. Design requires mathematics—mostly simple arithmetic. Some basic knowledge of algebra is assumed, as is the ability to convert to different units such as from amperes to milliamperes to microamperes, or from ohms to kilohms to megohms and so on. This information is readily available in various textbooks. Also assumed is a fundamental knowledge of electric circuits and a familiarity with basic hardware such as capacitors, resistors and inductors. Everyone reading this is probably as familiar with voltage, current, impedance and reactance, as he is with his postal ZIP code number; however, much of this will be reiterated throughout the book just for the sake of clarifying a more involved point.

The technical discussion must be initiated by describing two basic conventions concerned with the direction of current flow. In the heyday of vacuum tubes it was taken for granted that current flows from the negative terminal of a battery through the load and back to the positive terminal. This is the actual direction in which electrons flow. With tubes it is significant only because electrons flow from the heated cathode in the electron tube to the plate.

When talking about circuits involving semiconductors it is much easier to use conventional current flow as the standard. Here, current starts to flow from the positive terminal of the power supply, through the load, and back to the negative terminal. This direction is just the reverse of electron flow. The arrow in diode and transistor symbols indicates the direction of current—not electron flow. It is a great help when describing transistor circuits to remember that current flow is in the direction of the arrow drawn in the symbol of the particular semiconductor.

Basic circuit commonly used in hi-fi and other audio equipment are described in detail in the text. New developments using VFETs (Vertical Field-Effect Transistors) and pulse circuits in audio applications are likewise discussed. Microcircuits have also been integrated into audio equipment. Integrated circuits are introduced in Chapter 14 along with applications of these chips as well as applications using discrete components.

Digital circuits have found their way into many otherwise linear configurations. Chapter 13 is devoted to introducing the audio expert to concepts required in understanding and designing these circuits. Among the topics covered are binary numbers, logic circuits, BCD (Binary Coded Decimal) notation, registers and digital readouts. As many of these arrangements are available as integrated circuits, unnecessary theory is avoided.

I would like to thank the editor of *Radio-Electronics*, Larry Steckler, Gernsback Publications and M. Harvey Gernsback, the editor and publisher, for permission to use the material previously published in the magazine as the basis of this book.

Mannie Horowitz

Contents

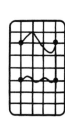

Chapter 1

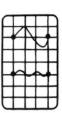

Fundamentals of Semiconductor Devices

Every experimenter is familiar with electrical conductors. Ordinary copper hookup wire used to connect two components in a piece of electronic equipment is a common example of a conductor. The chassis used to support the components of an audio amplifier is frequently used as a conductor.

Insulators are just as important in audio work as are the conductors. Air resists the flow of electricity at the most used voltage levels, and is thus an excellent insulator. Plastic, cotton, or enamel coverings over hookup wire are important insulators. These insulators are frequently rated by the amount of voltage they can safely withstand before they break down and start conducting.

Semiconductors, as the name implies, are materials that fall somewhere between conductors and insulators in their ability to conduct electricity. Although germanium and silicon are fair insulators in their pure state, the addition of impurities changes all this. Impure germanium and silicon are the basic materials of most semiconductors currently in use.

Characteristics of the semiconductor materials are determined by the impurities added. While one type of impurity will cause an excess of electrons to float around in the semiconductor material, a second type will provide a material lacking in electrons and is positive in nature. These materials are assigned names: N-type material contains an excess of electrons while P-type material is lacking in electrons.

JUNCTION DIODES

An independent piece of N-type or P-type material is of value as a component such as a thermistor, a varistor, a hall-effect generator and so on. If an N-type semiconductor is joined to a P-type semiconductor, the practical value of the resulting device is

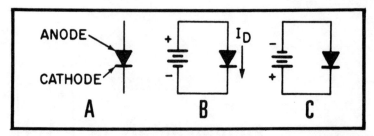

Fig. 1-1. Junction diode symbol (A). A diode can conduct when forward-biased (B) and cannot conduct when reverse-biased (C).

without bounds. This is the geometry of the PN junction diode. Depending upon the application and specific design, it may be called a silicon rectifier, a zener diode, a noise diode, a signal diode, a switching diode, as well as by many other designations.

The symbol of the junction diode is shown in Fig. 1-1A. The terminal with the arrow is made of P-type material and is referred to as the anode. The straight line is the cathode and is made of an N-type slab. Figures 1-1B and 1-1C indicate what happens if a battery is connected across the diode. Do not try this experimentally unless you include a resistor in series with the circuit to limit diode current to a safe value.

A diode will conduct (Fig. 1-1B) when the voltage supplied at the anode is positive with respect to that at the cathode. In other words the P-type material must be positive with respect to the N-type material if the diode is to conduct. This is an important fact to remember. It is also important to notice the direction in which the current will flow. It is indicated by the arrow next to and in the diode symbol. Current flows from the positive battery terminal, through the diode, to the negative terminal. In Fig. 1-1C the battery is connected in the reverse direction. Theoretically no current will flow. This last statement will be modified to some degree later.

Now let us turn our attention to the forward-biased diode. In this arrangement it conducts current. There is no intention of implying that a diode will conduct if a supply voltage is connected as shown in Fig. 1-1B; other conditions could prevent conduction. However, the voltage must be applied with the polarity shown if the diode is to conduct in the forward direction.

The amount of current a diode conducts depends on the circuit, the applied voltage and the characteristics of the particular diode. A typical forward-biased diode curve is shown in Fig. 1-2A. The solid line indicates the relationship between the current the diode passes and the voltage across the diode.

It is simple to determine from the curve just how much current will flow when a specific voltage is placed across the diode. Just draw a vertical line from the voltage axis (horizontal axis) in Fig. 1-2B, starting at a point equalling the voltage (V₁) across the diode. Extend the line until it touches the solid line diode characteristic curve. Now draw a horizontal line from the point where the diode curve and the vertical line just drawn intersect. Extend this line to the vertical current axis and read the current at the point where this line touches the vertical axis. Current I₁ flows through the diode when voltage V₁ is present across the diode.

Returning to Fig. 1-2A you will notice that at low voltages very little or no current flows. As the voltage is increased the amount of current that flows increases rapidly. This can be seen in a more instructive way in Fig. 1-3. Here the diode is in a circuit with a resistor and variable voltage power supply. Assume that voltage E is increased to very large values. Current that can flow will be

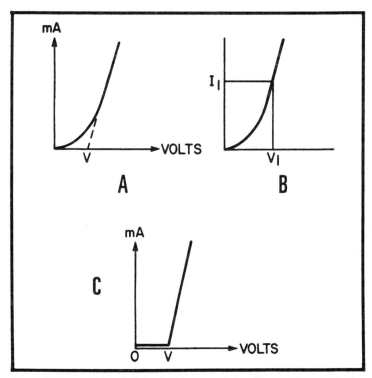

Fig. 1-2. Forward-biased diode curves. Curve A represents a forward-biased diode. Curve B shows the method of determining diode current. Curve C approximates a diode's characteristics.

11

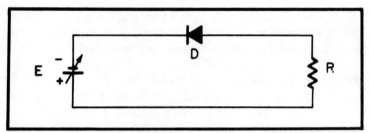

Fig. 1-3. This diode is forward-biased by a variable voltage source. Resistor R limits the diode current to a safe level.

limited by resistance R. Regardless of the current flowing the voltage across the diode will rise very slowly after voltage V has been exceeded. The bulk of voltage E will be developed across resistance R. Voltage across the diode will increase only somewhat above V in Fig. 1-2A.

It is interesting to stop here for a moment to see just what is happening. Input voltage E rises rapidly and the current flowing through the circuit increases rapidly. Yet the voltage across the diode remains at about V and rises only slightly above V. Voltage across a load in parallel with the diode will remain quite constant at V despite supply voltage variations. This is the basis of a voltage regulator.

Voltage V in Fig. 1-2A is quite important and is a basic factor in the approximate characteristic curve of the diode. Value V is determined by assuming that the straight portion of the curve is extended to the zero current axis. The total approximate curve for the forward-biased diode is shown in Fig. 1-2C. From 0 to V no current flows. Therefore, it can be assumed that no current flows when the voltage across the diode is less than V. As soon as the voltage across the diode is increased to, or is even slightly above V, current will flow; the voltage across the diode will remain at about V volts or rise slightly. The amount of current flowing through the circuit in Fig. 1-3 will be relatively independent of the diode; instead, it will depend primarily upon E and R.

Two important numbers should be remembered. For germanium diodes V ranges from 0.2 to 0.4 volt. For silicon devices it is about 0.6 or 0.7 volt. We use these approximations throughout this book. It should also be noted that these voltages are relatively accurate at room temperatures, 25° C. They decrease at about 2.5 millivolts (0.0025 volt) for each degree Celsius rise in temperature. The effect of this change in temperature moves the entire curve in Fig. 1-2A slightly to the left.

The diode is also characterized by its forward resistance. Figure 1-4 is a drawing of curves representing the forward characteristics of two different diodes. Curve A could be that of a silicon power rectifier, while curve B may have the curve of a point-contact germanium signal diode. The DC resistance of the diode is

$$r_{DC} = V/I$$

at any point on the curve. It is different at different points on each curve. As an example determine the DC resistance at 0.5 volt for both rectifiers. For power rectifier A the current flowing is 0.05 ampere and the DC resistance is

$$
\begin{aligned}
r_{DC} &= V/I \\
&= 0.5/0.05 \\
&= 10
\end{aligned}
$$

where r_{DC} is in ohms. For diode B the current flowing is 0.1 ampere and the DC resistance is

$$
\begin{aligned}
r_{DC} &= V/I \\
&= 0.5/0.1 \\
&= 5
\end{aligned}
$$

where r_{DC} is in ohms.

In this region the power rectifier has a higher DC resistance than the signal diode.

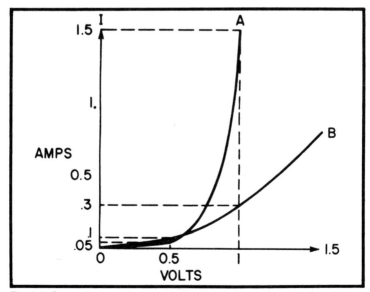

Fig. 1-4. Curves for two different types of diodes. Curve A represents a silicon power rectifier, while B may be the curve of a point- contact germanium type.

13

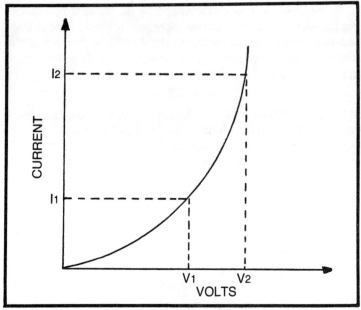

Fig. 1-5. Curves useful in calculating the AC resistance of a diode.

Now consider the DC resistance at 1 volt. Current flowing through the signal diode is 0.3 ampere and that flowing through the power rectifier is 1.5 amperes. The DC resistance of the signal diode is then

$$r_{DC} = V/I$$
$$= 1/0.3$$
$$= 3.33$$

where r_{DC} is in ohms. And the DC resistance of the power rectifier is

$$r_{DC} = V/I$$
$$= 1/1.5$$
$$= 0.67$$

where r_{DC} is in ohms.

This is the usual situation that exists under normal operating conditions. Power rectifiers have a lower resistance than point-contact germanium signal diodes. (Note that point-contact signal diodes have few, if any, audio applications; therefore, they are not discussed here. Point-contact diodes are used primarily in RF work. The structure does not consist of a junction of dissimilar semiconductors. It is introduced here only because of the distinct difference of the curve when compared with junction diode curves.) It will also

14

be found that the resistance of junction signal diodes is lower than that of point-contact devices, but is usually larger than that of power rectifiers.

A more important diode characteristic is the AC resistance. In the discussion above it was assumed that only direct current flows through the diode. In the more usual case the current is AC. The AC resistance can be readily and accurately determined from the diode curve. The procedure is described with the help of Fig. 1-5.

As you know as AC waveform is basically sinusoidal, varying over the 360° cycle. Assume an AC voltage is applied to the diode. When the AC signal is at a minimum the voltage across the diode is V_1, while at the maximum it is V_2. At these instants in the cycle the currents flowing through the diode are I_1 and I_2, respectively. The AC resistance, determined from the slope of the curve, is

$$r_{AC} = \frac{V_2 - V_1}{I_2 - I_1}$$

This is the actual resistance the sine wave sees. It will be found that the relative AC resistances of the various types of diodes are like the DC resistances in that power rectifiers exhibit the lowest resistances. Point-contact diodes have the highest resistances and silicon junction signal devices fall somewhere between the two, but close to the magnitude of the AC resistance of power rectifiers.

A convenient formula to remember for all junction diodes (not point-contact types) is

$$r_{AC} = 26/I_F \qquad\qquad (1\text{-}1)$$

where I_F is the average forward current flowing through the diode when this current is expressed in milliamperes mA (0.001 ampere). I_F is frequently midway between I_1 and I_2. At room temperature this formula will provide AC resistances close in value to those determined from the curves.

The complete equivalent circuit of a forward-biased diode can now be drawn as in Fig. 1-6. The arrow-line symbol represents the

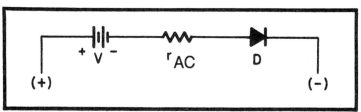

Fig. 1-6. Equivalent circuit of a forward-biased diode. The diode conducts when the applied voltage exceeds V.

15

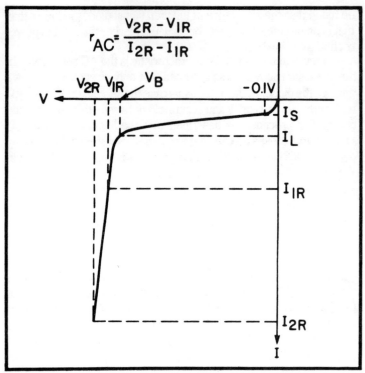

Fig. 1-7. Characteristics of reverse-biased diode.

ideal diode showing that current will flow only if the anode (arrow) is positive with respect to the cathode. For the ideal diode V in Fig. 1-2A is zero; however, V is not forgotten in the equivalent circuit. Battery V represents this cut-in voltage encountered in the description of Fig. 1-2A. It is assumed that a positive voltage greater than V must be applied at the terminal marked plus (+) in the equivalent circuit (or at the anode of a real diode) before the diode will conduct. Value r_{AC} in the equivalent circuit is the AC diode resistance discussed above and is drawn as a resistor in the equivalent circuit.

We now turn our attention to the reverse-bias characteristic. It is drawn graphically in Fig. 1-7. It was stated earlier, with reservations, that current will not flow through the diode when it is reverse biased. Actually, current will flow. When the reverse voltage is about 0.1 volt a saturation current flows. This current increases only with temperature. It doubles for every 10° C rise in temperature when the diode is made of germanium material. For silicon devices the current is assumed to double for every 6° C rise in

16

conservative designs. In actual devices this number can be anywhere between 6° C and 16° C, depending upon the diode used.

In addition to the undesirable reverse saturation current impurities associated with the diode add to the unwanted current, producing a leakage current. Size of this factor depends upon the reverse voltage.

As the reverse voltage is increased a breakdown voltage is reached, V_B, above which the current increases rapidly. Any slight increase in voltage results in a large increase in the amount of reverse current flowing through the diode. The reverse AC resistance can be determined for this or for other sections of the curve using the methods applied to Fig. 1-5. The sole difference here is that the arithmetic and construction are now accomplished in the third rather than in the first graphical quadrant. (See the mathematics and construction in Fig. 1-7). Note that Equation 1-1 does not apply to the reverse characteristic.

If you have a scope, a 12-volt RMS (about 17 volts peak) supply, a 9-volt zener diode and a 1500-ohm resistor, you can perform an interesting and instructive experiment. First it must be understood that the zener diode is merely a silicon diode with a fixed breakdown voltage, V_B. In this case it is equal to 9 volts. Forward characteristics are identical to those of any silicon device. The 1500-ohm resistor is necessary to limit diode current to safe values.

Now wire the circuit as shown in Fig. 1-8. Place your scope input leads across the 12-volt supply. If the sweep frequency and phase controls on your scope are properly adjusted you will see a sine wave as shown at the top of Fig. 1-9.

Now connect your scope across the zener diode. The trace should resemble the second curve in Fig. 1-9, approaching the shape of a square wave. Should your scope have a DC vertical amplifier you will find that the voltage increases sinusoidally above

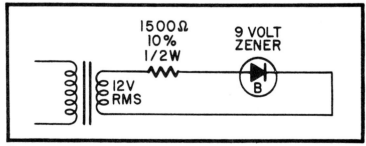

Fig. 1-8. Setup for an experiment to determine the characteristics of a zener diode.

the zero DC level (it is below the zero level if the connections to your scope are reversed) until the 9-volt reverse breakdown voltage of the diode is reached. The voltage across the diode remains flat at 9 volts despite the fact that the peak voltage applied to the circuit rises to 17 volts. Below the 9-volt breakdown, the curve is flat at 9 volts despite the curve is identical in shape to the upper sine-wave curve as applied to the circuit. This proves that the curve in Fig. 1-7 is proper because up to V_B the diode is an open circuit and the entire input voltage is across the diode. Above V_B the voltage remains relatively constant at V_B (9 volts in this case); however, the reverse diode current increases rapidly above V_B.

The second half of the middle curve (Fig. 1-9) shows the effect of the forward characteristic of Fig. 1-2. Here the voltage across the diode increases sinusoidally until V is reached. It remains at V (about 0.6 volt for silicon) until the applied sine-wave signal once again falls below V. In the forward direction this diode is an open circuit below V and is a relative short circuit when the voltage applied to the circuit is above V.

Current flowing through the diode is identical to that flowing through the 1500-ohm resistor. Since the waveforms of the voltage and current across a resistor are identical, a scope across the resistor will show a display of the voltage across the resistor and the current flowing through the resistor and the zener diode. If the scope is properly connected, you should see a curve similar to the bottom curve in Fig. 1-9. Note that in the first half of the cycle, when the diode is reverse biased, no current flows until the breakdown voltage of the diode is exceeded. Current flowing through this portion of the cycle increases with the voltage applied to the circuit due to cyclic variations. But note once again that in the middle drawing the voltage across the diode remains at 9 volts despite the increase in current during this portion of the cycle.

In the forward direction current flows practically throughout the entire cycle. (See the 180° to 360° section of the lower drawing.) This is because conduction starts at a low forward diode voltage (V). Once again, note in the middle drawing that the voltage across the diode will remain constant at V, regardless of the amount of current the diode is conducting.

BIPOLAR TRANSISTORS

If a slab of P-type semiconductor is placed in intimate contact with a piece of N-type material, the resulting device is a junction diode. Now, add a second N-type slab in close contact with the other side of the P-type material. The new configuration is an NPN bipolar

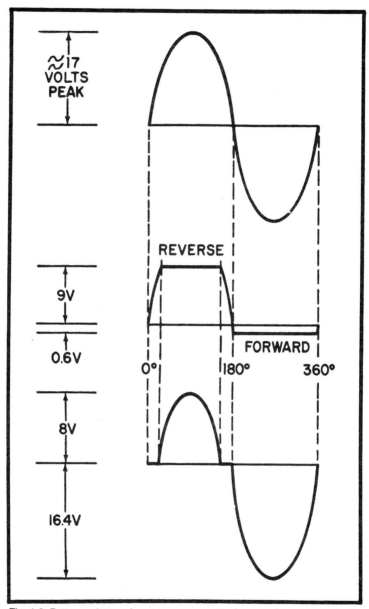

Fig. 1-9. Patterns observed on a scope connected across the components in Fig. 1-8. The top pattern is a sine wave across the secondary winding of a transformer. The middle curve shows the voltage across the zener diode. In the reverse-biased direction it is clamped to the zener breakdown voltage, while when forward-biased it is at about 0.6 volts. The bottom pattern shows the current and voltage across the resistor. The sum of the voltage across the zener and the voltage across the resistor equals the voltage at the secondary of the transformer.

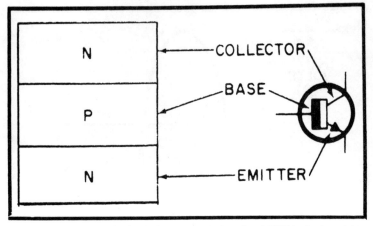

Fig. 1-10. Physical and schematic representation of an NPN bipolar transistor.

transistor. Figure 1-10 shows both a physical representation and a schematic drawing of the transistor. The three semiconductor slabs are assigned names—emitter, base and collector.

Note that the base and emitter form one diode and the base and collector a second diode. In audio applications the base-emitter junction is forward biased and the base-collector junction is reversed biased. In the case of the NPN transistor, the base is made positive with respect to the emitter and negative with respect to the collector. As is the case with the diode, electron current flows opposite to the direction of the arrow in the schematic. In the NPN transistor shown, it flows from the emitter to the base and collector.

Emitter current I_E consists of the sum of two currents—collector current I_C and base current I_B. Stated mathematically,

$$I_E = I_C + I_B$$

One important relationship between the currents is the ratio of collector direct current to emitter direct current. This ratio is assigned the Greek letter alpha (α). The direct current gain of the transistor, α_{DC}.

$$\alpha_{DC} = I_C/I_E. \qquad (1\text{-}2)$$

As I_C is less than I_E, α_{DC} is always less than one. In most transistors it is so close to this limiting value that it is indistinguishable from unity.

To establish a second relationship between α_{DC} and the various currents assume for the moment that the emitter current is equal to 1 ampere. The collector current is α_{DC} while the current flowing through the base is

$$I_B = 1 - \alpha_{DC}$$

where I_B is in amperes.

Another important ratio to be remembered is the collector direct current relationship to the base direct current. The Greek beta (β) is the letter representing this ratio. The direct current gain from the base to the collector is β_{DC}.

$$\beta_{DC} = I_C/I_B \tag{1-3}$$

I_C is usually much greater than I_B. β_{DC} normally ranges from 2 to 1000.

A bit of arithmetic manipulation can be used to establish the relationship between α and β.

$$\alpha = \beta/(\beta + 1) \tag{1-4}$$

$$\beta = \alpha/(1 - \alpha) \tag{1-5}$$

A Bipolar Circuit

Terms α_{DC} and β_{DC} are actually the current gains of a transistor. If current I_B is fed into the base the collector current should be, from Equation 1-3, about

$$I_C \approx \beta_{DC} \times I_B$$

about in this statement stems from leakage factors to be discussed below.

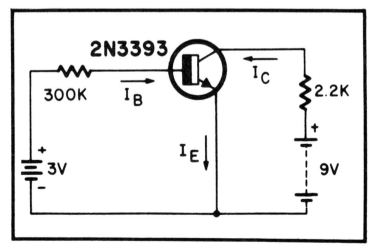

Fig. 1-11. Transistor in an experimental circuit.

Put a transistor into the circuit shown in Fig. 1-11. The transistor used is the 2N3393, specified as having a beta somewhere between 100 and 300. We will assume a nominal beta of 200. We will also assume zero DC base-emitter junction resistance and zero volts across the base-emitter diode. Set up the circuit and see if the results you find through measurements are as predicted in the calculation below. Base current is

$$I_B = E_B/R_B$$
$$= 3/300 \times 10^3$$
$$= 1 \times 10^{-5}$$

where I_B is in amperes. The collector current should be about

$$I_C \approx \beta \times (1 \times 10^{-5})$$
$$\approx 200 \times 10^{-5}$$
$$\approx 2 \times 10^{-3}$$

where I_C is in amperes. If this is true the voltage across the 2200-ohm resistor is

$$E_R = I_C \times R_R$$
$$= (2 \times 10^{-3})(2200)$$
$$= 4.4$$

where E_R is the voltage in volts.

This voltage can be checked accurately with an ordinary VOM if the resistance of the meter range used is much higher than 2200 ohms. Otherwise, use a TVOM or VTVM.

Variations will occur. The beta of the 2N3393 can be anywhere between 100 and 300. Assume that the beta is at one extreme—100. Then

$$I_C = \beta \times I_B$$
$$= 100 \times (1 \times 10^{-5})$$
$$= 1 \times 10^{-3}$$

where I_C is in amperes. Voltage across the 2200-ohm resistor is then 2.2 volts. Should beta be at the upper extreme of the range at 300, the collector current is

$$I_C = \beta \times I_B$$
$$= 300 \times (1 \times 10^{-5})$$
$$= 3 \times 10^{-3}.$$

where I_c is in amperes. Voltage across the 2200-ohm resistor is 6.6 volts.

The voltage across the resistor can vary at least from 2.2 volts to 6.6 volts, depending upon the particular 2N3393 transistor used in the circuit. Methods have been devised to reduce the size of this variation.

PNP Transistors

Only one form of transistor is shown in Fig. 1-10. Should N-type material be sandwiched between two slabs of P-type material as shown in Fig. 1-12, a second form of the bipolar transistor is formed. This is the PNP transistor. Everything that has been written here about the NPN device applies equally to the PNP transistor, except the polarities of the power supplies must be reversed. For the base-emitter junction to be forward biased the base must be negative with respect to the emitter. Following this logic the base must be positive with respect to the collector if there is to be no conduction through this junction.

Although PNP and NPN devices are made from either germanium or silicon semiconductor materials, silicon transistors are primarily NPN and germanium are mostly PNP. Since silicon transistors currently dominate the field, our discussion generally considers NPN devices; however, all facts are applicable to PNP transistors as well. Only the polarity of the power supplies must be reversed to accommodate these devices.

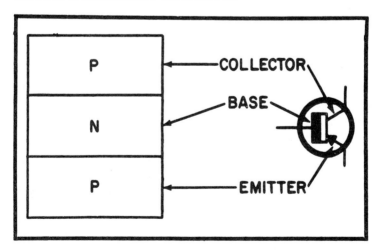

Fig. 1-12. Physical and schematic representations of a PNP bipolar transistor.

AC Alpha & Beta

Terms α_{DC} and β_{DC} define the current gain for the transistor at one point of operation. In the example when 10^{-5} amperes (10 microamperes) is fed to the base, a current of 2×10^{-3} amperes (2 milliamperes) flows through the collector circuit, assuming β_{DC} is 200.

Now feed an alternating current to the base with a peak-to-peak value of 5×10^{-6} amperes (5 microamperes). Assume this current to be riding on top of the 10^{-5} amperes of DC. The situation is shown in Fig. 1-13. Since the peak alternating current is 0.25×10^{-5} amperes, the current fed to the base at this instant is

$$I_B = (1 \times 10^{-5}) + (0.25 \times 10^{-5})$$
$$= 1.25 \times 10^{-5}.$$

where I_B is in amperes. At the crest of the signal the current fed to the base is

$$I_B = (1 \times 10^{-5}) - (0.25 \times 10^{-5})$$
$$= 0.75 \times 10^{-5}$$

where I_B is in amperes. Considering β_{DC} as 200 the collector current at the instant of peak base current is

$$I_C = 200 (1.25 \times 10^{-5})$$
$$= 2.5 \times 10^{-3}$$

where I_C is in amperes. At the moment the current fed to base is at minimum the collector current is

$$I_C = 200 (0.75 \times 10^{-5})$$
$$= 1.5 \times 10^{-3}$$

where I_C is in amperes. The peak-to-peak output current is

$$I_{P-P} = (2.5 \times 10^{-3}) - (1.5 \times 10^{-3})$$
$$= 1 \times 10^{-3}$$

where I_{P-P} is the peak-to-peak output current in amperes. Thus with an AC input to the base of 5×10^{-6} amperes the output of the collector is 1×10^{-3} ampere. The AC gain in this example is

$$(1 \times 10^{-3})/(5 \times 10^{-6}) = 200$$

In this very approximate example the AC gain is identical in value to the DC beta. AC beta, or β_{AC}, is usually very close in value to β_{DC}. β_{AC} is defined as the ratio of the difference of two DC current levels:

$$\beta_{AC} = \frac{I_{C2} - I_{C1}}{I_{B2} - I_{B1}} = \frac{\Delta I_C}{\Delta I_B} \qquad (1\text{-}6)$$

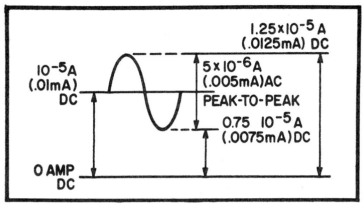

Fig. 1-13. AC input signal superimposed on the DC base bias current.

Similarly,

$$\alpha_{AC} = \frac{I_{C2} - I_{C1}}{I_{E2} - I_{E1}} = \frac{\Delta I_C}{\Delta I_E} \qquad (1-7)$$

where I_{C2} is the collector current flowing when I_{B2} or I_{E2} is fed to the base or emitter, respectively. I_{C1} is the collector current flowing when I_{B1} or I_{E1} is fed to the base or emitter, respectively. Δ is a symbol indicating a change of value, such as ΔI_C is a change of collector current, ΔI_B is a change in base current, etc.

FIELD-EFFECT TRANSISTORS

The input impedance of a bipolar transistor is relatively low due to the forward bias requirement of the input base-emitter diode. An important comparative characteristic of the field-effect transistor is the higher input impedance. The input circuit is reverse biased.

Field-effect transistors (FETs) can be divided into two basic groups. One type is abbreviated JFET for junction field-effect transistor and the other is known by the letters IGFET for insulated gate field-effect transistor, or MOS for metal oxide semiconductor field-effect transistor. The IGFET is identical to the MOSFET. The structure of the JFET differs from that of the IGFET. The former is currently more applicable to audio circuits due to its inherent lower noise characteristic.

JFETs

The physical representation and schematic of the N-channel JFET are shown in Fig. 1-14. An N-type semiconductor channel connects two terminals known as the drain and the source. Current

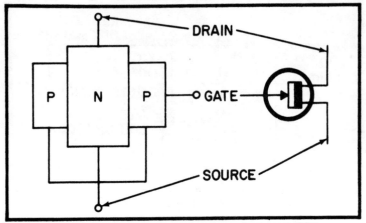

Fig. 1-14. Structural and schematic symbols for an N-channel JFET.

flows through this channel. A third terminal, the gate, is connected to P-type slabs. These P-type slabs form a junction with the channel. The relative voltage on the gate with respect to the source determines the amount of current flowing through the channel. In the usual bias arrangement the drain is made positive with respect to the source while the gate is made negative.

Resistance from the source to the drain is merely the resistance of the N-type slab. It is usually only several hundred ohms. Electron current flows through this slab from the negative source to the relatively positive drain.

Gate and source are normally the input terminals of the JFET. Should the gate-source junction be forward biased, in which case the gate is made positive with respect to the channel (and more positive than the +0.6 volts cut-in voltage discussed with respect to forward-biased diodes) there would be conduction between the gate and the channel. Input impedance would be that of a forward-biased diode. But this junction is normally reverse biased. Negative voltage controls the quantity of current flowing from the source to the drain. An increase in negative voltage reduces the source-drain current.

Should the channel be made of a P-type semiconductor and the gate of N-type slabs, the resulting configuration is a P-channel transistor. The schematic change is but a reversal of the arrow representing the gate. The operation is exactly as described for the N-channel device; however, here the bias must be reversed to make the drain negative with respect to the source and the gate positive with respect to this latter lead.

Since the input impedance is high, the FET is a voltage-activated device. Whereas for bipolar transistors, β_{AC} is the ratio of currents equal to $\Delta I_C / \Delta I_B$, the AC gain here is the ratio of the change of drain current, ΔI_D, to the change of gate voltage, ΔV_G.

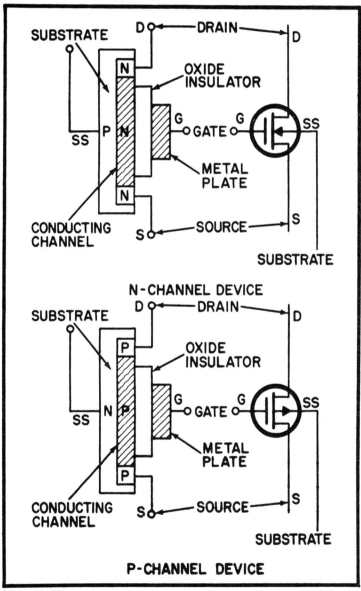

Fig. 1-15. Structural and schematic symbols for a depletion-type IGFET.

This ratio is known as transconductance. Using the symbol g_m for this factor:

$$g_m = \frac{\Delta I_D}{\Delta V_G} \qquad (1\text{-}8)$$

Assume for the moment that you have a transistor with a transconductance of 5000 micromohs (equal to 0.005 mho). Should 0.2 volt AC be applied between the gate and source, the output drain current is

$$I_D = (g_m)(V_G)$$
$$= (0.2)(0.005)$$
$$= 0.001$$

where I_D is in amperes, or 1 mA AC.

The AC voltage developed across a load resistor that may be in the drain circuit is the drain current flowing through that resistor, 1 mA, multiplied by the resistance of the components.

IGFETs

As in the case of the JFET the input impedance of the IGFET is extremely high. The magnitude of this impedance is emphasized by the fact that a static charge can be and frequently is induced at the various elements of the device. (Large amounts of static charge can be generated across extremely high impedances.) This static voltage can be so high that it requires special precautions to be taken when handling an IGFET. To avoid damage to the IGFET due to the static charge all leads must be shorted together until after the IGFET has been soldered into its circuit.

Drawings of the physical structures of the N- and P-channel depletion-type IGFETs, along with the schematic representation of each, are shown in Fig. 1-15. The following discussion centers around the N-channel device. Once again, everything refers to the P-channel transistor as well, except the types of material and the polarities of the applied voltages are reversed.

Two N-slabs of the N-channel IGFET are diffused (joined) to, or put in intimate contact with, a highly resistive P-type semiconductor foundation known as a substrate. A medium resistance N-type material connects the two N-type slabs. One of the two N-type slabs serves as the source and the other N-type slab is the drain. The gate is made out of metallic material and is insulated from the semiconductors by an oxide. Should the drain be made positive with respect to the source, current will flow between the two semiconductors. A negative voltage on the gate will affect the amount of source-to-drain current flowing. The current will be reduced as the gate is made more negative with respect to the source. This is referred to as the depletion mode of operation.

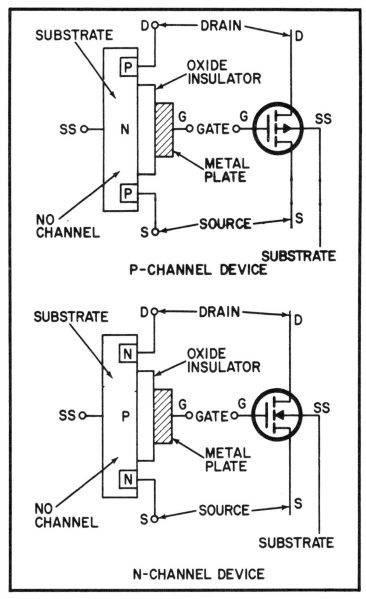

Fig. 1-16. Structural and schematic symbols for an enhancement-type IGFET.

An additional feature of the IGFET over the junction type of transistor is that more source-to-drain current will flow as the gate is made more positive. The IGFET gate can actually be made positive with respect to the source. This positive bias will not reduce the input impedance because the gate material does not form a junction with the channel, but is physically insulated from it by the oxide. When biased positively, the transistor is said to be operating in the enhancement mode.

Some IGFETs are strictly enhancement types. A drawing of this type is shown in Fig. 1-16. Considering the N-channel device, it is similar to the drawing of the types just discussed, with the exception that there is no N-type material connecting the source to the drain. Current flows between the source and drain only when the positively biased gate induces negative charges into the P-type substrate. This reduces the resistance between the two N-type slabs, allowing conduction.

As for gain, the definition of g_m discussed for the JFET applies here as well. The example discussed above does not change for this type of transistor; only the voltages involved at the gate have the additional flexibility of being either positive or negative. The substrate lead is normally tied to the source.

In all types of FETs there is also a DC transconductance characteristic, written g_{FS}. Term g_{FS} defines the ratio of drain current to the DC gate-to-source voltage.

Chapter 2
Biasing the
Bipolar Transistor

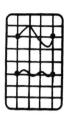

When a sine wave is fed to the input side of a transistor audio amplifier stage, the goal may be to recover this sine wave, unaltered except for amplitude, at the output of the device. In other types of amplifier stages, it may be desirable to recover half or even less than half of the sine wave at the output. A major factor in determining the type of signal that will appear at the output is the bias current, or the current flowing through the transistor when it is idling.

BIAS FOR COMMON-EMITTER CIRCUITS

A very rudimentary transistor circuit is shown in Fig. 2-1. It is referred to as the common- or grounded-emitter arrangement. In this type of circuit the output signal appears across load resistor R_C, which, as far as signal voltage is concerned, is between the collector and emitter. With this type of circuit, it is possible to get voltage, current and power gain.

Now let us start by examining the collector circuit. The maximum DC that can flow in this circuit is equal to (by Ohm's law) the supply voltage, E_{cc}, divided by all resistance in the circuit. This resistance consists primarily of R_C, the internal resistance of the battery and the collector resistance of the transistor. To facilitate matters the internal resistance of the supply is considered zero and may be entirely ignored. Since the maximum current flows when the voltage drop across the transistor is zero, the collector resistance may likewise be ignored. At times it is taken into consideration by assuming that there is 1 volt across the transistor when the maximum DC flows. This 1 volt, opposing the battery voltage, may then be subtracted from E_{cc} when making the calculations.

With little error it can then be assumed that the maximum current, I_C (max), that will flow in the collector circuit is

$$I_{C(MAX)} = E_{CC}/R_C.$$

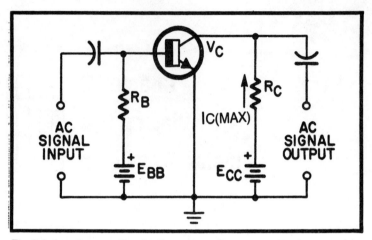

Fig. 2-1. A common-emitter circuit provides voltage, current and power gain.

Voltage V_C at the collector is then equal to the supply voltage, E_{CC}, less the voltage drop across the collector resistor. That is,

$$V_C = E_{CC} - (I_{C(MAX)})(R_C)$$

but

$$E_{CC} \approx (I_{C(MAX)})(R_C)$$

therefore

$$V_C = 0$$

The minimum collector current, I_C (min), that can flow is zero, of course. With no current flowing no voltage is developed across R_C; so the collector voltage is equal to the supply voltage less the zero volts across R_C, or simply the supply voltage. Now,

$$V_C = E_{CC}.$$

Let us now assume that a complete sine wave must be reproduced at the output. Collector current must flow at all times throughout the cycle. At the peak of the cycle, the current required to flow must never exceed E_{CC}/R_C and the required voltage at the collector must never be less than zero. A circuit which has collector current flowing through the entire cycle is defined as biased in a class A mode of operation.

The best way of establishing a class A state is to set the idling or quiescent conditions so that half the maximum collector current flows in the absence of audio signal. In this way the collector current will be capable of swinging equal amounts during both halves of the cycle—from zero to $\frac{1}{2}I_{C(MAX)}$ during one-half of the cycle and from $\frac{1}{2}I_{C(MAX)}$ to $I_{C(MAX)}$ during the second half of the cycle. The identical condition is established if the collector voltage is set at ½Ecc so that Vc can then swing from zero to ½Ecc and from ½Ecc to Ecc on alternate halves of the cycle. Ideal collector current and collector voltage conditions would then exist simultaneously.

A set of curves describing the collector characteristics of a hypothetical transistor is shown in Fig. 2-2. Each curve shows the amount of collector current that flows when a specific amount of current is flowing into the base. Note that the collector current is just about independent of the voltage, V_{CE}, present between the collector and emitter of the transistor, since the characteristic curves are almost horizontal. For the actual transistor there is a sizeable dependence since the I_B curves do vary from the horizontal and rise somewhat with increasing collector-emitter voltage.

Using the curves the amount of collector current that flows can be determined from the amount of base current flowing. Two equations must be plotted on one graph to determine the one point (or series of points) relating the output to the input. The first and extremely complex equation describes the transistor curves. No mathematical relationship need be stated, as the plot is already present in Fig. 2-2. The second equation relates components in the collector circuit of Fig. 2-1. It is:

$$E_{CC} = I_C R_C + V_{CE}.$$

(2-1)

Plot this equation on the graph, as shown in Fig. 2-3, to establish a solution to the simultaneous equations. The combination of these two equations will determine the operating points of the transistor.

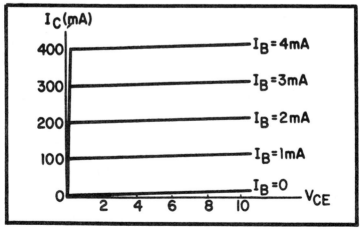

Fig. 2-2. Collector curves of a hypothetical transistor with a beta equal to 100.

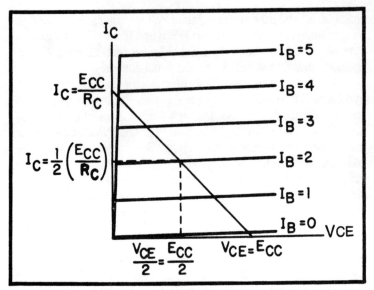

Fig. 2-3. Plot of the collector load line on transistor curves to determine the operating locus.

From the equation stated, when I_C is zero, V_{CE} is E_{CC}. Plot this one point on the graph. It is on the horizontal V_{CE} axis. A second point can be found from the equation when V_{CE} is zero. Now,

$$I_C = E_{CC}/R_C.$$

Plot this point on the vertical I_C axis. Connect these two points. This line is known as the load line for the circuit. Circuit operation is defined by the intersection of the load line and the various characteristic curves. For any value of current fed to the base there is a specific voltage and current flowing, as determined from the various points of intersection. All conditions of operation must lie along this load line.

Try a numerical example. Assume the transistor has a beta of 100. The collector supply is 12 volts and R_C, the load, is 3000 ohms. A sine wave is amplified by the transistor and a sine wave is to appear at the output. Plot the load line on the curve of the transistor in Fig. 2-4 as follows.

When no collector current flows, I_C is zero. Since there is no voltage across the 3000-ohm resistor, the voltage at the collector is equal to the supply voltage. Then I_C is zero when V_{CE} is 12 volts on the graph.

When the maximum current flows, the voltage at the collector is zero. At that instant,

$$Ic = Ecc/Rc$$
$$= 12/3000$$
$$= 4 \times 10^{-3}$$

where Ic is in amperes, Ecc is in volts and Rc is in ohms. The 3000 ohms is assumed to be the only resistance in the collector circuit. Plot this point and then connect it with a straight line to the point previously plotted. This is the load line.

Choose an idling current at a point midway on the load line. Use the point where Vce is 6 volts and Ic is 2×10^{-3} amperes. This is the quiescent collector current.

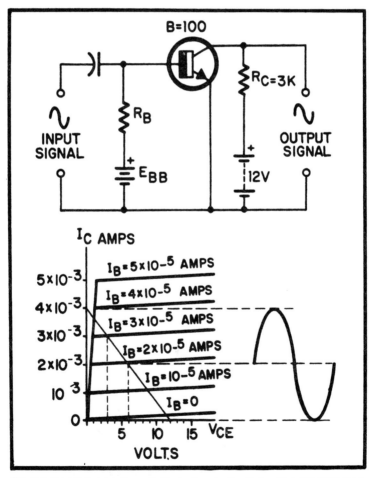

Fig. 2-4. Transistor circuit used in the text example, along with a plot of the load line.

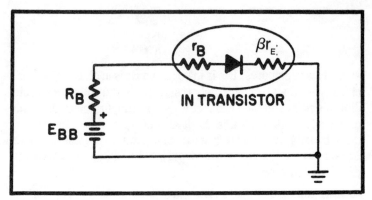

Fig. 2-5. The equivalent circuit seen from the input side of the transistor consists of a diode, a DC base resistance r_B, and a DC emitter resistance multiplied by beta, βr_E.

Let the sine wave at the input to the transistor swing the base current up to 3×10^{-5} amperes. The base current crosses the load line at a point corresponding to 3 volts and 3×10^{-3} amperes. Should the peak of the sine wave force the base current further up to 4×10^{-5} amperes the collector current would be 4×10^{-3} amperes, while the collector voltage is zero. At the crest, if the base current is forced to zero, the collector would swing to 12 volts with zero current flowing. The maximum sinusoidal output is possible only if the collector voltage is set at $\frac{1}{2}E_{CC}$ and the collector current is at one-half its maximum value.

In the above example, if the input signal drives the base so hard that it will conduct more than 4×10^{-5} amperes at the peak, the collector current would be limited to 4×10^{-3} amperes. One peak of the signal would be flattened at 4×10^{-3} amperes of collector current or at zero collector volts. Likewise, if the base current were forced below zero, a similar flattening of the other end of the curve would occur at the output.

Should the bias be set so that collector current flows for only one half of the cycle the condition is referred to as class B operation. In this case the base current is normally set at zero. Only the positive portion of the input signal would cause the transistor to conduct. It would not conduct during the negative portions of the cycle; however, now the swing of the conducting half-cycle is not limited to $\frac{1}{2}E_{CC}$ as in class A but can swing the collector the entire E_{CC}.

Normally, class AB is used in audio output stages. In this case the transistor conducts for slightly more than one-half of the cycle.

The quiescent base bias current is easily established once the requirement has been determined.

An equivalent of the forward-biased base-emitter circuit is shown in Fig. 2-5. A number of factors must be considered in this circuit. First, a voltage supply is necessary to establish the forward base current. Then there is the DC resistance in the base material, r_B and the DC resistance in the emitter material, r_E. Both of these items may be considered as negligible. The only resistance in the circuit of any significance is R_B, the external resistor used to establish the base bias current. Finally, there is the voltage drop across the base-emitter junction. As in the case with the diodes, about 0.2 volt appears across this junction if the transistor is made of germanium semiconductor material and 0.6 volt if it is a silicon device. From Ohm's law the base bias current is

$$I_B = (E_{BB} - 0.6)\,/R_B$$

for a silicon device.

The effect of r_E is negligible only because r_E is very small. If a sizable resistor, R_E, were placed in the emitter circuit, between the emitter lead and the common ground, the effect of the resistor would be far from negligible. The emitter resistor appears to the base bias circuit as if it were a resistor in series with the base but multiplied by beta. Actually it is multiplied by beta + 1, but only a small error is involved if the 1 is omitted from the multiplication operation. For example, if the resistor in the emitter lead were 270 ohms and the beta of the transistor were 100, it would appear as

$$(270)(100) = 27,000$$

ohms in series with R_B.

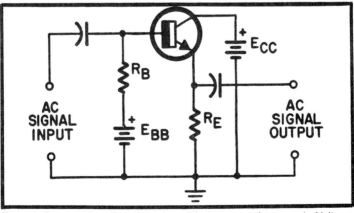

Fig. 2-6 The common collector circuit provides current and power gain. Voltage gain is almost 1 The stage has a high input and a low output impedance

37

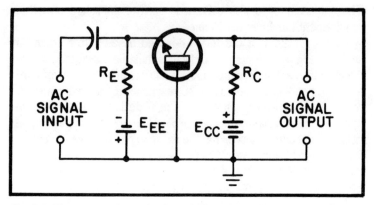

Fig. 2-7. The common-base circuit provides power and voltage gain. Current gain is almost 1.

BIAS FOR COMMON-COLLECTOR CIRCUITS

The common-collector arrangement does not require a resistor in the collector circuit, but does use a load resistor in the emitter. The basic amplifier stage is shown in Fig. 2-6. The input signal is fed between the base and collector while the output appears between the emitter and collector. This may not be obvious at first, but can be seen clearly when it is recalled that a battery or most other DC voltage supplies have zero resistance. They appear as short circuits to all AC or signal voltages.

The output load resistor is R_E. All output voltages appear across this resistor. The load line is drawn as before for the common-emitter circuit, this time using R_E as the load resistor.

In calculating the base current R_E is a very important factor here due to its size. Base bias current for the silicon transistor in Fig. 2-6 is

$$I_B = \frac{E_{BB} - 0.6}{R_B + \beta\, R_E}$$

BIAS FOR COMMON-BASE CIRCUITS

Voltage gain and power gain greater than 1, are characteristics of the common-base circuit in Fig. 2-7. The current gain is slightly less than 1. The input signal is applied between the emitter and base while the output is developed across R_C between the collector and base. (The supply is a short circuit for all signal frequencies.) A set of characteristic curves for this mode of operation is shown in Fig. 2-8. In the curves drawn collector current is plotted against the collector-to-base voltage. Each line indicates how the collector current varies with V_{CB} for various magnitudes of emitter current. The load line can be plotted as before, but this time on a different set of axes.

In establishing the bias here, the quiescent emitter current is adjusted to provide the desired quiescent collector current. The idling emitter current in the circuit in Fig. 2-7, for a silicon transistor, is

$$I_E \approx \frac{E_{EE} - 0.6}{R_E}$$

Should there be a resistor R_B in the base circuit its presence is reflected in the emitter circuit as R_B/β.

BIAS CIRCUIT CONFIGURATIONS

There are numerous bias circuits that can be applied to all the circuit arrangements. Each is detailed below. The reasons for many of these variations may not be evident now, but will become more obvious when stability is discussed. Here we will also divert from the previous notation for indicating a power supply in the schematic. Up to this point a battery with a voltage and polarity marked was our symbol for a voltage source. From here on the battery symbol will be omitted. Only a notation indicating a supply and the polarity of one end of the voltage source will be marked on the schematic. It should always be understood that the remaining end of the supply is connected to a common or ground return point.

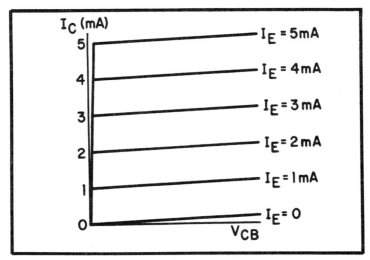

Fig. 2-8. Common-base curves show that the emitter current exceeds the collector current. I_E is slightly greater than I_C.

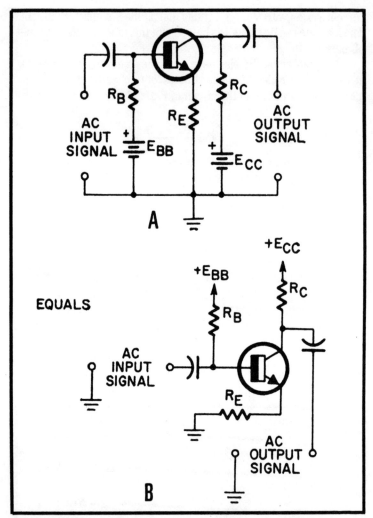

Fig. 2-9. Power supply designations in B simplify the circuit diagram.

Figure 2-9 shows the simplicity of the power supply notation we will be using compared with the one used until now. It is also a drawing of the simplest of bias methods, sometimes referred to as fixed bias. This method was discussed above when bias requirements were presented. The design procedure begins with deciding on the idling voltage needed at the collector. Next, determine the quiescent collector current from Ohm's law:

$$Ic = (Ecc - Vc)/Rc$$

where Vc is the voltage at the collector. The base current, IB, is equal to Ic/β.

Now look at the base circuit. The base supply voltage in Fig. 2-9 is EBB, although the collector supply, Ecc, frequently doubles in this function. The current flowing into the base starts at +EBB, flows through RB, the base-emitter junction, and finally through RE. Assuming a silicon transistor where the voltage drop across the base-emitter junction is about 0.6 volt, the base current is

$$I_B = \frac{E_{BB} - 0.6}{R_B + \beta R_E}$$

Note: through the remainder of the discussion of bias, the 0.6 volt base-emitter potential will be ignored. This voltage is usually negligible when compared to EBB. If you wish to include it in your calculations, you should merely subtract it from the base voltage supply considered, such as VTH below.

If we take the circuit in Fig. 2-9 and add a resistor, RX, from the base to ground, the more complex but more stable circuit of Fig. 2-10 results. For a first approximation, RX is usually specified at less than ten times the size of RE.

In order to analyze this circuit the simple but extremely useful Thevenin's theorem is most helpful. By applying this theorem any linear complex circuit consisting of a voltage source and a passive network can be reduced to an equivalent series combination of a voltage source and a series resistor. This can be accomplished in a few easy steps. For an example of the procedure the circuit in Fig. 2-10 will be "thevenized." Follow the procedure using Fig. 2-11.

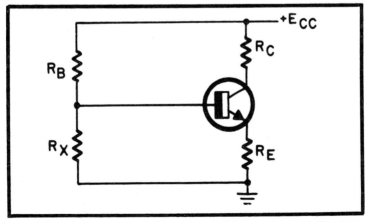

Fig 2-10 This bias arrangement improves stability over the one in Fig. 2-9

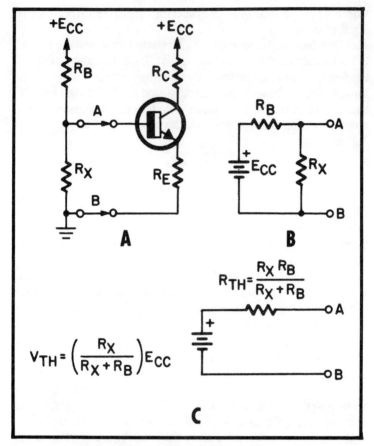

Fig. 2-11. Thevenin equivalent circuit derived for the bias arrangement in Fig. 2-10.

The simplification of the circuit begins with the splitting of the power supply for the base and collector circuits. Since both circuits are connected to one supply, E_{CC}, the splitting is done by simply indicating two identical supplies in the schematic, one for the collector circuit and the second for the base circuit. Now for the various steps to apply Thevenin's theorem.

1. Separate the supply circuit from the load circuit. In the case of Fig. 2-11A this means breaking the circuit at points A and B. Redraw the circuit to the left as shown in Fig. 2-11B.

2. Next find the voltage across the terminals where the load was formerly connected. This is the Thevenin voltage,

V_{TH}. In the example R_X and R_B form a simple voltage divider so that the voltage across points A and B is

$$V_{TH} = \frac{E_{CC} \, R_X}{R_X + R_B}$$

3. The third step is to determine the resistance looking into the open terminals. This is done by simply shorting all voltage sources in the original circuit. In the example E_{CC} is shorted so that the end of R_B, formerly connected to $+E_{CC}$, is now connected to point B. Resistor R_B is effectively in parallel with R_X. Thevenin resistance R_{TH} is this parallel resistance, that is,

$$R_{TH} = \frac{R_B R_X}{R_B + R_X.}$$

4. Draw the complete Thevenin equivalent circuit. For the bias network in Fig. 2-10, see Fig. 2-11C.

Returning to our bias circuit it can be analyzed by connecting the Thevenin equivalent network back to the base circuit, as shown in Fig. 2-12. By applying this theorem the circuit reverts to the one previously discussed for Fig. 2-9.

Here the base current is

$$I_B = \frac{V_{TH}}{R_{TH} + \beta \, R_E}$$

while the collector current is once again

$$I_C = I_B\beta.$$

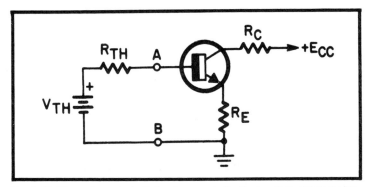

Fig. 2-12. Thevenin equivalent circuit connected to the transistor input, replacing the original circuit. The final arrangement reverts to the form of the simple circuit in Fig. 2-9.

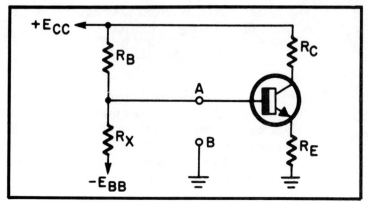

Fig. 2-13. Two voltage sources are used to bias the transistor base circuit.

A common variation of the circuit in Fig. 2-10 involves the addition of a second power supply connected to the bottom of R_X. The circuit is shown in Fig. 2-13. In this case, in addition to the Thevenin equivalent circuit, the superposition principle must be used. This method dictates that when more than one supply is used in a circuit the effect of each supply upon a circuit factor must be considered individually. Then the sum of the effects of all supplies are totaled algebraically.

Let us apply this method to the circuit in Fig. 2-13. Use the steps outlined below. Refer to Fig. 2-14 for clarification.

1. First, break the connections between the load and the supply circuit at points A and B. This is identical to the procedure used above.

2. Short the negative supply. The voltage across points A and B due to $+E_{CC}$ alone is

$$\frac{E_{CC} \, R_X}{R_B + R_X.}$$

3. Next short the $+E_{CC}$ supply. The voltage across points A and B due to $-E_{BB}$ is

$$\frac{-E_{BB} \, R_B}{R_B + R_X.}$$

If this is not too obvious, remember that when E_{CC} is shorted the top of R_B is connected to ground or point B. Resistances R_X and R_B thus form a voltage divider.

4. The total Thevenin voltage is the sum of the voltages due to these two sources. It is

$$V_{TH} = \frac{E_{CC}\,R_X}{R_B + R_X} \quad - \quad \frac{E_{BB}\,R_B}{R_B + R_X} \qquad (2\text{-}2)$$

5. Short **both** voltage sources. Looking into terminals A and B, R_B is in parallel with R_X. The Thevenin resistance is this parallel combination or:

$$R_{TH} = \frac{R_B\,R_X}{R_B + R_X} \qquad (2\text{-}3)$$

Now, draw the total Thevenized circuit in conjunction with the base circuit of the transistor. This is shown in Fig. 2-14B. Once again, the quiescent base current is:

$$I_B = \frac{V_{TH}}{R_{TH} - \beta R_E} \qquad (2\text{-}4)$$

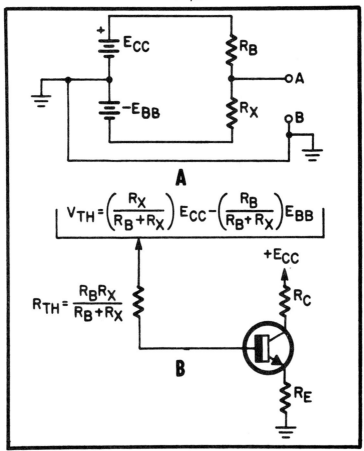

Fig 2-14 In these drawings, the superposition and Thevenin methods are applied to the circuit in Fig 2-13

45

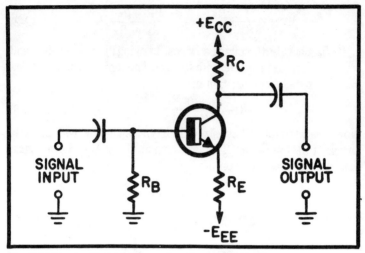

Fig. 2-15. Circuit with the bias supply voltage in the emitter

and the idling collector current is beta multiplied by I_B.

Figure 2-15 shows another method of biasing a transistor. It uses an emitter supply rather than a base voltage source. It should be recalled that a resistor in the emitter is reflected as a resistor in the base circuit, but multiplied by a factor of beta. Thus R_{E} appears as a resistor, βR_E, in series with the base lead.

In a similar manner any resistor in the base circuit is reflected into the emitter circuit as a resistor divider by beta. Resistance R_B appears as resistor R_B/β in series with R_E. The emitter (and collector) current flowing through the transistor is

$$I_E = E_{EE}/(R_E + \frac{R_B}{B})$$ (2-5)

The base current is this value divided by beta.

The final circuit to be considered, sometimes referred to as the self-bias circuit, as shown in Fig. 2-16. It should be noted that the sum of the collector current and base current flows through R_C. Current flowing through the collector resistor is

$$\frac{E_{CC} - V_C}{R_C} = I_B + I_C$$ (2-6)

while the base current is

$$I_B = \frac{V_C}{R_B + \beta R_E}$$ (2-7)

46

STABILIZING THE BIAS

There are two primary factors which lead to instability in transistor bias circuit: parameter variations with collector current and parameter variations with temperature.

Parameter Variations with Collector Current

Since the emitter and collector currents are about equal, any increase in collector current I_C is followed by a similar increase in emitter current I_E. Alpha and beta do not necessarily vary with collector current, except that they normally increase rapidly as I_C becomes very large. Consequently, the base current I_B, which is equal to the collector current divided by a relatively constant beta, will also increase at moderate values of I_C.

The AC emitter resistance r_e, since it is equal to $26/I_E$, will obviously decrease as the emitter and collector current rise.

An AC resistance, r_c, exists between the collector and base of transistors arranged in common-base circuits. Resistance r_c is large when the input impedance is low, as is the case for the common-base arrangement. It can range up to 1 megohm.

Common-emitter and common-collector circuits are characterized by high impedances in the input base circuit. The collector-to-emitter resistance is thus low compared to r_c. It is assigned the symbol r_d, which is approximately equal to r_c/B. Resistance r_c, and consequently r_d decrease with any increase in I_C.

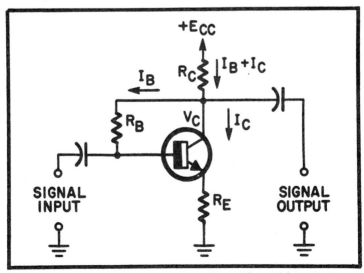

Fig. 2-16. Bias circuit using a combination of both AC and DC feedback.

Here is an important voltage to watch: V_{BE}. This is the base-to-emitter voltage of the forward-biased transistor junction. It is a primary factor in stability considerations. The base-emitter voltage has been approximated at 0.2 volt for germanium transistors and 0.6 volt for silicon devices. It was implied that these values are constants regardless of the current flowing through this junction. Well, this is almost so. Actually, the voltage does increase with base and collector current.

Parameter Variations with Temperature

Voltage V_{BE} also varies with temperature. For a good general approximation it is assumed to decrease at 2.5 millivolts (0.0025 volts) for every degree Celsius that the temperature rises. This is significant, for as V_{BE} decreases, the voltage bucking the base circuit power supply is reduced. Should the base supply voltage remain constant, the reduced base-emitter voltage will result in an increase of base current and, consequently, will produce an increase in collector current. Under most circumstances, alpha and beta will also increase with temperature.

The third important factor which increases with temperature is leakage current, I_{CBO}. This leakage current is significant when germanium transistors are involved, but it loses its primary importance with silicon devices. This leakage is discussed in the next section. At the moment it should be remembered that for germanium transistors I_{CBO} doubles for about every 10°C rise in temperature. When designing circuits around silicon transistors, it is best to assume that I_{CBO} doubles every time the temperature increases 6°C. In reality, the doubling of I_{CBO} for silicon devices can vary from 6°C to 16°C. Due to I_{CBO} the collector current will increase rapidly with any rise in temperature.

Leakage Current

The transistor has been described as consisting of two junction diodes arranged as in Fig. 2-17. In the normal mode of operation for audio amplification purposes the base-emitter junction is forward biased. For the NPN transistor the base is made positive with respect to the emitter. At the same time the base-collector diode is reverse biased and the collector is positive with respect to the base. Theoretically, or more precisely, ideally, the base-collector diode does not conduct any current.

As with all diodes a leakage current does exist in the reversed-biased base-collector junction. Current flows through the

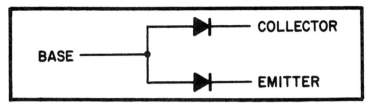

Fig. 2-17. Junction diodes form the equivalent circuit of a bipolar transistor. The NPN version is shown.

diode even though the cathode end is positve with respect to the anode. To be sure this leakage current is much smaller than any forward current that would flow had the diode been biased in the opposite direction. Leakage current is frequently of sufficient proportions to significantly affect the transistor collector idling current or bias. I_{CBO} is formally defined as the leakage or reverse current flowing through the collector-base junction while the emitter lead remains open.

Now, what would the leakage current do if the emitter lead were connected to the negative terminal of a voltage source while the base lead remained open? The base-collector diode is then reverse biased while the base-emitter diode is biased in the forward direction. Obviously, all the I_{CBO} leakage current will flow into the base and through the base-emitter diode. Since this leakage current flows into the base, the current flowing through the collector due to I_{CBO} would be this base current multiplied by the amplification factor of the transistor, or $\beta_{DC}I_{CBO}$. It is assigned the symbol I_{CEO}—the collector-emitter current that flows when the base lead is open.

In the common-emitter circuit bias equations the DC collector current has been noted roughly as $\beta_{DC}I_B$, the DC amplification factor multiplied by the base current. To determine the total collector current flowing leakage current must be added to the desirable current fed to the base so that the entire collector current is now:

$$I_C = \beta I_B + \beta I_{CBO}$$
$$= \beta(I_B + I_{CBO}) \qquad (2-8)$$

As for the common-base circuit collector current is no longer merely $\alpha_{DC}I_E$, the direct current amplification factor multiplied by the desirable current fed to the emitter, but it is:

$$I_C = \alpha I_E + I_{CBO} \qquad (2-9)$$

The emitter-follower also suffers from the effects of leakage current. The emitter current is approximately equal to the collector current modified by a small leakage factor:

$$I_E = I_C + I_{CEO} \qquad (2-10)$$

Major Stability Factors

Whatever the established bias current is, and regardless of the circuit used, it is important that that bias point be maintained. Of the various factors that can cause a transistor to drift away from the preset bias condition, the most important ones are:

Leakage Current. The leakage current is a primary factor in establishing the idling current. This current varies, as noted above, with temperature. For germanium transistors, leakage current just about doubles for every 10°C rise in temperature, while for silicon devices, conservative designs assume that it doubles for every approximate 6°C rise in temperature; however, it is usually a less significant factor where silicon transistors are used because in these devices the leakage current at 25°C is nearly non-existent.

Base Supply Voltage. Obviously, a variation in the supply voltage which establishes the quiescent base current will drastically affect the bias current. In theoretical drawings this supply voltage is drawn as a battery. But when practical circuits are used, the voltage is derived from the variable power supply generators at the electric company's plants. Furthermore, the bias supply voltage can and will vary with amplified signals, temperature, and the portion of the cycle in which the applied signal happens to exist. This supply voltage also has a significant influence on V_{BE}, the voltage across the forward-biased base-emitter junction.

Beta: This factor varies with temperature as well as with collector current. Beta is frequently at a peak at one specific value of collector current. It may also increase with temperature.

Although variations in beta due to temperature and collector current will affect the bias current, it is outshined by beta variations within device categories. Thus, for any transistor type, beta is specified as being somewhere within a range of values. Transistor circuits should be designed to accommodate devices with any of the beta values specified for a particular type of transistor.

Stability Criteria

The three primary factors determining the stability of a transistor in a particular bias circuit arrangement should be stated mathematically if the merits of the circuit are to be evaluated. In each case it is desirable to determine the change in collector current, ΔI_c, due to each of the three factors. Once the effect of each individual factor on I_c is established, the total effect can be determined by simply summing the individual ΔI_c values.

One stability factor, S, relates the change in collector current to the change in leakage current, ΔI_{CBO}. Stated mathematically, it is:

$$S = \frac{\Delta I_C}{\Delta I_{CBO}} \qquad (2\text{-}11)$$

In a similar manner stability factors can be established to determine the change of collector current due to the change in base supply voltage, ΔE_{BB}, and the change in collector current due to the change in beta, ΔB. These stability factors are assigned symbols S_E and S_B, respectively. Stated mathematically, they are:

$$S_E = \frac{\Delta I_C}{\Delta E_{BB}} \qquad (2\text{-}12)$$

$$S_\beta = \frac{\Delta I_C}{\Delta \beta} \qquad (2\text{-}13)$$

As an example in the use of the stability factors assume that for a particular bias circuit S is 5. If I_{CBO} increases from 1 milliampere at 25°C to 5 milliamperes at an elevated temperature, or if it increases a total of 4 milliamperes, the collector current will increase 20 milliamperes due to the rise in temperature. This is based on numbers being plugged into Equation 2-11, where

$$\Delta I_C = S(\Delta I_{CBO})$$
$$= 5(4 \text{ mA})$$
$$= 20 \text{ mA}.$$

Similar solutions can be derived if the stability factors S_E and S_β are known for a circuit and ΔE_{BB} and $\Delta \beta$ have been determined. In any problem or circuit it is desirable to maintain a stability factor as close to its minimum value of unity as is possible and practical.

Variation of collector current is of immense significance in the design of audio circuits. In order to explore this fact assume a common-emitter circuit with a 667-ohm load resistor in the collector. Plot the load line in Figs. 2-18A and 2-18B.

Now, suppose that at 25°C the transistor were biased at Q1 and that a fixed input signal would swing the collector current from 0.5 milliamperes to 5.5 mA. The output current swing is drawn alongside the collector current axis in Fig. 2-18A. The quiescent collector current for a perfect sine wave is midway in the swing of the output curve, at 3 mA in this example.

Next, suppose that the temperature rises and I_{CBO} increases, or some other factors cause β and E_{BB} to increase or different transistors of the same type are used where β and V_{BE} differ from the average device, or any one of a number of other factors causes

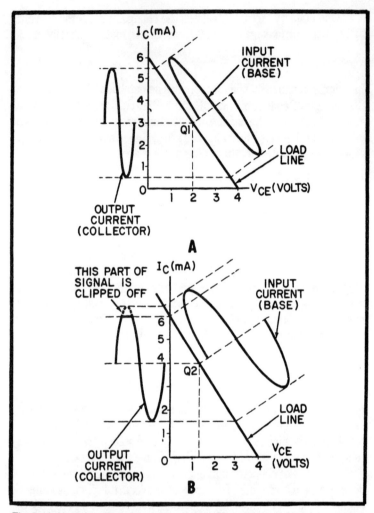

Fig. 2-18. Note the effect of the bias current shift on the output collector current and the flattened output signal. Transistor characteristic curves are omitted for clarity. All signal currents must travel along the load line. In A the bias current was set at Q1. In B the bias current shifted up to Q2.

the quiescent point to shift. All significant factors cause the quiescent collector current to increase. Assume it increases from 3 mA to 4 mA and is at quiescent point Q2. This condition is now drawn in Fig. 2-18B.

With the quiescent current at Q2 the negative portion of the input signal can still cause the negative portion of the collector current to swing the full 2½ mA to a low of 1½ mA. The positive

52

portion of the input signal can swing the collector current only to its maximum value of 6 mA. When the input signal tries to force I_C beyond the 6 mA, only 6 mA will be delivered at the collector. The output current curve will have a flat top during the period of time when the 6-milliampere collector current should be exceeded.

The designer should be capable of determining just how much leeway his or her circuit must have so that a full sine wave can be reproduced at the output at all times. It must be realized that the shift in quiescent conditions may be due to factors besides current and temperature variations in any one transistor. Different transistors of identical type vary somewhat in their characteristics. In some types beta can vary by as much as 5 to 1, although it is frequently held to a 2-to-1 ratio. V_{BE}, a significant factor in determining collector current, is usually specified with a maximum rating, while a 0.05-volt spread between different transistors of the same type is not unusual.

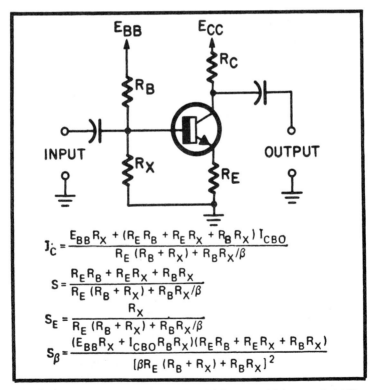

$$I_C = \frac{E_{BB}R_X + (R_E R_B + R_E R_X + R_B R_X)\, I_{CBO}}{R_E\,(R_B + R_X) + R_B R_X/\beta}$$

$$S = \frac{R_E R_B + R_E R_X + R_B R_X}{R_E\,(R_B + R_X) + R_B R_X/\beta}$$

$$S_E = \frac{R_X}{R_E\,(R_B + R_X) + R_B R_X/\beta}$$

$$S_\beta = \frac{(E_{BB}R_X + I_{CBO}R_B R_X)(R_E R_B + R_E R_X + R_B R_X)}{[\beta R_E\,(R_B + R_X) + R_B R_X]^2}$$

Fig. 2-19.Bias circuit using resistors Rx and Re to establish a good stability factor approximating unity.

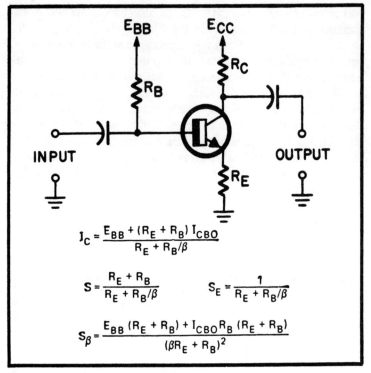

$$J_C = \frac{E_{BB} + (R_E + R_B)\, I_{CBO}}{R_E + R_B/\beta}$$

$$S = \frac{R_E + R_B}{R_E + R_B/\beta} \qquad S_E = \frac{1}{R_E + R_B/\beta}$$

$$S_\beta = \frac{E_{BB}\,(R_E + R_B) + I_{CBO}\, R_B\,(R_E + R_B)}{(\beta R_E + R_B)^2}$$

Fig. 2-20.The bias circuit in Fig. 2-19 with Rx omitted.

Stability Factors & Bias Circuits

Three stability factors, S, S_E and S_β, were just defined. Each of these stability factors can be calculated from the bias circuits and the components used in the particular circuit. Then the calculated values of S, S_E and S_β can be substituted into Equations 2-11, 2-12 and 2-13, respectively. Changes in collector current ΔI_C for each factor can be calculated by multiplying the specific stability factor by the change involved.

Once S has been determined from the equations stated in Figs. 2-19 through 2-23, it should be multiplied by the change in leakage current, ΔI_{CBO}, to determine the change in collector current due to this item. In a similar manner determine S_E from the equations and multiply it by the change in base supply voltage, ΔE_{BB}, to establish the change in collector current due to ΔE_{BB}. Likewise, the product of S_ρ (as determined from the equations in the figures) and the change of beta, Δ_β, will provide the data required to find the collector current change due to this variation.

One of the bias circuits which was discussed with respect to Fig. 2-10 is redrawn in Fig. 2-19. The collector current flowing through Rc, as well as the stability factors, can be approximated from the equations in the drawing. It should be noted here that the equations are not to be memorized but are to be used for simply determining circuit characteristics. They may appear complex, but step-by-step substitution of circuit component values will indicate just how easily they can be utilized.

As can be seen in Fig. 2-20 the equations for this circuit are simpler than those applying to the single-battery bias circuit in Fig. 2-19. This is due to the absence of Rx. The two sets of equations are identical, but in the latter figure, Rx was made infinite in value. Should the circuit be further simplified to that in Fig. 2-21 where Rᴇ is omitted, the equations in that figure are to be used. Stability here is at its worst for no external circuitry is used to minimize variations.

The bias circuit in Fig. 2-22 is similar to the one in Fig. 2-19, but with the addition of DC feedback. This arrangement provides the best stability of all when using simple resistor circuits for compensation. Once again the equations are stated in the figure. The circuit in Fig. 2-22 will still exhibit good stability characteristics if Rₓ is omitted, as in Fig. 2-23. Equations here are identical to those stated in Fig. 2-22 if Rx in that figure is considered infinite.

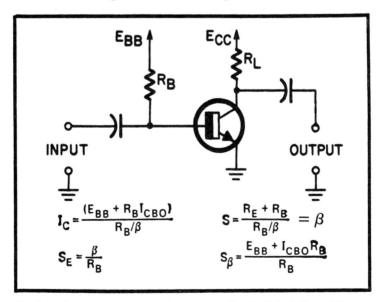

Fig. 2-21. Further simplification of the circuit in Fig. 2-19. Both Rx and Rᴇ are omitted. Stability is at its worst here.

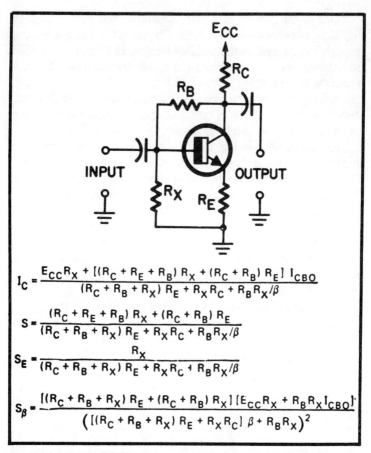

$$I_C = \frac{E_{CC}R_X + [(R_C + R_E + R_B)\,R_X + (R_C + R_B)\,R_E]\,I_{CBO}}{(R_C + R_B + R_X)\,R_E + R_X R_C + R_B R_X/\beta}$$

$$S = \frac{(R_C + R_E + R_B)\,R_X + (R_C + R_B)\,R_E}{(R_C + R_B + R_X)\,R_E + R_X R_C + R_B R_X/\beta}$$

$$S_E = \frac{R_X}{(R_C + R_B + R_X)\,R_E + R_X R_C + R_B R_X/\beta}$$

$$S_\beta = \frac{[(R_C + R_B + R_X)\,R_E + (R_C + R_B)\,R_X]\,[E_{CC}R_X + R_B R_X I_{CBO}]}{\left([(R_C + R_B + R_X)\,R_E + R_X R_C]\,\beta + R_B R_X\right)^2}$$

Fig. 2-22. Very stable bias circuit using DC feedback from the collector to the base.

Collector current and stability equations for the emitter bias circuit in Fig. 2-24 are similar to the equations for the fixed bias circuit in Fig. 2-20. Just substitute E_{EE} for E_{BB}.

One last bias circuit, discussed in the interest of stability, is shown in Fig. 2-25. This configuration looks very similar to the one drawn in Fig. 2-19, but with the addition of a forward-biased diode. Voltage across D1 is identical to that across the forward-biased diode junction composed of the transistor base and emitter, and varies with temperature in accordance with the voltage change across the base-emitter junction. Stability equations in Fig. 2-19 can be used for this circuit, but the actual stability will be much better than indicated by the calculations.

Design Procedures

Stability equations are great for checking the circuits after they have been designed. But how should one proceed to execute a good stable design? A few general rules can be deduced from the equations. In all bias circuits Rx should be made as small as practical and Re should be as large as possible.

If germanium transistors are used where Icbo is usually a very important factor affecting stability, S is reasonably small if Rc is large and Rb is minimized. Vbe and beta vary with temperature regardless of the transistor type. Furthermore, beta can have any of a large range of values within any specific transistor category. Stability factors concerning these items are best limited if Rb and Rc are larger resistors.

Using these basic rules a design example will illustrate procedures. Suppose you want to design an audio preamplifier using a 12-volt battery supply. The low-noise 2N3391A silicon transistor is to be used. The beta range is 250 to 500, with a mean average of

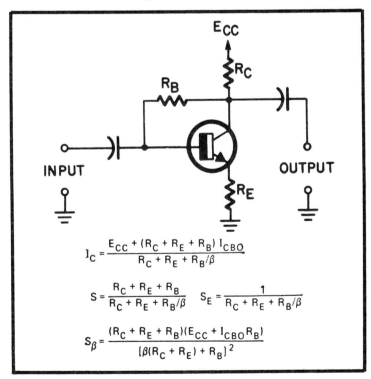

$$I_C = \frac{E_{CC} + (R_C + R_E + R_B)\, I_{CBO}}{R_C + R_E + R_B/\beta}$$

$$S = \frac{R_C + R_E + R_B}{R_C + R_E + R_B/\beta} \qquad S_E = \frac{1}{R_C + R_E + R_B/\beta}$$

$$S_\beta = \frac{(R_C + R_E + R_B)(E_{CC} + I_{CBO} R_B)}{[\beta(R_C + R_E) + R_B]^2}$$

Fig. 2-23. Circuit in Fig. 2-22 with Rx removed. Stability suffers to some degree.

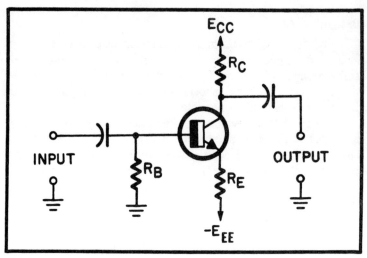

Fig. 2-24. Emitter bias circuit based on the same equations as in Fig. 2-20. Here, EEE is substituted for EBB

375, and the leakage current at 25°C is 0.1 microampere (10^{-7} ampere or 0.0000001 ampere). The transistor is to be used in an ambient temperature ranging from 25°C to 55°C. The common-emitter circuit is to have a minimum AC voltage gain of 10 and a maximum output impedance of 6000 ohms. The maximum input signal it should accommodate is 0.8 volt peak to peak and the output voltage must be capable of swinging a minimum of 8 volts (0.8 × 10).

Start with the design of the circuit by establishing the output load resistor value. The maximum output impedance is stated as 6000 ohms. To assure this put a load resistor of less than 6000 ohms in the collector circuit. Using the next lower EIA standard value, let Rc be 5600 ohms.

Minimum AC gain of the circuit has been specified at 10. AC voltage gain is approximately equal to the ratio of the resistor in the collector circuit to the resistor in the emitter circuit, or

$$A_V = R_C/R_E$$

for high beta transistors. Consequently for a minimum gain of ten, RE must be less than 560 ohms. To compensate for losses we will make RE equal to 470 ohms. Appropriate gain should then be about

$$A_V = 5600/470 = 12$$

Now plot the load line. It is to represent the sum of Rc and RE or

$$5600 + 470 = 6070$$

ohms. A plot of a 6000-ohm load line will suffice. See the plot drawn in Fig. 2-26A, based on a 12-volt supply. Actual transistor characteristic curves, unnecessary for this discussion, have been omitted from the drawing in the interest of clarity.

It has been stated that an 8-volt peak-to-peak output voltage swing is required to accommodate the 0.8-volt peak-to-peak maximum input signal. The peak-to-peak collector current swing is then

$$\frac{8 \text{ volts}}{6000 \text{ ohms}} = 1.33 \text{ mA.}$$

The bias must be arranged so that the collector current can swing 1.33 milliamperes. Should the bias be set at a minimum extreme position while accommodating the swing, the current will vary from 0 to 1.33 milliamperes. At the opposite extreme position the collector current will accommodate this swing if it will vary from $2 - 1.33$ milliamperes or 0.67 milliampere up to 2 milliamperes. These two borderline conditions are shown in Figs. 2-26B and 2-26C, respectively. Obviously the idling bias currents are at the middle of each curve, or

$$\frac{1.33 - 0}{2} = 0.67 \text{ mA}$$

in one case and

$$\frac{2 - 0.67}{2} + 0.67 = 1.34 \text{ mA}$$

for the second case.

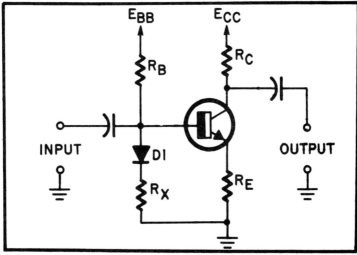

Fig. 2-25. Bias circuit in which diode D1 compensates for the forward-biased base-emitter junction voltage variation with temperature.

Plot B may be considered the condition at one extreme when the transistor is operating in a 25°C ambient temperature and beta is at the minimum end of its specification range. In this case I_{CBO} is at its minimum specified value. V_{BE}, the forward-biased base-emitter voltage, is at the maximum of about 0.2 volt for germanium devices and 0.6 volt for silicon transistors.

Plot C, the other possible extreme, assumes the transistor is operating at the maximum temperature while beta is at a maximum of its range on the 2N3391A specification sheet. It also assumes that V_{BE} has dropped at about 2.5 millivolts for each degree the transistor ambient temperature has risen above 25°C, while I_{CBO} has increased to its maximum value under the stated temperature limit.

From this analysis we are then able to determine that the idling collector current change must be limited to

$$1.34 - 0.67 = 0.67 \text{ mA}$$

(the difference of the two idling currents) as the transistor temperature rises from 25°C to 55°C.

We also determined that at 25°C the idling current must be adjusted to 0.67 mA (calculated above from Fig. 2-26B). The adjustment at 25°C assumes the minimum beta and I_{CBO} and the maximum V_{BE}.

The remainder of the design procedure begins by surveying the various bias circuits that can be used. Initially, select the simplest logical one, design it using procedures outlined in the early parts of this chapter and then substitute the component values in the appropriate stability equations. Note the effect of changes of I_C on the initially designed circuit, considering each stability factor individually. Find the total change of I_C by summing the individual effects. Then, check if the resulting idling current (the initial quiescent current plus the sum of the ΔI_C values) is compatible with the plot in Fig. 2-26C. Thus, ΔI_C from all causes should not exceed 1.34 mA − 0.67 mA if the circuit is to operate properly under all desired conditions.

Should the change in I_C exceed the required value (0.67 mA in this case) compute the components needed for the next bias circuit in the complexity sequence. Once again calculate the stability factors and determine the ultimate effect on I_C. Add circuit complexities until you find an arrangement which will provide you with the desired results.

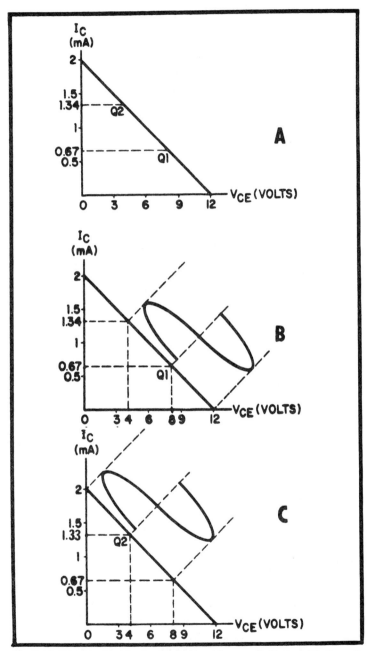

Fig. 2-26. Plot of the load line for the problem discussed in the text (A). Curve B is the quiescent point at one possible extreme position, and curve C is the second possible extreme position for quiescent point.

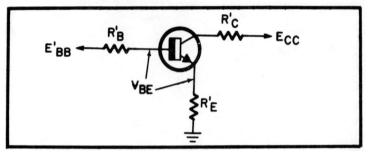

Fig. 2-27. Basic circuit used in the extreme point method of engineering stability into a design.

An alternate and somewhat more sophisticated design method uses extreme points in the engineering procedure. It starts by assuming the simple bias circuit in Fig. 2-27. Two equations are established for the base circuit. The first assumes one extreme of collector current, the minimum value, where $I_C = I_{C(min)}$ and the transistor operates under its minimum temperature condition. Here I_{CBO} is at its minimum value, $I_{CBO(min)}$, V_{BE} is at its maximum, $V_{BE(max)}$, and beta is at its minimum, $\beta_{(min)}$. Assume $I_C = I_E$. The base supply voltage is then equal to

$$E'_{BB} = I_{C(min)} \, R'_E + \frac{R'_B}{\beta_{(min)}} \quad - \quad I_{CBO(min)} \, R'_B + V_{BE(max)} \qquad (2\text{-}14)$$

A second equation assumes the maximum collector current, temperature and beta. The base-emitter voltage is at its minimum. The base supply voltage at this extreme condition becomes

$$E'_{BB} = I_{C(max)} \left(R'_E + \frac{R'_B}{\beta_{(max)}} \right) - I_{CBO(max)} \, R'_B + V_{BE(min)} \qquad (2\text{-}15)$$

One of the two equations is subtracted from the other. The various values of maximum and minimum collector current, beta, leakage current and base-emitter voltage are then substituted into the resulting formula to establish a relationship between R'_E and R'_B. All these values can be determined from the data derived above. In some instances, such as for base-emitter voltage, actual data may not be supplied by the transistor manufacturer. But actual data might not actually be required, because since Equation 2-14 was subtracted from Equation 2-15, the terms in the final equation will contain the differences of two values rather than the absolute values. The difference of the two values of V_{BE}, for example, can easily be calculated from the temperature difference involved, since $V_{BE(max)} - V_{BE(min)}$ is approximately equal to 2.5 millivolts multiplied by this temperature difference.

Chapter 3

Biasing
JFET Amplifiers

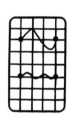

Bias circuits designed for bipolar transistors serve two primary functions. The first is to set the quiescent base current with the ultimate goal of establishing a specific collector idling current. The second and equally essential intent is to stabilize the quiescent collector current against changes due to temperature variations, supply voltage fluctuations and parameter tolerances in specific transistor categories. FET bias circuits perform similar functions.

This discussion deals primarily with biasing the JFET, although many of the characteristics and procedures can be applied to the IGFET. The obvious partiality to the JFET is due to the extreme predominance of this type of FET in small signal and power audio applications.

Only N-channel JFETs are discussed, but everything said with regard to this device can be applied to the P-channel JFET; however, the supply and element voltage polarities must be reversed. As for the bias mechanism the gate-to-source idling voltage, V_{GS}, is set to establish a desirable quiescent drain current, I_D, in the output circuit. Stability of the required drain current must be maintained against variables similar, in some respects, to those plaguing the bipolar devices.

JFET CHARACTERISTICS

Figure 3-1 shows a typical N-channel transistor schematic and a display of drain characteristic curves. Curves here resemble those of the pentode vacuum tube. The display can be conveniently and functionally divided into two basic sections—the ohmic or on region and the pinchoff or off region. In audio amplifier applications the ohmic region is just about ignored.

These curves are essentially horizontal for all gate-to-source voltages, V_{GS}, in the pinch-off region. It can be stated with reasonable accuracy that the drain current is virtually independent of the drain-to-source voltage, V_{DS}, although the current does increase slightly with the voltage. Drain current I_D flowing when V_{GS} is equal to zero is assigned the special symbol I_{DSS}—the zero gate-to-source-voltage drain current.

It is obvious from the curve that the gate of the N-channel JFET is made negative with respect to the source. The gate-source junction is reverse biased. As you may recall a reverse-biased junction of any diode conducts practically no current. From Ohm's law the impedance of any device is the voltage across the device divided by the current flowing through it. Because the current flowing through a reverse-biased junction is just about zero the impedance of the junction, by Ohm's law, approaches infinity. The impedance of the reverse-biased gate-source junction similarly approaches infinity.

Despite not being shown on the graph positive V_{GS} curves are applicable up to about +0.5 volt. Impedance remains high despite the forward-bias voltage applied to the junction. This follows from the diode characteristic where the forward-biased silicon junction does not conduct until that voltage exceeds about +0.5 volt.

As the gate-to-source voltage is made more negative the collector current becomes very small, approaching infinitesimal proportions. Gate-to-source voltage generating this condition is referred to as the pinchoff voltage, V_P, of the transistor. This is similar to the concept of cutoff voltage in relation to the vacuum tube. As an acceptable standard the gate-to-source voltage is considered at pinch-off when the drain current is one thousandth to one hundredth of I_{DSS}, or less than 50 microamperes.

A broken-line curve is superimposed on the graph in Fig. 3-1. This trace is the sum of the drain-to-source voltage, V_{DS}, and the gate-to-source voltage, V_{GS}, with the polarity of both values ignored. The sum is equal to the pinch-off voltage. The mathematical statement for this curve is

$$V_P = V_{DS} + |V_{GS}|.$$

It is obvious from the equation that when V_{GS} is equal to zero

$$V_P = V_{DS}.$$

This is a point on the $V_{GS} = 0$ curve at the start of the horizontal pinch-off region. Pinch-off voltage can then be determined from this curve, as shown in Fig. 3-1, as well as from the value of V_{GS} which causes I_D to be very small.

Earlier it was noted that the set of drain characteristics is separated into two regions. This broken-line plot of the equation is

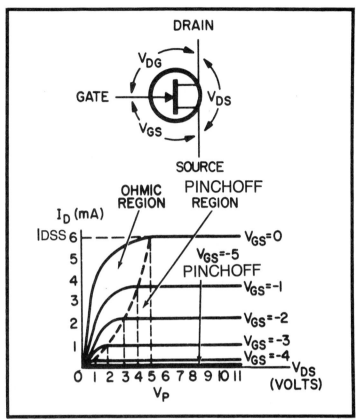

Fig. 3-1. The N-channel transistor symbol, associated voltages and a set of characteristic curves.

the dividing line. To be certain that you are designing audio amplifiers well within the linear pinch-off region of the plot, it is conventional that the minimum drain-to-source voltage be made 1½ times the specified pinch-off voltage.

The ohmic region to the left of this line is very valuable in some applications because each curve is a plot of a distinct drain resistance. The resistance is equal to the ratio of the change in drain-to-source voltage, ΔV_{DS}, to the change in drain current, ΔI_{DS}. Since this resistance is different for each V_{GS} curve, the drain resistance of the JFET will vary with the gate-to-source voltage. This characteristic is very useful should you wish to design a circuit such as a volume compressor utilizing the JFET resistance change.

Getting back to the pinch-off region it is obvious from the drawing that the quiescent drain current, I_D, is dependent upon V_{GS}.

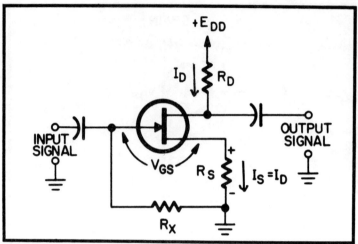
Fig. 3-2. Self-bias circuit for a JFET.

Although not equally as evident drain current is related to V_P and I_{DSS}. The important relationship is:

$$I_D = I_{DSS}\left(1 - \frac{|V_{GS}|}{|V_P|}\right)^2 \qquad (3\text{-}1)$$

where $|V_{GS}|$ is the absolute value of V_{GS} and $|V_P|$ is the absolute value of V_P. As you know the absolute value of numbers disregards the + or − signs in front of the numbers.

BIAS CIRCUITS

Quiescent drain or bias current can be calculated using Equation 3-1. Quantities I_{DSS} and V_P depend on the particular transistor used. As these factors remain relatively constant for any one transistor the drain current depends only on specific values of V_{GS}. It is then necessary to find circuits to set the required V_{GS} to establish the desired quiescent drain current. The self-bias circuit in Fig. 3-2 performs this function simply.

This circuit is similar to the one most commonly used for vacuum tube bias. Electron current starts at the negative ground side of the supply, flows through R_S, through the transistor and R_D and on to the positive terminal of the supply $+E_{DD}$. Conventional current flow is in the opposite direction, as shown in Fig. 3-2. Source and drain currents are essentially equal. A voltage with the polarity shown is developed across R_S and is equal to $I_D R_S$. No voltage appears across R_X (a statement to be modified below). The

66

only voltage between the source and gate is that across R_S. Considering this,

$$V_{GS} = I_D R_S$$

For stability and low distortion considerations it is desirable to make R_S large. A voltage supply bucking the voltage developed across R_S can be placed in series with R_X as shown in Fig. 3-3. The voltage between the gate and source is then about

$$V_{GS} = I_D R_S - E_{GG}.$$

Since the gate-to-source voltage and the drain current must be identical to that determined for the previous circuit, the only variable factor in the equation is R_S. Resistance R_S must be larger in value here than it was for the circuit in Fig. 3-2 to compensate for the effect of the additional E_{GG} supply.

This circuit is not practical because a second power supply must be used for the E_{GG} voltage. An arrangement using but one supply is shown in Fig. 3-4. Voltage is developed across R_X due to the current, I_G, generated by $+ E_{DD}$ which flows through R_G and R_X. It is of the proper polarity to buck the $I_D R_S$ voltage. The circuit is frequently designed so that I_G is equal to one-tenth of the drain current. Gate-to-source voltage then becomes

$$\begin{aligned} V_{GS} &= I_D R_S - I_G R_X \\ &= I_D R_S - 0.1 I_D R_X \\ &= I_D (R_S - 0.1 R_X). \end{aligned}$$

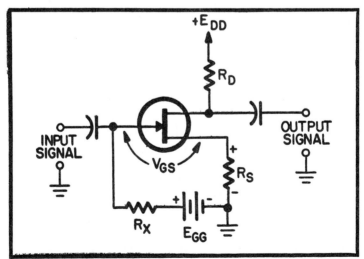

Fig. 3-3. Combined fixed-and self-bias circuit designed so that Rs can be made large.

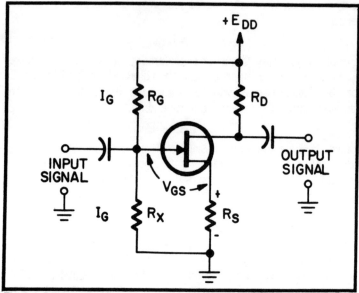

Fig. 3-4. Practical version of the circuit in Fig. 3-3 using only one power supply.

Gate current I_G may be much less than one-tenth of the drain current, but it must be at least 10 times the leakage current to be discussed below.

Resistors R_G and R_X may, at times, be too low in value to satisfy the requirements of an input signal source feeding the transistor. Input impedance is the parallel combination of R_G and R_X or $R_G R_X / (R_G + R_X)$. Should the circuit be modified to that in Fig. 3-5 the input signal will see a load equal to R_A in series with the parallel combination. As no current flows through R_A it is not a factor in determining the bias voltage.

In the interest of stability one additional change is frequently added to the circuit in Fig. 3-4. Instead of connecting R_G to the power supply it is connected to the drain as in Fig. 3-6. Any advantages are due to the DC voltage feedback from the drain to the gate through R_G. Of course R_A can be added here as it was in Fig. 3-5 should additional resistance be required to increase the input impedance presented to a source.

LEAKAGE CURRENT

In the bipolar transistor discussion we encountered a leakage current flowing in reverse-biased junctions. One leakage current is I_{CBO} due to the reverse current flowing between the collector and base. As for the JFET the channel encompasses both the source and drain. The channel is reverse biased with respect to the gate. A leakage current flows between the channel and gate. This leakage current, I_{GSS}, is defined as the reverse current flowing from the gate when the source and drain are connected to each other. The current is proportional to the square of the voltage applied between the elements.

As is characteristic of all leakage currents I_{GSS} increases with temperature. Depending upon the particular transistor, I_{GSS} doubles with every 6° C to 15° C of temperature elevation. In this book we will use 10°C as a good average for all JFETs.

Leakage current for a JFET is usually very low. For example, at 25°C it can range from 0.1 nanoamperes (0.1×10^{-9} ampere) for a 2N5558 up to 1 nanoampere for a 2N4304; however, it is significant at high temperatures, especially if R_x in the gate circuit is large. This can be illustrated using the bias circuit in Fig. 3-2. Bias voltage V_{GS} was stated as equal to $I_D R_s$. A voltage developed across R_x, due to I_{GSS}, is equal to $I_{GSS} R_x$. To calculate V_{GS} more precisely than before, $I_{GSS} R_x$ must be subtracted from the originally determined bias voltage.

TRANSCONDUCTANCE

Among the important JFET parameters that change with temperature are I_{DSS}, I_{GSS} and g_m. The first two items were just

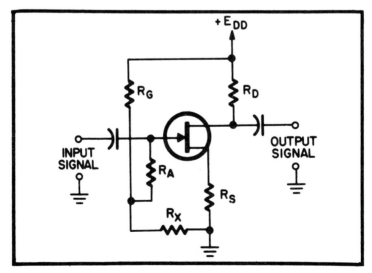

Fig 3-5. The circuit in Fig. 3-4 is shown modified to present a higher impedance to the input signal.

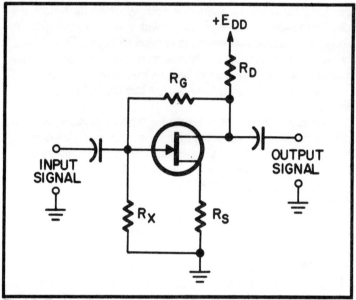

Fig. 3-6. The bias circuit is improved by adding DC feedback from the drain to the gate.

discussed in detail while g_m, the AC transconductance, was defined in Chapter 1. Transconductance relates the output current to the input voltage by the equation:

$$g_m = \left(\frac{\Delta I_P}{\Delta V_{GS}} \right) \qquad (3\text{-}2)$$

where g_m is in mhos, and ΔI_D is a change in drain current (amperes) due to ΔV_{GS}, a change in gate-to-source voltage (volts). This can be shown graphically with the help of Figs. 3-7 and 3-8. In Fig. 3-7 the plot of drain current against the gate-to-source voltage (the transfer characteristic curve) is derived from the drain characteristic curves.

At the left-hand side of Fig. 3-7, the drain characteristic curves in Fig. 3-1 have been redrawn. The horizontal drain current lines for each value of gate-to-source voltage have been extended to the vertical drain current axis in the graph at the right of the figure. The horizontal axis of the second graph in the right-hand portion of Fig. 3-7 is calibrated in gate-to-source voltage. A vertical line is drawn from the gate-to-source voltage on the horizontal axis up to the horizontal current line which represents the drain current that flows for the specific V_{GS}. This procedure is repeated for each discrete value of V_{GS}. All necessary information is available in the original

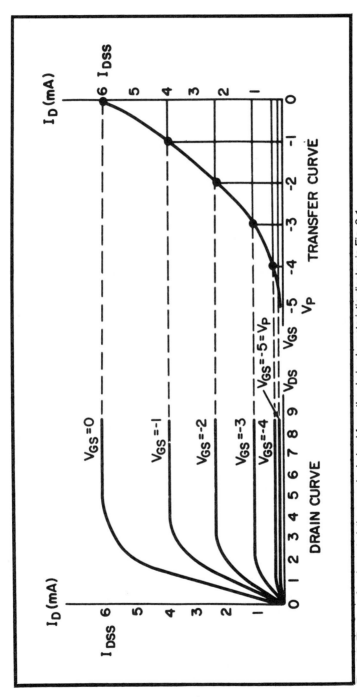

Fig. 3-7. The transfer characteristic curve is derived from the drain characteristic display in Fig. 3-1.

drain characteristic plot at the left. A dot is placed at the point where the related curves cross. All dots are connected to form the transfer characteristic curve.

Because the curve is a plot of the drain current against the gate-to-source voltage, the slope of the curve at any one point is the transconductance of the JFET for that particular current value. Variation of the slope from point to point on the curve indicates that g_m varies with drain current.

Initially, two AC transconductance values are of interest to us. The first, referred to as g_{mo}, is the transconductance at I_{DSS}, where the gate-to-source voltage is zero (see Fig. 3-8). Assume the transistor is biased so that the quiescent drain current is I_D. Put a dot on the curve at this drain current. This is the second significant point at which the transconductance must be determined. Refer to this transconductance simply as g_m.

An average value of transconductance, $\overline{g}_m$, is $(g_m + g_{mo})/2$, the mean value of the two transconductances. An equation can be derived from Fig. 3-8 to determine $\overline{g}_m$ from other circuit and transistor characteristics. It requires that I_{DSS} be connected to I_D in Fig. 3-8 with a straight line. Applying Equation 3-2:

$$\overline{g}_m = \frac{I_{DSS} - I_D}{V_{GS} - 0} \qquad (3\text{-}3)$$

or stated in a more useful form:

$$I_D = I_{DSS} - \overline{g}_m V_{GS} \qquad (3\text{-}3a)$$

V_{GS} is the gate-to-source voltage when the current flowing in the drain circuit is I_D.

We have by now defined all the transistor parameters necessary to design a stable circuit. It is necessary to stabilize the transistor against the wide tolerances that exist in the specifications of any particular type as well as against parameter variations with temperature and drain current. Let us now summarize the parameters that do concern us. They vary with temperature in the following manner.

1. For the JFET, I_{DSS} increases as the temperature decreases. As for the IGFET it doubles for every 10°C rise in temperature.
2. Transconductance g_m is an inverse function of temperature. It also changes with drain current.
3. V_P increases at about 2.2 millivolts for each degree Celsius that the temperature increases.

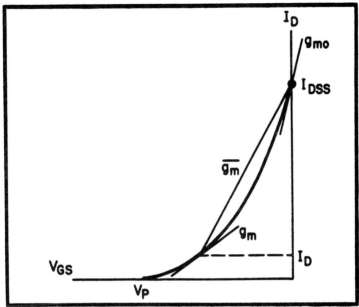

Fig. 3-8. Plot of transconductance on the transfer characteristic curve. Slope of the tangential lines are transconductances at various points on the curve. Slope of the line connecting I_{DSS} and I_D is the average transconductance.

4. I_{GSS} doubles for about every 10°C rise of the JFET's temperature. As for the IGFET, I_{GSS} is minute and the change with temperature is negligible.

5. Quantity r_{DS} (on) is the resistance from the drain to source when the transistor is biased fully in the ohmic region. It increases with temperature.

Now let us turn to the specified transistor tolerances. Parameters such as I_{DSS}, V_P and g_{mo} are specified as having a range of values for any transistor type, rather than a specific value. For example, the I_{DSS} of a 2N4303 can be anywhere between 4 and 10 mA and still be specified as a standard 2N4303.

Applying these facts we describe two procedures which can be used to design stable circuits. The first assumes a thoughtful manufacturer who provides the designer with all pertinent information and limits. In this case the paper design will usually suffice. The second design procedure assumes that you have been provided with a minimum of detailed information. Many approximations must be made. The end result using any procedure should be checked in the laboratory. This is especially true of the latter, more inexact, approach.

STABILIZING A DESIGN USING COMPLETE DATA

The exact method assumes the manufacturer supplied the data for or the curves in Fig. 3-9. As explained in the figure, transistors are specified to be within any one category if their characteristics fall within a specific set of limiting values. The curves marked 25°C represent the two extremes within which all transistors of a particular type must fall when the ambient temperature is 25°C. Should the ambient temperature change the curves are displaced accordingly.

The plots show the transfer characteristic curves within specific I_{DSS} limits at various temperatures. If these curves are not presented as such in the manufacturer's data, plots at 25°C may usually be derived from the drain characteristic curves using the procedures exercised in Fig. 3-7.

Design procedure is based on transistor operation limited by the boundaries of two of the curves. It can best be illustrated with a practical example. Assume that a circuit such as that in Fig. 3-3 is to be designed. The required output from the circuit is a minimum of 6 volts peak-to-peak across a 5600-ohm load resistor. The transistor must operate properly from +25°C to +125°C.

Temperature range is the first item to be considered. From the plots in Fig. 3-9 choose the 125°C broken-line curve for the lower extreme characteristics and the 25°C solid-line curve for the second limiting factor. All plots defining the characteristics of the particular transistor type between +25°C and +125C are included between these curves; hence, these curves as boundaries satisfy all temperature requirements. Redraw the limiting curves in Fig. 3-10. Now, place a 5600-ohm resistor in the drain circuit so that the output load will be the specified value. The 6-volt peak-to-peak requirement dictates a minimum drain current swing of 1.07 milliamperes (6 volts/5600 ohms).

We proceed to plot a bias point on each of the two curves and set the extremes in idling current. It is undesirable to bias the transistor at or near pinch-off because this region is nonlinear and the transconductance is low. If we place the bias on the lower I_{DSS} curve at approximately 1.75 milliamperes we will operate at a reasonably linear portion of the curve. It will also allow the 1.07-milliampere peak-to-peak current to swing the maximum range without getting into pinch-off at one end and not reaching the zero V_{GS} limit at the other extreme. Call this point I_D (min) and plot it on the broken-line curve. Drop a vertical line from this point to the horizontal axis. The line crosses the axis at the 0.75-volt gate-to-source point. Refer to this as V_{GS} (min).

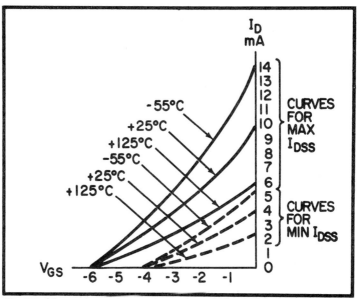

Fig. 3-9. At normal room temperatures, the solid line 25° C plot is the transfer characteristic curve for the maximum I$_{DSS}$ value of a hypothetical JFET. The broken-line 25°C curve represents the transfer characteristic for the minimum value of I$_{DDS}$. The other curves are maximum and minimum values at extreme temperatures.

Since the required 1.07-milliampere excursion is a small portion of the possible transistor current variation, we have wide latitude in choosing the maximum value of drain current on the upper limiting curve. Select I$_D$ as 4 milliamperes and plot it on the solid-line curve. Extend the lines to the vertical and horizontal axis. The vertical line crosses the gate-to-source axis at 2.9 volts. The point on the upper curve is then defined by

$$I_{D(max)} = 4 \text{ mA}$$

and

$$V_{GS(max)} = 2.9V.$$

Connect the points plotted on the two limiting curves with a straight line.

In the next step source resistor R$_S$ is to be calculated for Fig. 3-3. It is the slope of the line connecting the two points on the graph. Resistance R$_S$ is equal to the difference in the gate-to-source voltages divided by the difference in the drain currents, or:

$$R_S = \frac{2.9 - 0.75}{4 \times 10^{-3} - 1.75 \times 10^{-3}} \tag{3-4}$$

$$R_S = \frac{2.15}{2.25 \times 10^{-3}}$$

$$= 956$$

where R_S is in ohms. Use the next higher Electronic Industries Association 10% resistor value of 1000 ohms.

The next task is to determine E_{GG} from the plot. Circuit theory dictates the relationship:

$$E_{GG} = I_D R_S - V_{GS} \qquad (3-5)$$

Using the minimum values of V_{GS} and I_D ($V_{GS(max)}$ and $I_{D(max)}$ can be used instead), we find:

$$E_{GG} = (1.75 \times 10^{-3})\,(1000) - 0.75 \qquad (3-6)$$

$$= 1$$

where E_{GG} is in volts.

Resistance R_X is chosen so that the voltage developed across it by I_{GSS} at the highest temperature is negligible compared to the E_{GG} of 1 volt. Assume that one-tenth of E_{GG} or 0.1 volt is a negligible value. If it were specified that I_{GSS} is 1 nanoampere (10^{-9} ampere) at 25°C, and that it doubles for every 10°C rise in temperature up to 125°C, the maximum I_{GSS} is about 1 microampere or 10^{-6} ampere. Then the maximum R_X may be 0.1 volt/10^{-6} ampere = 100,000 ohms.

Minimum drain supply voltage still remains to be determined. It is equal to the sum of three factors: (1) the maximum voltage across R_S, or $I_{D(max)} R_S$; (2) the minimum voltage across the transistor, $1.5 V_P$, where V_P is the maximum pinch-off voltage for the transistor (V_P should be multiplied by about 1.5 to be certain that the transistor is operating in the linear portion of the pinch-off region); and (3) the maximum voltage across R_D, or $I_{D(max)} R_D$. It should be noted that since R_D and R_S are 10% resistors, the values referred to in factors 1 and 3 are 10% above the nominal values of both resistors. Thus, the R_S in question is 1000 ohms +10% of 1000 ohms or 1100 ohms and R_D is 5600 ohms +10% of 5600 ohms or 6160 ohms. In our example, the minimum supply voltage is

$$E_{DD} = I_{D(max)} R_S + 1.5 V_P + I_{D(max)} R_D \qquad (3-7)$$

$$= (0.004)(1100) + (1.5)(6) + (0.004)(6160)$$

$$= 4.4 + 9 + 24.64$$

$$= 38.04$$

where E_{DD} is in volts. Use a 40-volt supply.

Should you wish to use the circuit in Fig. 3-4 instead of that in Fig. 3-3 and eliminate the second supply the E_{GG} voltage must be developed across R_X. Assuming that I_G is about ten times the maximum I_{GSS} determined above, or 10^{-5} amperes, and that E_{GG} is 1 volt as previously calculated, then

$$R_X = E_{GG}/I_G$$
$$= 1/10^{-5}$$
$$= 100,000 \text{ or } 100 \text{ kilohms.}$$

Since E_{DD} is 40 volts, the remaining 39 volts must be developed across R_G. The same 10^{-5} amperes that flows through R_X flows through R_G; hence,

$$R_G = 39/10^{-5}$$
$$= 3.9 \times 10^6$$

or 3.9 megohms, which is a standard Electronic Industries Association (EIA) 10% resistor value.

It should be noted here that the simple circuit in Fig. 3-2 can be used successfully to fulfill all stability requirements. Bias points on

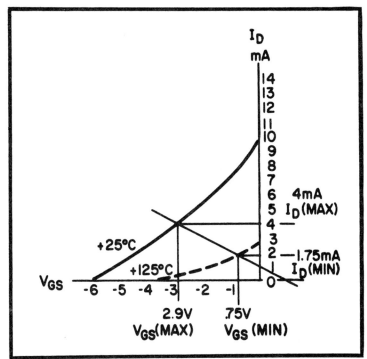

Fig. 3-10. Curve describing the limits for solving a problem using the exact design method.

the two curves can be chosen to determine only a value for R_S and the E_{GG} supply is unnecessary; however, the complication was added to indicate a procedure rather than to solve a tight problem.

STABILIZING USING AN APPROXIMATE METHOD

Let us now turn to a second method of determining the components in the circuits. This time assume that the manufacturer did not furnish the curves in Fig. 3-9. To effect a solution we start with the assumption that all temperature variations, with the possible exception of I_{GSS}, have little effect on determining the circuit components. Actually changes with temperature are usually negligible when compared to the variations in I_{DSS} due to transistor tolerances.

Several pertinent relationships should now be established. From Fig. 3-8, is evolved Equation 3-3a in order to state a relationship between drain current I_{DSS}, V_{GS} and average tranconductance, g_m. This equation, repeated here for convenience, is:

$$I_D = I_{DSS} - \overline{g_m}V_{GS} \qquad (3\text{-}3a)$$

In many instances we do not know the actual transconductance, g_m, at a particular quiescent current. It can be determined mathematically, for it is related to g_{mo}, the transconductance at I_{DSS}, by the equation:

$$g_m = g_{mo} \left(\frac{I_D}{I_{DSS}} \right)^{\frac{1}{2}} \qquad (3\text{-}8)$$

Equation 3-9 relates $\overline{g_m}$ to g_{mo} and g_m:

$$\overline{g_m} = \frac{g_{mo} + g_m}{2} \qquad (3\text{-}9)$$

for as an average value, $\overline{g_m}$ is midway between the values of g_m and g_{mo}. It should also be noted that g_{mo}, V_P and I_{DSS} are related to each other by the equation:

$$g_{mo} = \frac{2\, I_{DSS}}{|V_P|} \qquad (3\text{-}10)$$

where $|V_P|$ is the absolute pinch-off voltage, disregarding polarity.

All factors in Equations 3-3a, 3-8, 3-9 and 3-10 are assumed to be average values. In order to apply these equations properly the average values for the various parameters must be calculated from the limited data supplied by the manufacturer of the device. Initially we must also assume that all operations take place at 25°C ambient temperature.

We will apply the approximate method to the problem solved above using the complete data. In the problem we assumed a transistor with a minimum I_{DSS} of 4 mA and a maximum of 10 milliamperes. Both currents are specified at 25°C. The average current, $\overline{I_{DSS}}$, is midway between the two limits, or

$$\overline{I_{DSS}} = \frac{4 + 10}{2}$$
$$= 7$$

where the limits and $\overline{I_{DSS}}$ are in milliamperes. From the curves in Fig. 3-9 we note that pinch-off voltages range from 4 to 6 volts. The average pinch-off voltage, $\overline{V_P}$ is 5 volts.

V_{GS} should never be allowed to swing to pinch-off to avoid the crowded region of the display and the consequent distortion. As a rule of thumb V_{GS} should not be more than three-fourths of the minimum value of V_P. In this case V_{GS} should be less than 3 volts; however, it may be allowed to swing somewhat beyond zero at the other extreme, for the transistor will not conduct until V_{GS} is more than +0.5 volt. An average gate-to-source voltage, $\overline{V_{GS}}$, would then be

$$\overline{V_{GS}} = \frac{3 - 0}{2}$$
$$= 1.5$$

where all of the above units are in volts. Substituting this into Equation 3-1 the average drain current is

$$\overline{I_D} = 0.007 \left(1 - \frac{1.5}{5} \right)^2 \tag{3-11}$$
$$= 0.00343$$

or 3.43 milliamperes. If gain is important, $\overline{I_D}$ should be determined from Equation 3-3a using the $\overline{g_m}$ term rather than Equation 3-1.

Average transconductance should be calculated from g_m and g_{mo}. Use Equation 3-10 to determine g_{mo}. It is

$$g_{mo} = \frac{2(0.007)}{5}$$
$$= 0.0028$$

ampere per volt. Equation 3-8 dictates that the transconductance at the average drain current is

$$g_m = (0.0028) \left(\frac{0.00343}{0.007} \right)^{1/2}$$
$$= 0.00196$$

ampere per volt; hence, the average transconductance

$$\overline{g}_m = \frac{g_{mo} + g_m}{2}$$

$$= \frac{0.0028 + 00196}{2}$$

$$= 0.00238$$

ampere per volt from Equation 3-9. To summarize the important data:

$$\overline{I}_{dss} = 7 \text{ mA}, \qquad \overline{g}_m = 0.00238 \text{ mhos},$$
$$\overline{I}_D = 3.43 \text{ mA}, \qquad \overline{V}_{GS} = 1.5V, \text{ and}$$
$$\overline{V}_P = 5V, \qquad I_{GSS} = 1 \ \mu A \text{ at } 25°C$$

I_{GSS} at the elevated temperature was calculated in the previously discussed procedure.

Using the above data, initially design the simple self-bias circuit in Fig. 3-2. R_D is 5600 ohms as specified for all circuits. The entire gate-to-source voltage is developed across R_S. Since

then
$$\overline{V}_{GS} = \overline{I}_D R_S$$
$$R_S = \frac{\overline{V}_{GS}}{\overline{I}_D}$$

$$= \frac{1.5}{0.00343}$$
$$= 437$$

where R_S is in ohms, $\overline{V}_{GS}$ is in volts and $\overline{I}_D$ is in amperes. Use a standard 470-ohm resistor. As before, $R_X = 100,000$ ohms, for the considerations here are the same as they were in the example with the more exact solution.

The circuit in Fig. 3-3 is of greater interest because the E_{GG} voltage which bucks $I_D R_S$ will permit R_S to be increased in size while retaining the desired V_{GS}. The equation for the gate voltage is:

$$\overline{V}_{GS} = \overline{I}_D R_S - E_{GG} - I_{GSS(max)} R_X \qquad (3\text{-}12)$$

Substituting the calculated values into the equation yields:

$$1.5 = (3.43 \times 10^{-3}) R_S - E_{GG} - (10^{-6})(10^5) \qquad (3\text{-}13)$$

so that the gate supply voltage is related to the source resistor by:

$$E_{GG} = -1.4 + (3.43 \times 10^{-3}) R_S \qquad (3\text{-}14)$$

Resistance R_S must be bigger than determined for the circuit in Fig. 3-2. Doubling the 470 ohms to the EIA resistor value of 1000 ohms is a good estimate. Then E_{GG} will be $-1.4 + 3.43 = 2.03$ volts from Equations 3-14. This is a logical solution not unlike that derived using the more exact methods. The results should be checked in the laboratory.

The required drain supply voltage should now be determined. The procedures used above also apply here. The voltage across the drain resistor is

$$\overline{I_D}R_D = (0.00343)(5600)$$
$$= 19.2 \text{ volts.}$$

The minimum voltage across the transistor is $(1.5)\ \overline{V_P}$, as derived above, or $1.5\,(5\text{ volts}) = 7.5$ volts. The voltage across R_S must be at least that calculated for Fig. 3-2, or $\overline{I_D}R_S = (3.43 \times 10^{-3})\,(438) = 1.5$ volts. The average supply voltage is the sum of these factors, or $19.2 + 7.5 + 1.5 = 28.2$ volts. Add about 30% to compensate for peak values in drain current and pinch-off voltage. The required supply will then be approximately 40 volts.

The practical circuit in Fig. 3-4 can be determined from the data which has already been accumulated. Although R_X remains at 100,000 ohms, R_G can be calculated as before. Voltage across R_G is E_{DD} less the voltage R_X, or 40 volts -2.03 volts ≈ 38 volts (2.03 is E_{GG}, the voltage across R_X). As I_G, the current flowing through R_G is about the same as the current flowing through R_X, or

$$\frac{2.03}{10^5} \approx 2 \times 10^{-5} \text{ amperes}$$

Resistance R_G is calculated then by dividing the voltage across it by the current through it; that is,

$$R_G = \frac{38}{2 \times 10^{-5}}$$
$$= 1.9 \times 10^6$$

or 1.9 megohms. Use a standard EIA 1.8-megohm resistor. Should the more stable circuit in Fig. 3-6 be desired the quiescent voltage across R_G is that at the drain, V_D, less, E_{GG}, the voltage across R_X. Because the quiescent drain current is 3.43 milliamperes and the resistor in the drain circuit is 5600 ohms the voltage across R_D is

$$(0.00343)\,(5600) \approx 19 \text{ volts.}$$

The voltage across R_G is

$$19 - 2.03 \approx 17 \text{ volts.}$$

Assuming that I_G is equal to the 2×10^{-5} amperes determined above R_G for this current is

$$\frac{17}{2 \times 10^{-5}} = 8.5 \times 10^5$$

or 850 kilohms. A standard 820-kilohm resistor may be used here.

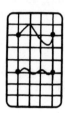

Chapter 4
Bipolar
Amplifiers

The ultimate goal of an audio amplifier is to provide gain for the input signal. However important the bias and stability considerations are, a circuit must be designed to enable the amplifier stage to furnish voltage, current and power amplification. At the output the signal delivered to a load should be an enlarged and undistorted version of the input.

Reference was made in Chapter 2 to the three most commonly used transistor circuits. These are, of course, the common-base, common-emitter and common-collector arrangements. For any circuit built around each of these arrangements we must know the current, voltage and power gains, as well as the input and output impedances. These factors can be determined by plotting the appropriate circuit information on collector characteristic curves. Procedures of this type are quite accurate for any one transistor, but are at the same time cumbersome.

Small-signal amplifiers are more readily analyzed using equivalent circuits. These circuits involve the semiconductor device and the associated components. Two different equivalents are widely used—the *hybrid equivalent circuit* and the *equivalent T-circuit*. Both circuits have been previously explained, although they may not have been recognized as such in the text. The hybrid equivalent is briefly discussed because some important parameters are based on this method of analysis. Greater emphasis is placed on the equivalent T-circuit methods since low-frequency design requirements are easily satisfied using these procedures. Relationships will be established between the two sets of parameters.

HYBRID EQUIVALENT CIRCUIT

The hybrid model of the circuit assumes the transistor, in any configuration, has a pair of input terminals and a pair of output

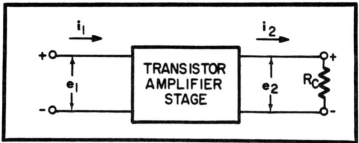

Fig. 4-1. Circuit used to develop hybrid parameters. Rc is the resistor in the transistor collector circuit.

terminals. In Fig. 4-1 the input voltage and current fed to the transistor are e_1 and i_1 respectively. Similarly, the voltage and current at the output are e_2 and i_2. Four important ratios evolve from this block representation.

1. When a short is placed at the output, e_2 is zero. A ratio of short-circuit output current to the input current, i_2/i_1, is assigned the symbol h_f or h_{21}. In a common-emitter circuit this is referred to as the β_{AC} of the transistor. For a common-base circuit the ratio is α_{AC}. (For the remainder of the book, we will drop the AC subscripts after the alpha and beta symbols. Should DC conditions be considered, the DC subscript will be employed.) These current gain factors are discussed thoroughly in Chapter 1.

2. Maintaining a shorted output circuit we can establish the relationship e_1/i_1. Symbols for this ratio are h_i and h_{11}. These symbols represent the input impedance of the transistor—but only when the output circuit is shorted.

3. Output impedance can be determined from the condition when the input is open circuited and i_1 is zero. It is the ratio e_2/i_2. The reciprocal of this ratio, i_2/e_2, the output admittance, is assigned the symbols h_o and h_{22}.

4. Final symbols h_r and h_{12} also assume the input circuit is open and i_1 is zero. They are equal to e_1/e_2, where e_1 is the voltage fed back through the transistor from the output circuit to the input and e_2 is the output voltage.

A hybrid equivalent circuit can be drawn for the transistor using the relationships just noted. Although all arrangements (common-base, common-collector and common-emitter) use the same basic circuit, the second subscript at the h-parameter symbols indicates which circuit is involved. In Fig. 4-2 the equivalent for the common-emitter circuit is used; so all h parameters end

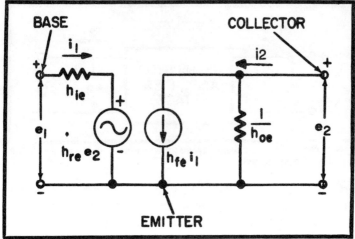

Fig. 4-2. Hybrid equivalent for a common-emitter transistor circuit. Only the equivalent circuit of the transistor proper is shown. Polarity markings show the relative phases at one instant.

with an e, such as h_{fe}. Similarly, a b added to the subscript indicates that a common-base parameter is involved, while the addition of a c means the parameter is for a common-collector circuit. Values of the parameters depend upon the particular circuit arrangement in which the transistor is being used.

In Fig. 4-2 only the transistor is represented in the equivalent circuit. The impedance looking into the base of the transistor is h_{ie} modified by the presence of $h_{re}e_2$. Similarly, the output impedance of the transistor itself is $1/h_{oe}$ in parallel with the current source $h_{fe}i_1$. Voltage, current and power gains can also be determined from the two loops in Fig. 4-2.

The practical circuit in Fig. 4-3 has components which modify the characteristics of the transistor. For example, the output impedance presented by the transistor is $1/h_{oe}$. Output impedance presented by the circuit is the transistor output impedance in parallel with R_C. Similarly, the input impedance must be modified by the presence of R_G. The effect of the overall circuit can easily be determined using the equivalent-T-model.

EQUIVALENT-T CIRCUIT

The equivalent T-model of the transistor is shown in Fig. 4-4A. It looks more like the actual transistor than does the hybrid equivalent network. The common-emitter equivalent has been drawn. In Fig. 4-4B the input source and output load have been added to the transistor network. Input is applied between the base and emitter, while the output from the amplifier stage is developed between the collector and emitter.

An AC resistor representing the internal resistance of each transistor element is in series with each terminal inside the device. A current source, representing the gain of the device, appears across the collector resistance, r_d. Point b' is inside the transistor. All resistances from the transistor elements are connected to this point. Emitter resistance r_e is determined as follows:

$$r_e = \frac{26}{I_E}$$

where I_E is the quiescent emitter current expressed in milliamperes. Quantity r_b is the base resistance usually ranging from 200 to 800 ohms. The collector resistance is r_d for the common-emitter and common-collector circuits, usually assuming values between 10,000 and 100,000 ohms. The collector resistance for the common-base circuit is r_c, and is approximately determined by

$$r_c \approx \beta \, r_d.$$

Resistances r_c and r_d are large when the input impedance to the transistor is small.

Various bits of data about the circuit in Fig. 4-3 can be determined by analyzing the equivalent T-circuit when it is connected to

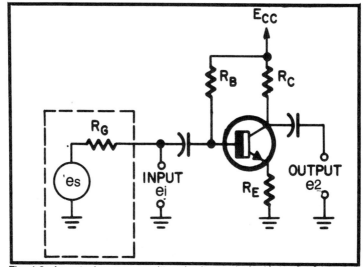

Fig. 4-3. An actual common-emitter circuit complete with input and output components and input signal generator.

all resistors and sources in the associated circuit, as in Fig. 4-4B. The voltage source sees an impedance when looking into the transistor. It is equal to base resistance r_b, in addition to the sum of emitter resistance r_e and external emitter resistor R_E, when the latter two are multiplied by beta. (All resistances when reflected from the emitter into the base circuit appear in the base circuit as the emitter resistors multiplied by the beta of the transistor.) Consequently, the total transistor input resistance seen by the generator is:

$$R_{IN} = r_b + \beta (r_e + R_E) \qquad (4\text{-}1)$$

R_{IN} is shunted by the bias resistor R_B in Fig. 4-3. The source feeding the transistor sees R_B in parallel with R_{IN}.

In the drawing, $R_C + r_d$ (the collector load resistor and the internal collector resistance, respectively) are shown as shunting $r_e + R_E$; however, they do not appear in Equation 4-1 since they are much larger than all emitter resistors. The effect of R_C and r_d on the parallel combination is indeed minor.

In a similar manner, with like considerations, all the other statistics for the common-emitter arrangement can be determined using the equivalent T-model. R_{OUT} represents the impedance the collector load resistor sees by looking back into the transistor, while A_V is the voltage gain of the circuit in Fig. 4-3, and A_i and G are the current and power gains, respectively. Approximate equations derived for the common emitter arrangements are:

$$R_{OUT} = \frac{r_d\left[(r_b + R_G) + \beta(r_e + R_E)\right]}{r_b + r_e + R_G + R_E} \qquad (4\text{-}2)$$

$$A_V = \frac{\beta R_L}{r_b + \beta(r_e + R_E)} \approx \frac{R_L}{R_E} \qquad (4\text{-}3)$$

$$A_i = \beta \qquad (4\text{-}4)$$

$$G = A_V A_i \approx \frac{\beta R_L}{R_E} \qquad (4\text{-}5)$$

In Equation 4-2 if the resistor in the bias circuit, R_B, is less than ten times the size of the source resistance, R_G, then R_G stated in Equation 4-2 should be modified to $R_G R_B/(R_G + R_B)$. This is the expression for R_G in parallel with R_B.

Now let us return to the hybrid parameters we described so carefully above. Some transistor manufacturers supply only these parameters in their data books. How can numbers be used for the various impedances in Equations 4-1 through 4-5 if only h parameters are provided? Simple! Let us set up equations relating the hybrid parameters to those in the equivalent T-circuit as follows:

$$r_b = \frac{h_{rb}}{h_{ob}} = h_{ie} - \frac{h_{re}h_{fe}}{h_{oc}} \qquad (4\text{-}6)$$

$$r_c = \frac{1 - h_{rb}}{h_{ob}} = \frac{h_{fe}}{h_{oe}} = h_{fe}r_d \qquad (4\text{-}7)$$

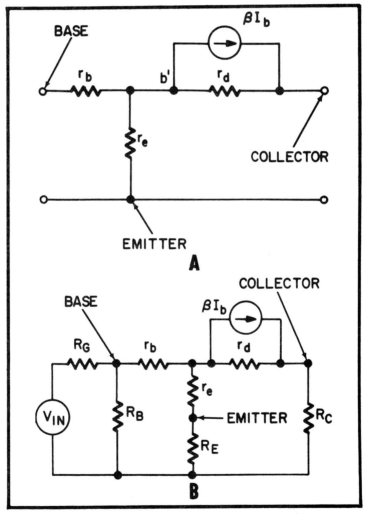

Fig. 4-4. T-equivalent circuit of only the transistor when used in a common emitter arrangement. At B, the input and output components have been added to the transistor circuit for a complete equivalent of Fig. 4-3.

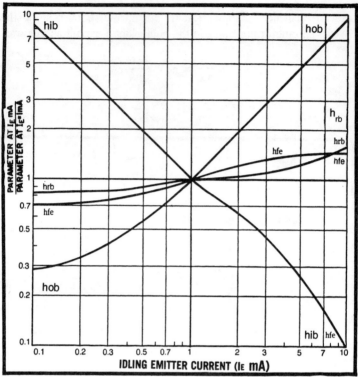

Fig. 4-5. Variation of h-parameters with the quiescent emitter current.

$$r_e = h_{ib} - \frac{h_{rb}(1 + h_{fb})}{h_{ob}} = \frac{h_{re}}{h_{oe}} \qquad (4\text{-}8)$$

$$\alpha = -h_{fb} = \frac{h_{fe}}{1 + h_{fe}} \qquad (4\text{-}9)$$

$$\beta = h_{fe} = \frac{-h_{fb}}{1 + h_{fb}} \qquad (4\text{-}10)$$

Next, calculate the various equivalent T-elements from the relationship in Equations 4-6 through 4-10. Substitute the calculated values of r_b, r_c, r_d, r_e and β into Equations 4-1 through 4-5. Calculate the various statistics about a particular circuit using T-model parameters.

Various h parameters vary with emitter current and collector-to-emitter voltage. Curves such as those shown in Figs. 4-5 and 4-6 are normally supplied by manufacturers to describe how these parameters vary. As an example assume the values for the h parameters are presented on a specification sheet at $I_C = 1$ mA and $V_{CE} = 5$ volts. If the value of h_{ob} at these quiescent conditions is 5×10^{-5} mhos, and it is required to know the h_{ob} at $I_C = 10$ milliamperes and $V_{CE} = 10$ volts, the following mental gymnastics must be performed.

1. From Fig. 4-5 the ratios of the actual h_{ob} at 10 mA to h_{ob} at 1 mA is 9. Then due to the current deviation from the specified value, $h_{ob} = 9 \times (5 \times 10^{-5}) = 4.5 \times 10^{-4}$ mhos.

2. From Fig. 4-6 the ratio of the actual h_{ob} at 10 volts to the h_{ob} at 5 volts is 0.7. Multiply this by the solution found in step 1 and the required $h_{ob} = 0.7 \times (4.5 \times 10\text{-}4) = 3.15 \times 10^{-4}$.

3. Repeat this procedure for the other hybrid parameters before substituting these factors into Equations 4-6 through 4-10.

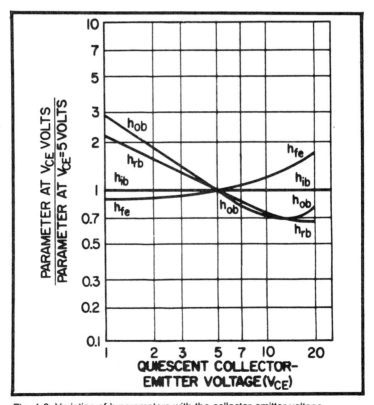

Fig. 4-6. Variation of h-parameters with the collector-emitter voltage.

89

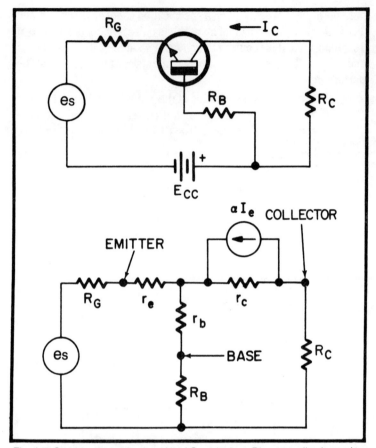

Fig. 4-7. Common-base circuit and its AC equivalent. Direct coupling is used to avoid complicating the analysis.

Vital statistics for the common-base and common-collector circuits in Figs. 4-7 and 4-8, respectively, are noted below. The equivalent T-circuits are also shown in the figures. As for the common-emitter circuit discussed above, Equations 4-6 through 4-10 can also be used here to convert from the h to the T-circuit parameters if only the hybrid parameters are stated in the specifications for the device. For the common-base circuit the equations are:

$$R_{IN} = r_e + \frac{r_b + R_B}{\beta} \tag{4-11}$$

$$R_{OUT} = \frac{r_c[r_b + R_B + \beta(r_e + R_G)]}{\beta(r_b + R_B + r_e + R_G)} \tag{4-12}$$

$$A_V = \frac{\beta R_L}{r_b + R_B + \beta\,(r_e + R_G)} \approx \frac{R_L}{R_G} \qquad (4\text{-}13)$$

$$A_I = \alpha \qquad (4\text{-}14)$$

$$G = \alpha A_V \qquad (4\text{-}15)$$

Common-collector circuits are described by the following equations:

$$R_{IN} = r_b + \beta(r_e + R_E) \qquad (4\text{-}16)$$

$$R_{OUT} = r_e + \frac{r_b + R_G}{\beta} \qquad (4\text{-}17)$$

$$A_V = 1 \qquad (4\text{-}18)$$

$$A_I = \beta \qquad (4\text{-}19)$$

$$G = \beta \qquad (4\text{-}20)$$

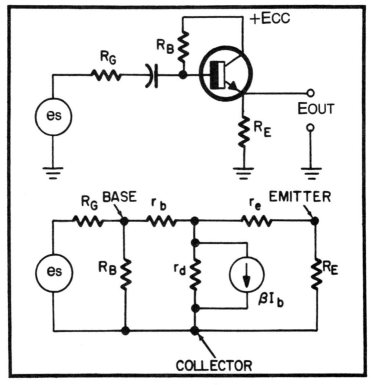

Fig. 4-8. Common-collector circuit and its AC equivalent.

As noted earlier if R_B is comparable in size to R_{IN} or R_G in Equations 4-16 and 4-17, both R_{IN} and R_G should be modified. The actual R_{IN} and R_G are to be made equal to the resistance of the parallel combination of the resistances involved with R_B. A resistor shunting the input in Fig. 4-7 dictates similar modifications in Equations 4-11 and 4-12.

EQUATIONS FROM LOGIC

The equations stated above should not be memorized, but with a little applied logic and some rules of thumb you can derive many of the equations when analyzing a circuit or doing a design.

Start with R_{IN}. We know that the CC (common-collector) circuit presents the highest impedance to a source, while the CB (common-base) circuit is the lowest. The CE (common-emitter) circuit falls somewhere between the two. We also know that any resistor in the emitter, such as r_e and R_E, when referred to the base circuit, is to be multiplied by the beta of the transistor. It follows logically that any resistance in the base circuit such as r_b, R_G, R_B, etc., is to be divided by β when reflected into the emitter circuit.

For the common-emitter circuit the input resistance in the base circuit is the sum of the base resistance of the transistor, r_b (about 200 to 800 ohms and usually negligible), added to the product of beta with the sum of $r_e + R_E$ in the emitter circuit. The source sees these resistors shunted by bias resistor R_B. This is the same resistance the input source sees for the CC arrangement, only the value of R_E in this latter case is much larger than it is for the CE circuit. As for the CB circuit quantities $v_b + R_b$ is divided by beta when reflected back into the input emitter circuit, while also being added to the emitter resistance, r_e. The combination is in series with R_E, a resistor that may be in series with the emitter lead.

R_{OUT}, the output resistance of the transistor, is seen by load resistor R_C when it looks back into the collector circuit in the CE and CB arrangements and by R_E when it looks back into the emitter circuit for the CC configuration. As for the latter the load sees the resistors in the base circuit divided by beta, $(r_b + R_G)/\beta$, added to the emitter resistance, r_e. Don't forget to put R_B in parallel with R_G if they are of comparable size. For the CE and CB circuits R_{OUT} resistances are more difficult to determine, but they are somewhat less than r_d and r_c, respectively; hence, the CB circuit has the highest output impedance, the CC arrangement has the lowest, with the CE circuit falling somewhere between the two.

Voltage gain is very close to unity for the CC circuit (emitter follower), while it closely approximates the ratio of the resistor in the collector, R_C, to the resistance in the emitter, $r_e + R_E$, for the CE and CB arrangements. Current gain for the CB circuit is alpha, while for the CE and CC arrangements it is beta. Power gain is the product of the respective voltage and current gains for each circuit.

Calculated values for impedance and gain of the transistor itself are modified by external circuits. While we will analyze only a one-transistor circuit in this chapter, in Chapter 9 we will see how the factors discussed here are affected by coupling the one-transistor stage to another transistor as well as to other types of devices.

THE SINE WAVE

The basic function of the audio amplifier is to magnify the input so that the output voltage, current, or power is an enlarged version of the input signal. Most experimental work is done using the sine wave. Before proceeding with the solution of a practical problem we will pause here to review the characteristics of the sine wave. Data accumulated in this section of the book will be useful in the design of all types of small-signal and power amplifiers as well as in the design of power supplies.

As you are aware fixed DC voltage and fixed direct current are theoretically constant at all times. Disregarding aging, the voltage at the positive post of a battery is always a fixed amount *above* that at the negative terminal.   The reverse is never true. This is not so with sinusoidal voltages and alternating currents.

With respect to one voltage terminal of the AC generator the voltage at the second terminal varies as shown in Fig. 4-9. The single cycle in Fig. 4-9 is repeated many times a second, depending

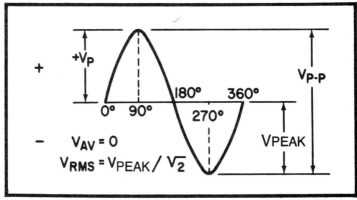

Fig. 4-9. Characteristics of the ordinary sine wave.

upon the frequency involved. It is repeated 60 times a second for a 60-hertz power supply. As you see each cycle is divided into 360 integral portions known as degrees. The amplitude varies from zero at 0° to a positve peak, V_P at 90°, back to zero and on to a negative peak at 270°, then returning to zero.

This very basic description was introduced here to enable us to discuss, define and get a complete insight into the meaning of RMS, average, peak and peak-to-peak voltage.

Average DC voltage is the constant voltage at the terminals of a battery. Average AC voltage of a sine wave is zero over the complete cycle because the equal portions—the positive and the negative—add vectorially and cancel.

The sine wave does deliver power despite the fact that the average voltage over the complete cycle is zero. The ability to deliver power is due to the availability of voltage (and current) in each individual half of the cycle. The power is delivered due to an effective or RMS voltage which is equal to

$$V_{RMS} = \frac{V_{P.}}{\sqrt{2}}$$
$$= 0.707 V_P$$

Now let us assume that the negative half of the sine wave is flipped over so that it is always positive as shown in Fig. 4-10. Since the same varying voltage and current appear as before (only the polarity of one-half of the cycle is changed, not the amplitude) it can deliver as much power as the cycle in Fig. 4-9. The RMS voltage will remain unchanged at 0.707 V_{PEAK}. But since it delivers current and voltage in one direction, there is also an average value for the voltage differing from zero. This is

$$V_{AV} = \frac{2V_{PEAK}}{\pi}$$

where π is equal to 3.14.

Average and RMS Voltages

It is important to clearly understand the difference between average and RMS voltages. Average voltage has nothing to do with power. It just tells you what voltage you would have if the amplitudes of the sine wave were added at each point on the curve, then divided by the number of points considered. It is as if the sinusoidal voltage were flattened by squashing the upper part of the curve down to a flat level and the bottom part brought up to that level. The area under the flat curve is equal to that under the sinusoidal form.

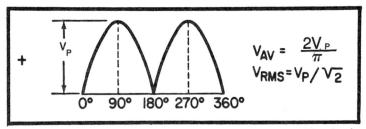

Fig. 4-10. Characteristics of a waveform consisting of repetitive positive sinsoidal pulses.

On the other hand the RMS voltage involves power and is derived from considering the power delivered to a load by the fluctuating sine wave. DC voltage capable of delivering this power into the same load is considered as the basis of comparison. AC and DC voltages are assigned identical numbers when they deliver identical amounts of power. AC voltage, known as RMS, is then compared to the peak sinusoidal voltage, and a relationship between peak and RMS is established.

One last but important consideration: what happens if the negative pulse of the actual sine wave is entirely eliminated and only the pulse from 0° through 180° remains? The voltage is zero from 180° through 360° in each cycle. See Fig. 4-11. The average voltage is half that for the curve in Fig. 4-10, while the RMS voltage is that in Fig. 4-10 divided by $\sqrt{2}$ or $V_P/2$.

A Typical Example

New magnetic phonograph cartridges frequently deliver less output voltage than do those of years ago. In our problem we are assuming that you have a good amplifier with a 47-kilohm input impedance that requires a 5-millivolt (mV) peak output from the cartridge. But if you have a new high quality record player and the excellent new cartridge you chose delivers but 2 millivolts peak at an average velocity of 5cm/second, what should you do? Problems of this type can be solved by simply adding a stage of gain between the new cartridge and the amplifier.

The voltage gain of the amplifier stage to be designed must be at least equal to the ratio of the sensitivity of the old amplifier to the output from the new cartridge, or

$$\frac{5 \text{ mV}}{2 \text{ mV}} = 2.5$$

Adding some leeway a gain of three will be fine. A low-noise

95

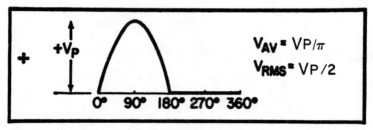

$$V_{AV} = VP/\pi$$
$$V_{RMS} = VP/2$$

Fig. 4-11. Characteristic of a single sinusoidal pulse repeated only once each cycle.

transistor should be chosen for this application. The 2N3391A is a natural choice. Leakage current is just about negligible up to any practical temperature, the noise figure is low and the beta ranges from 250 to 500. An average value of 400 can be assumed.

The average cartridge is designed to operate into 47 kilohms; hence, the stage we are designing must present a 47-kilohm resistance to the cartridge. The output from this stage must look into the 47-kilohm resistance in the old amplifier. To assure that the amplifier will not load our stage of gain we will make the collector resistor in our design equal to one-tenth the resistance of the load it must see, or we set Rc equal to 4700 ohms.

Now, choose a circuit. Since the voltage gain is to be more than unity, the CC circuit is not usable. The requirement of a fairly high input impedance makes the CB circuit impractical. We must then turn to the remaining CE arrangement in Fig. 4-3. You will find this circuit the most practical in many designs because of its gain and impedance characteristics.

The cartridge is the next consideration. Peak voltage output from an average size signal is 2 mV. For high amplitude signals the peak voltage output from the cartridge may be as much as ten times this value or 20 mV. Across 4700-ohm load resistor Rc of the amplifier stage, the output voltage must be capable of swinging

$$20 \times 3 = 60 \text{ mV}.$$

As you recall the gain of the stage must be at least three. The minimum collector current swing is then

$$\frac{60 \text{ mV}}{4700\Omega} = 12 \ \mu A.$$

Low-noise considerations dictate that the collector bias current and voltage be very small. On the other hand for a low-distortion figure the quiescent current and voltage must be out of the leakage current and saturation regions of the collector characteristic curves. A good compromise is to use the idling conditions of $V_{CE} = 2$ volts and $I_C = 0.5$ mA. The quiescent voltage across R_C is then

$$0.5 \times 4700 = 2.35 \text{ volts.}$$

Since leakage current is no factor, the bias circuit can be very simple. The circuit in Fig. 4-12 can be used. The components and characteristics we have already determined are noted in the drawing.

An idling current of 0.5 mA means that the resistance in the transistor is

$$r_e = \frac{26}{I_E}$$

or 52 ohms. In order to have a voltage gain of three,

$$R_E + r_e = \frac{R_C}{3}$$

so that

$$R_E + r_e = \frac{4700}{3}$$

$$= 1567\Omega.$$

Subtracting r_e (52 ohms) and using the nearest EIA resistor value we will make R_E equal 1500 ohms.

The idling voltage across R_E is (1500 ohms) (0.5 milliampere) $= 0.75$ volt for $I_C \approx I_E$. Supply voltage E_{CC} is equal to the sum of the

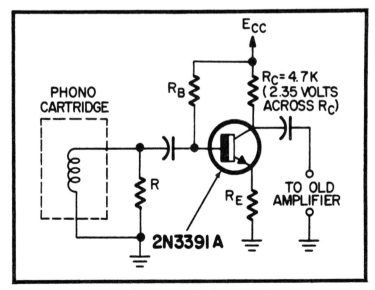

Fig. 4-12. Phono preamplifier designed for the text problem.

quiescent voltages across R_E and R_C, added to V_{CE}, or $0.75 + 2.35 + 2 = 5.10$ volts. Use a small 6-volt battery for E_{CC} to power the circuit.

Bias resistor R_B can now be determined. The base current is the collector current, 0.5 milliampere, divided by the average beta of the 2N3391A, or 400. Doing the arithmetic, it is 1.25 microamperes (1.25×10^{-6} ampere). Current flowing through the base-emitter junction is E_{CC} divided by the sum of R_E reflected into the base circuit and R_B. Write the simple Ohm's law relationship for $I = E/R$, letting $V_{BE} = 0.6$ volt:

$$1.25 \times 10^{-6} = \frac{6 - 0.6}{R_B + \beta R_E} \qquad (4\text{-}21)$$

$$1.25 \times 10^{-6} [R_B + 400 (1500)] = 6 - 0.6 \qquad (4\text{-}22)$$

Solving for R_B we find 3.72×10^6 ohms. Use a EIA standard 3.9-megohm resistor.

The minimum overall resistance of the base circuit should now be calculated. If this resistance is more than the required 47 kilohms the cartridge must see, a resistor is to be placed across the cartridge in parallel with the base resistance. The combination of this resistor in parallel with the base circuit resistance must amount to about 47 kilohms.

The impedance reflected into the base due to $r_e + R_E$ for the minimum beta of 250 for the 2N3391A transistor is $250 (1500 + 52) = 388$ kilohms. The cartridge sees this resistance in parallel with R_B, or approximately 350 kilohms. If the cartridge is to see 47 kilohms a resistor must be placed across the cartridge to parallel the 350 kilohms. Using the usual equations for parallel resistors (R_P is equal to the resistance of the two resistors, R and R_1, connected in parallel),

$$\frac{1}{R_P} = \frac{1}{R} + \frac{1}{R_1} \qquad (4\text{-}23)$$

or

$$R_P = \frac{R\,R_1}{R + R_1} \qquad (4\text{-}23a)$$

we can calculate the resistor to be placed across the cartridge. Letting $R_P = 47$ kilohms and $R_1 = 350$ kilohms Equation 4-23 becomes

$$\frac{1}{47,000} = \frac{1}{R} + \frac{1}{350,000} \qquad (4\text{-}24)$$

hence

$$\frac{1}{R} = \frac{1}{47,000} - \frac{1}{350,000} \qquad (4\text{-}24a)$$

and

$$R = 54,290 \qquad (4\text{-}24b)$$

therefore, use a 56-kilohm 10% EIA standard resistor for R.

Output impedance as well as current and power gains are not important in this problem. Gains can easily be calculated by substituting the numbers into Equations 4-4 and 4-5, as follows:

$$A_i = \beta = 400$$
$$G = A_i A_v = 400 \times 3 = 1200$$

R_{OUT} is more difficult to calculate because the transistor manufacturers do not supply all the data required for substitution into the equation; however, the old amplifier sees the collector load resistor, R_c, of the single stage shunting R_{OUT}. As far as the old amplifier is concerned this stage has an output impedance of about 4700 ohms because R_c is much smaller than R_{OUT}.

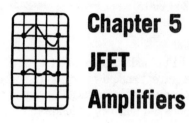

Chapter 5
JFET
Amplifiers

Bipolar amplifiers can be conveniently divided into two groups—the small-signal voltage-gain types and the large-signal groups designed to deliver high power. Until recently, there were no power FETs for use in entertainment equipment. Now, we have the VFET power transistor. In this chapter we parallel the discussion on small-signal bipolar amplifiers, disregarding the VFET for the moment.

Three basic circuit arrangements are frequently used: the common-source, common-drain (source follower) and common-gate configurations. They are similar to their bipolar transistor counterparts. The most useful one, the common-source type, is at the center of most discussions here, but characteristics of the remaining two circuits are not ignored.

CIRCUIT CHARACTERISTICS

As is the case with bipolar devices different equivalent JFET circuits are possible. An approximate equivalent of the transistor itself is shown in Fig. 5-1. It will also suffice as an equivalent circuit for the common-drain mode of operation when audio-frequency designs are considered.

At first glance there is one obvious difference between this circuit and that drawn for bipolar devices in Chapter 4. Capacitors are integral components in the FET equivalent circuits. Reactive components have a negligible effect when compared to the resistive elements in the small-signal bipolar equivalents, and are thus omitted from bipolar equivalent circuits. Because high impedance is an important attribute of the FET, shunt and series capacitors gain new significance at audio frequencies.

Significant capacitance exists between the gate and source, C_{gs}, and between the gate and drain, C_{gd}. The input voltage, e_i, sees capacitance rather than resistance. Therefore, we talk about the

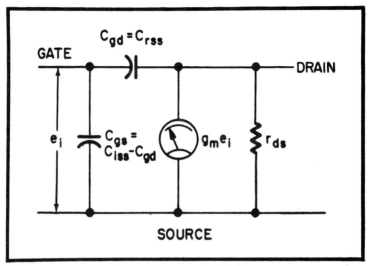

Fig. 5-1. Equivalent circuit of a JFET operating in the common-source mode.

input impedance, Z_{IN}, of a device rather than the input resistance. The above capacitances are instrumental in limiting the high-frequency response of an amplifier stage. It is fortunate that these capacitances are small, being but a few picofarads (pF) in size.

Two capacitances other than C_{gs} and C_{gd} are frequency stated in the specifications. These are C_{iss}, the input capacity when the drain is bypassed to the source, and C_{rss}, the gate-to-drain capacity with the gate bypassed to the source. While $C_{rss} = C_{gd}$, $C_{iss} = C_{gs} + C_{gd}$. The latter relationship is obvious for by the definition of C_{iss}, C_{gs} is shunted by C_{gd} when the drain is connected to the source.

For JFETs the output capacitance between the drain and source is negligible and is not shown in the equivalent circuit. In this chapter we consider all capacitances in the equivalent circuit as negligible. This is not a wild approximation when designing circuits that apply to all but the top frequencies in the audio spectrum. Nevertheless, it is important to realize that the frequency limitations do exist: therefore, we must keep in mind the capacitance relationships just discussed.

The channel drain-to-source resistance, r_{ds}, and the current source, $g_m e_i$, are significant and important factors in determining the characteristics of the device in a circuit at any frequency. These factors, when added to components in the surrounding circuit, are used in various equations to describe the performance of a particular arrangement.

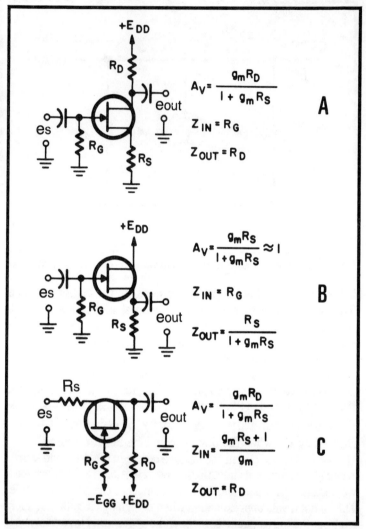

Fig. 5-2. FET circuit arrangement with formulas to calculate the characteristics of each circuit. A is a common-source circuit. B is a common-drain circuit (source follower) and C is a common-gate circuit.

Input impedance Z_{IN} and output impedance Z_{OUT} are two important characteristics of the circuits. The only other characteristic of importance needed to describe an audio JFET circuit is voltage gain A_V. Unlike the bipolar device current and power gains are insignificant factors. The effects of the capacitors in the equivalent circuits are discussed later.

Various circuit arrangements and the significant approximate equations describing the circuits are shown in Fig. 5-2. Input and output impedances are seen by looking into the transistor from the e_s source and the e_{OUT} terminals, respectively. Various symbols in the equations require elaboration. Several modifications must also be included to account for circuit components not shown in the drawings.

Start with R_D. In the equations it is the load resistor in the drain circuit. Should the transistor manufacturer specify a drain-to-source resistance, r_{ds}, that is comparable to R_D, then R_D in Fig. 5-2 is no longer the resistance to be used in the equation. Instead, substitute R_L for R_D, where R_L is a resistance equal to the parallel combination of R_D and r_{ds}.

Take this one step further. If the load at the output terminals is similar in size to R_D it must also be considered as paralleling R_D and r_{ds} to form R_L. Resistance R_D is stated in the equation rather than R_L because in audio designs, r_{ds} and other paralleling loads are usually (not always) negligible when compared with R_D.

Now, let us turn our attention to R_S and R_G. Any resistor of comparable size shunting either of these will automatically make the equation results inaccurate. Shunting components must be added in parallel with these resistors before numbers are plugged into any of the equations. This calculation must be made regardless of the paralleling component, be it a shunting resistor, capacitor or inductor. In the latter two cases, the shunting impedance due to an inductance is 6.28fL and the impedance due to a capacitor is 1/6.28fC, where f is the frequency in hertz, L is the inductance in henrys and C is the capacity in farads.

The final symbol of interest in the equations is g_m. Quantity g_m is the actual transconductance of the FET at a specific quiescent drain current, I_D. It is related to g_{mo}, the transconductance when the drain current is equal to I_{DSS}, by the equation:

$$g_m = g_{fs} = y_{fs}{}^* = g_{mo} \left(\frac{I_D}{I_{DSS}}\right)^{\frac{1}{2}} \tag{5-1}$$

I_{DSS} is the drain current when the gate-to-source voltage, V_{GS}, is equal to zero. As a rule of thumb, g_{mo} is approximately equal to $1/r_{dso}$, where r_{dso} is the drain-to-source resistance as determined

---

* In Equation 5-1, y_{fs} is equated to g_m and g_{fs}. And g_m and g_{fs} are identical. At low frequencies, they are equal to y_{fs}, the common-source transadmittance. Since y_{fs} includes the capacitor in the equivalent circuit, it is much larger than g_{fs} at high frequencies, where g_{fs} is more significant.

from the $V_{GS} = 0$ curve in the ohmic region. Both g_{mo} and I_{DSS} can be found on transistor specification sheets.

A range rather than a single value of g_{mo} is usually stated in the specification sheets. Pinchoff voltage and I_{DSS} are treated in a like manner on data sheets. (See Fig. 3-1 for a plot describing V_P and I_{DSS}.) Should one or the other of these factors be missing in the data it can be found from the equation:

$$g_{mo} |V_P| = 2 I_{DSS} \qquad (5\text{-}2)$$

where $|V_P|$ is the pinchoff voltage with the polarity disregarded.

A PROCEDURAL EXAMPLE

It would be simple here to pursue the standard procedures when presenting an example in the design of an amplifier stage. Design would follow a carefully chosen set of steps and all calculations would produce whole numbers. Unfortunately little can be learned from this. No design is as straightforward as it appears on the printed page. In the example that follows, I present a method used by many design engineers. Solutions are tried and discarded for different reasons, even after many calculations. In the problem it is first attempted to use a less expensive FET. Finally a slightly more expensive device is found necessary to satisfy all requirements. In the final circuit much of the original work is discarded in favor of a better, simpler and cheaper design.

This is a procedure concluding with a design. It is detailed here to present facts as well as to indicate to you the mental gymnastics you must go through to derive the compromise between the best and the most economical circuit. Parameter variations with temperature are disregarded since they are thoroughly discussed in Chapter 3.

A procedure detailed in Chapter 4 concerns the design of a stage of gain using a bipolar transistor. The basic design included a voltage signal source with a maximum 20-millivolt peak output for high-amplitude signals feeding a voltage amplifier stage with a gain of three. The voltage across the load resistor at the output of this stage was designed to be capable of a minimum swing of

$$\pm\, 20 \times 3 = \pm 60 \text{ mV}$$

The stage was required to present a 47-kilohm load to the source and its output was to look into a 47-kilohm resistor. Let us redesign this stage, but this time use an N-channel JFET.

In choosing a circuit the common-drain arrangement must be excluded because the voltage gain here is less than three (actually it is somewhat less than unity). The common-gate circuit cannot be used because the input impedance is about R_S, and R_S is normally much less than the required 47 kilohms. By the process of elimination only the common-source circuit remains. Start by designing for the circuit in Fig. 5-2A.

The drain resistor is chosen here on the same basis as the collector resistor was chosen for the bipolar device. The effect of any load on the circuit must be negligible. R_D, the drain resistor, should be less than one-tenth the size of the load it must feed, or 10% of 47 kilohms. Let $R_D = 4700$ ohms. The current swing across this resistor is at least

$$\frac{\pm 60 \text{ mV}}{4700\Omega} \approx \pm 13 \ \mu A.$$

This is indeed a very small current.

Let us try an initial paper design by choosing an inexpensive 2N4302 to do the job. Due to transistor tolerances within this type I_{DSS} can be any value between 0.5 milliamperes and 5 milliamperes, and the device can still pass as a standard 2N4302. From the curves supplied by the manufacturer it is estimated that the pinchoff voltage is 0.8 volt when I_{DSS} is 0.5 milliampere and 3.3 volts when I_{DSS} is 5 mA. Using Equation 5-2 the respective g_{mo} values are 1.25 $\times 10^{-3}$ mohs and 3×20^{-3} mhos.

Now determine if this transistor can do the job. Draw the approximate transfer characteristic curves as shown in Fig. 5-3. This is executed by connecting the maximum I_{DSS} point to the respective maximum pinchoff voltage point on the V_{GS} axis with a straight line; then repeat this procedure for the minimum values of these characteristics.

Quiescent drain current and drain-to-source voltage are the next items to be considered. It is obvious from the drain characteristic curve in Fig. 3-1 that V_{DS} should not be allowed to drop below 1.5 times the pinchoff voltage if we are to operate within the linear pinchoff region of the curves. Idling gate-to-source voltage V_{GS} should be about two-thirds of the pinchoff voltage at a minimum so that drain current changes with V_{GS} will be relatively linear.

Idling current is most critical on the lower curve in Fig. 5-3 because the current swing is limited to only 0.5 milliampere. Minimum idling V_{GS} limited to two-thirds V_P can be set at 0.5 volt so the idling current becomes 0.19 milliampere. It can easily swing the required ± 13 microamperes around this value without forcing the JFET into pinch-off.

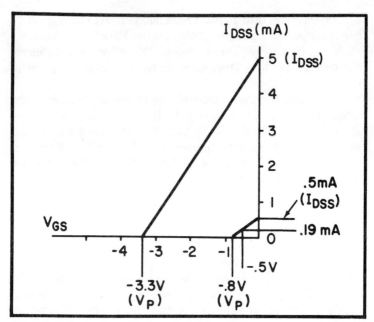

Fig. 5-3. Approximation of the transfer characteristic curves for the 2N4302.

Transconductance at a 0.19-milliampere drain current from Equation 5-1 is

$$g_m = g_{mo} \left(\frac{I_D}{I_{DSS}}\right)^{\frac{1}{2}} \tag{5-3}$$

$$= (1.25 \times 10^{-3}) \left(\frac{0.19}{0.5}\right)^{\frac{1}{2}} \tag{5-3a}$$

$$= 0.76 \times 10^{-3} \tag{5-3b}$$

where transconductance g_m is in units of mhos. Using the common-source equation in Fig. 5-2A the maximum possible gain, assuming $R_s = 0$, is

$$g_m R_D = (0.76 \times 10^{-3})(4.7 \times 10^3)$$
$$= 3.6$$

At first glance the gain of 3.6 is satisfactory. Consider that source resistor R_s must be shorted to obtain this gain. The source resistor is important. Distortion-reducing feedback voltage is normally developed across R_s. For example, if the gain were to be 6 rather than 3.6, half the gain may be discarded by developing a feedback voltage across the source resistor. This feedback will cause the distortion generated in this amplifier to be reduced by a factor of two. Although using a 2N4302 is nearly satisfactory, we should do better.

We can choose a somewhat higher gain and higher priced transistor such as the 2N4303. It has a minimum g_{mo} of 2000. Do the rough estimations to determine if this device will work. Specifications for the 2N4303 reveal the following characteristics. Current I_{DSS} can assume values anywhere between 4 and 10 mA. The respective pinchoff voltages are 2.9 and 5 volts. Using Equation 5-2 it can be shown that $g_{mo} = 2.75$ times 10^{-3} mhos for a device in which the $I_{DSS} = 4$ mA and $g_{mo} = 4$ times 10^{-3} for a 2N4303 with an I_{DSS} of 10 mA. Draw the approximate transfer characteristic curves for this transistor as in Fig. 5-4.

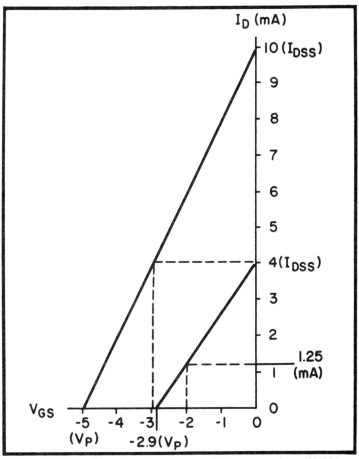

Fig. 5-4. Approximation of the transfer characteristic curves for a 2N4303.

Minimum quiescent V_{GS} is chosen on the lower curve at ⅔V_P or at about 2 volts. Idling current for the 2N4303 with this extreme characteristic is 1.25 mA. The g_m at this idling current from Equation 5-1 is

$$g_m = (2.75 \times 10^{-3}) \, (\frac{1.25}{4})^{1/2}$$
$$= 1.5 \times 10^{-3} \text{ mhos.}$$

The maximum possible gain is

$$g_m R_D = (1.5 \times 10^{-3}) \, (4.7 \times 10^3)$$
$$= 7.$$

This gain is more satisfactory than was possible with the 2N4302.

As for a transistor with characteristics approximated by the upper transfer curve the idling gate-to-source voltage at about two-thirds of V_P is 3 volts while the quiescent drain current is 4 milliamperes. The g_m at this current is

$$g_m = (4 \times 10^{-3}) \, (\frac{4}{10})^{1/2}$$
$$= 2.5 \times 10^{-3} \text{ mhos.}$$

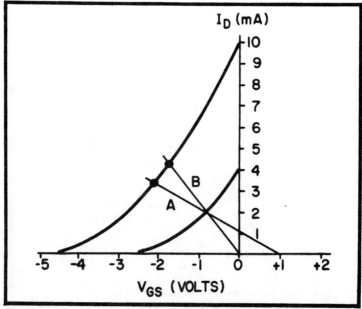

Fig. 5-5. Plot of reasonably exact transfer curves for a 2N4303 at 25°C. The curves represent the two extremes of the characteristics for this type. Line A is a plot of 1/Rs for the circuits in Fig. 5-6. Line B is a plot of 1/Rs for the circuit in Fig. 5-7.

Table 5-1. Points on curves in Fig. 5-5.

Determination of transfer characteristic curves from equation $I_D = I_{DSS} (1 - |V_{GS}|/|V_P|)^2$ for 2N4303 transistor. The equation is used to derive the curves for the extreme conditions when $I_{DSS} = 4$ mA, $|V_P| = 2.9$ volts and when $I_{PSS} = 10$ mA and $|V_P| = 5$ volts.

For $I_{PSS} = 4$ mA, $V_P = 2.9$ volts

V_{GS} volts	$I_{PSS} (1 - |V_{GS}|/|V_P|)^2$	I_D mA
0	$4(1 - 0/2.9)^2$	4
1	$4(1 - 1/2.9)^2$	1.71
2	$4(1 - 2/2.9)^2$	0.38
2.9	$4(1 - 2.9/2.9)^2$	0

For $I_{DSS} = 10$ mA, $V_P = 5$ volts

0	$10 (1 - 0/5)^2$	10
1	$10 (1 - 1/5)^2$	6.4
2	$10 (1 - 2/5)^2$	3.6
3	$10 (1 - 3/5)^2$	1.6
4	$10 (1 - 4/5)^2$	0.4
5	$10 (1 - 5/5)^2$	0

The maximum possible gain for this particular device is, therefore,

$$(2.5 \times 10^{-3}) (4.7 \times 10^3) = 11.8.$$

Gain using a 2N4303 with an I_{DSS} of 10 milliamperes is as satisfactory as the gain of the 2N4303 with the I_{DSS} at the lower extreme.

Convinced that we have a good chance to complete the design using a 2N4303, draw fairly exact transfer characteristic curves for this device. This can be accomplished using the equation in Chapter 3:

$$I_D = I_{DSS} \ (1 - \frac{|V_{GS}|}{|V_P|})^2 \qquad (3\text{-}1)$$

where I_D is the drain current that will flow when $|V_{GS}|$, the absolute value of the gate-to-source voltage, is applied between these leads. Substituting numbers into the equation yields the curves in Fig. 5-5. One curve is for a device where I_{DSS} is at its maximum of 10 milliamperes and the other for a 2N4303 with an I_{DSS} at 4 milliamperes. We will assume operation is at 25°C. See Table 5-1 for the various points to be plotted as determined from the equation.

On the lower curve the orginally estimated quiescent voltage was $V_{GS} = -2$ volts. Using the exact transfer characteristic curve in Fig. 5-5 we now find that the actual drain current at $V_{GS} = -2$ volts is $I_D = 0.38$ milliampere. The actual g_m at this current is

$$g_m = (2.75 \times 10^{-3}) (\frac{0.38}{4})^{1/2}$$

$$= 0.84 \times 10^{-3} \text{ mhos.}$$

And the maximum gain,

$$A_V = g_m R_D$$

as determined from these exact curves, is

$$A_V = (0.84 \times 10^{-3}) (4.7 \times 10^3)$$
$$= 3.95.$$

This gain is too close to the required gain of three. We should actually have a minimum gain of about six without feedback so that we can apply 6 dB of feedback to reduce the gain and distortion to half. To establish this as the minimum gain on the lower curve use the following procedure. Substituting numbers into the gain equation,

$$A_V = g_m R_D$$

and solving for g_m; that is,

$$g_m = \frac{A_V}{R_D}$$

we find that

$$g_m = \frac{6}{4.7 \times 10^3}$$

$$= 1.28 \times 10^{-3} \text{ mhos.}$$

The minimum drain current for this g_m can be derived using Equation 5-1, where

$$g_m = g_{mo} \left(\frac{I_D}{I_{DSS}}\right)^{\frac{1}{2}}$$

Solving for I_D we find that

$$I_D = 4 \times 10^{-3} \left(\frac{1.28 \times 10^{-3}}{2.75 \times 10^{-3}}\right)^2$$

$$= 0.87 \text{ mA.}$$

Solving for I_D we find that it must be at least 0.87 milliampere. We will arbitrarily select the value of 2 milliamperes for I_D since it is an easy number to work with and it is greater than 0.87 milliampere. Set V_{GS} to -0.82 volt and the bias point on the lower curve.

As for the upper curve the orginally estimated quiescent voltage was $V_{GS} = -3$ volts. Using the exact curve in Fig. 5-5 we note that $I_D = 1.6$ milliamperes. This value, 1.6 milliamperes, is less than the quiescent current just calculated for the lower curve. Proceed up the $I_{DSS} = 10$ mA curve and select a point where the idling current will be higher than that chosen for the lower curve. Let us use, for example, $I_D = 3.4$ milliamperes, and $V_{GS} = -2.1$ volts. At this drain current

$$g_m = (4 \times 10^{-3}) \left(\frac{3.4}{10}\right)^{\frac{1}{2}}$$

$$= 2.33 \times 10^{-3} \text{ mhos}$$

so that the maximum gain for a transistor with characteristics along the maximum I_{DSS} curve is

$$A_v = (2.33 \times 10^{-3}) (4.7 \times 10^3)$$

$$\approx 11$$

Connect the point determined on the upper curve to the point on the lower curve with line A. The reciprocal of the slope of this line is the resistance of R_S; that is,

$$R_S = \frac{2.1 - 0.82}{0.0034 - 0.002}$$

$$= 914 \ \Omega.$$

Use a standard EIA 910-ohm 5% resistor for R_S. Extend line A to the horizontal axis at +1 volt. This positive voltage must be placed between the gate and ground. (See Chapter 3.) The circuit will initially take the shape shown in Fig. 5-6A. We must now proceed to determine the remaining components in the circuit.

The minimum drain supply voltage, E_{DD}, is the sum of the maximum voltage across R_D and R_S added to the minimum voltage that can be placed between the source and drain of the FET. To be certain that the FET is operating in the pinch-off region, the minimum voltage across the transistor should be

$$1.5V_{P(max)} = 1.5(6) = 9 \text{ volts.}$$

The maximum pinch-off voltage is specified by the manufacturer of the 2N4303 as 6 volts. The maximum voltage across R_D and R_S is

$$I_{D(max)} (R_D + R_S) = (3.4 \times 10^{-3}) (4700 + 910)$$

$$= 19 \text{ volts.}$$

It follows then that E_{DD} must be at least

$$19 + 9 = 28 \text{ volts}$$

Use a 30-volt supply.

Using the information that $E_{DD} = 30$ volts and that 1 volt must be across R_X we can now write two simultaneous equations to determine R_X and R_G. The circuit must present a 47-kilohm resistance to the signal source. As far as the input is concerned, R_X is in parallel with R_G. Therefore, one equation is

$$\frac{R_G R_X}{R_G + R_X} = 47,000$$

And 1 volt is to be dropped across R_X. Resistances R_G and R_X form a voltage divider with 30 volts, E_{DD}, applied across them. The second equation is

$$1 = 30(\frac{R_X}{R_G + R_X}).$$

An approximate solution to the two equations yields

$$R_X = 49K$$

and

$$R_G = 1.5M.$$

The 910-ohm resistor in the source reduces the gain due to feedback. From the $I_{DSS} = 4$ mA curve, where g_m is 1.95×10^{-3} mhos, the overall gain of the circuit using the equation in Fig. 5-2 is

$$A_V = \frac{(1.95 \times 10^{-3})(4.7 \times 10^3)}{1 + (1.95 \times 10^{-3})(910)}$$
$$= 3.3$$

This is somewhat less than the required gain of three. To get a gain of 4.5, the maximum R_S is determined from the same gain equation; that is,

$$R_S = \frac{g_m R_D - A_V}{g_m A_V.}$$

And solving the equation by substituting the known quantities we find that

$$R_S = \frac{(1.95 \times 10^{-3})(4.7 \times 10^3)\,4.5}{(1.95 \times 10^{-3})(4.5)}$$
$$= 532\,\Omega$$

Let's use 560 ohms for the value of R_S. Since 560 ohms is less than the 910 ohms calculated from the curves the 910-ohm resistor can be split into two parts, 560 ohms and 350 ohms. (See Fig. 5-6B.) The 350-ohm resistor is to be bypassed with a large capacitor so that it will not affect the gain but will still be in the circuits to help set the quiescent bias voltage. Feedback voltage affecting gain and distortion will be developed only across the 560 ohms. The capacitor across the 350-ohm resistor should be large enough to short the resistor at the lowest audio frequency to be amplified.

An alternate method can be used to eliminate resistor R_G. This is desirable since any ripple in the power supply is fed through this resistor to the gate and amplified by the JFET. To accomplish this

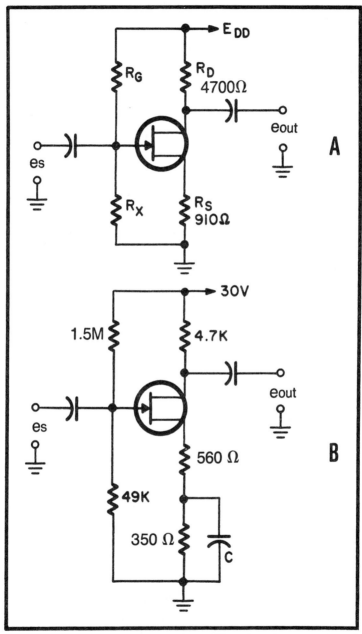

Fig. 5-6. Designs using a 2N4303 with a positive voltage between gate and ground to buck the negative voltage developed across Rs. The initial rough design is shown at A. At B the circuit is slightly altered to add feedback across the 780-ohm resistor.

113

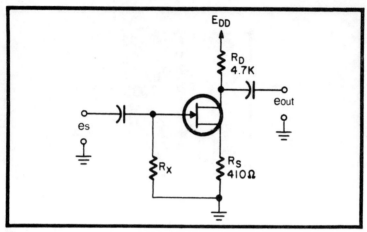

Fig. 5-7. This simplified circuit saves the cost of two resistors and a large electrolytic capacitor.

goal extend line B in Fig. 5-5 from the point on the lower I_{DSS} curve to a zero V_{GS} point on the axis so that no positive voltage will be required across Rx. The reciprocal of the slope of curve B is

$$R_S = \frac{0.82 - 0}{0.002 - 0}$$
$$= 410\Omega.$$

Since this is less than the maximum $R_S = 560$ ohms above the gain will be more than satisfactory, although the feedback and distortion reduction will not be as pronounced. The simplified circuit in Fig. 5-7 can now be used, omitting the capacitor in the source, the 1.5-megohm resistor and one of the source resistors.

Input resistor Rx is the 47 kilohms the source must see. Maximum idling current is 4.25 milliamperes, determined by extending line B to the upper curve in Fig. 5-5. The minimum drain voltage supply is

$$E_{DD} = I_{D(max)} (R_D + R_S) + 1.5V_{P\ (max)}.$$

Solving this equation by inserting the known values we find that

$$E_{DD} = (4.25 \times 10^{-3}) (4700 + 410) + 1.5(6)$$
$$= 30.7 \text{ volts.}$$

A 30-volt supply will suffice. The JFET will just work a bit closer to the rounded pinch-off voltage portion of the characteristic curve in Fig. 3-1.

Which design is more desirable? Try both and decide for yourself. Some adjustment to both circuits may be necessary in the laboratory.

Chapter 6
Noise in
Audio Amplifiers

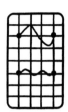

Any undesirable voltage or current associated with a signal may be classified as noise. It is intolerable when it interferes with the enjoyment of the signal or completely obscures it.

Noise associated with amplifying devices can be due to environmental radiation from arcing electrical devices and phenomena, or induction from AC electric supplies. The methods of minimizing interference from sources of this type are discussed in Chapter 12.

The random noise generated by passive and active devices in a circuit is of more immediate concern. When designing a circuit, it is frequently necessary to keep noise at a minimum. This is especially true in the high-gain first stage of an amplifier because noise generated here is boosted by all succeeding transistors.

Signal-to-noise is a measurement of the relative amount of noise present in reproduced intelligence. Conventional methods of measuring this involve feeding a midfrequency signal of average amplitude to the input of an amplifier, and noting the voltage, e_{so}, across the output load. Next remove the signal, place a resistor at the input equal to the impedance of the transducer or signal source to be used and once again measure the voltage. This second reading is the amount of noise voltage e_{no} riding along with the signal. The fraction of measured signal voltage to measured noise voltage is the signal-to-noise ratio for the amplifier.

Signal-to-noise fractions can also be power ratios. To determine the power ratio e_{so} and e_{no} are measured across the same output load resistor of the amplifier stage. Assume this load is R_L so that signal power P_{so} across the load is

$$P_{so} = \frac{e_{so}^2}{R_L}$$

and noise power P_{no} is

$$P_{no} = \frac{e_{no}^2}{R_L}$$

The signal-to-noise power ratio is

$$\frac{P_{so}}{P_{no}} = \left(\frac{e_{so}}{e_{no}} \right)^2.$$

The two signal-to-noise ratios, as defined from each other. The decibel, dB is defined as ten times the log of a ratio of two powers. Using a slight mathematical manipulation, dB can also be defined as twenty times the log of the ratio of two voltages when both voltages are measured across the same or equal resistors. The signal-to-noise ratio when expressed in dB, is the same regardless of the factor involved in the ratio—whether it be voltage or power. The equation relating to these ratios is:

$$dB = 10 \log \frac{P_{so}}{P_{no}}$$

$$= 20 \log \frac{e_{so}}{e_{no}} \qquad (6\text{-}1)$$

Table 6-1 is a chart that can be used with Equations 6-1 to relate any ratio in dB to the power and voltage ratios. If the voltage or power ratio is not shown in the table, the dB equivalent can easily be calculated from the data supplied. For example, a measured voltage ratio of 20:1 is not shown as such in Table 6-1. But ratios 4:1 and 5:1 are stated, and the product of the two ratios is 20:1. The ratio in dB for 4:1 is 12 dB and for 5:1 is 14 dB. These are added together—not multiplied as were the actual ratios. A voltage ratio of 20:1 is thus equivalent to 12 dB + 14 dB = 26 dB. The rule is: multiply two or

Table 6-1. Decibel voltage and power ratios.

POWER RATIO	VOLTAGE RATIO	dB
1:1	1:1	0
1.3:1	1,1:1	1
1.6:1	1.3:1	2
2:1	1.4:1	3
4:1	2:1	6
5:1	2.2:1	7
10:1	3.2:1	10
15.9:1	4:1	12
20:1	4.5:1	13
25:1	5:1	14
50.1:1	7:1	17
100:1	10:1	20
10000:1	100:1	40
10^6:1	10^3:1	60

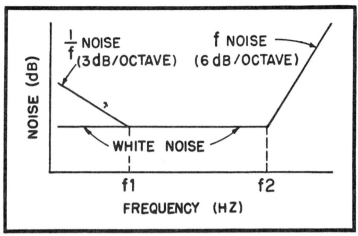

Fig. 6-1. Noise spectrum of a transistor.

more power or voltage ratios to equal a measured ratio, then add all the values representing these ratios.

A second example using identical procedures assumes a measured power ratio of 2.5:1. The 5:1 ratio *divided* by the 2:1 ratio will yield 2.5:1. The 5:1 ratio *divided* by the 2:1 ratio will yield 2.5:1. The respective ratios in dB are 7 and 3. Since one ratio is divided by the other, the numbers in dB must be *subtracted* from each other; hence a 2.5:1 power ratio is identical to 7 dB-3 dB = 4 dB.

ANALYZING THE NOISE SPECTRUM

The noise found in any transistor amplifier falls roughly into three groups. As shown in Fig. 6-1 there is one type of noise which covers the entire frequency spectrum. Identified as *white noise*, it delivers identical power at all frequencies. It can be generated by the random motion of particles in a conductor due to the energy imparted to these particles by heat. Because the noise is related to temperature it is also referred to as *thermal noise*. Any noise due to a resistor in the base or gate circuit is amplified by the bipolar transistor or FET. Bias resistors at the input circuit, or even the base resistance of bipolar transistors, are important sources of this type of noise.

Noise power produced by any resistor, P_{ni}, is governed by the equation:

$$P_{ni} = 1.37 \times 10^{-23} (273° + °C) B \qquad (6\text{-}2)$$

where the quantity is the temperature in degrees Celsius and B is the effective noise bandwidth. B is not the bandwidth of an amplifier in the usual sense of the word. Normally bandwidth is defined by the quantity $f_H - f_L$ where f_H and f_f are the high and low frequencies, respectively, at which the gain of the amplifier has dropped 3 dB (50 % reduction) from its center value. Noise bandwidth as applied to the equation is equal to the sum of the products of the gain and the respective frequency at each point of the entire frequency range divided by the maximum gain of the amplifier. It is quite a difficult and lengthy operation to derive B, even if integral calculus is used in the procedures. It is best to remember that in the usual case, where the rolloff of an amplifier is 6 dB per octave, the noise bandwidth, B, is 1.57 multiplied by the bandwidth of the amplifier at the 3 dB points.

When measurements are made the meter readings will correlate with Equation 6-2 if B is assumed to be the bandwidth just defined; however, this may not relate to the audible noise. Characteristics of the ear must be considered. From data it seems that the ear is most sensitive to approximately 2500 Hz and that the sensitivity decreases at frequencies on either side of this. Many tests have been performed and different standards established, each claiming to be the actual rolloff characteristic of the ear. From all of these it would seem reasonable to let $f_L = 800$ hertz and $f_H = 8000$ hertz so that audible B is

$$B = 1.57 \ (8000 - 800)$$
$$= 11.304 \text{ kHz.}$$

However inaccurate this figure may be, we will assume it to be valid in this book. It is sure to agree with someone's auditory characteristics. Arguments can be presented against this assumption, but it must be remembered that no two people have identical hearing curves. All other factors in Equation 6-2 are constants.

Available noise power is the maximum power that can be transferred from the noisy source resistor to the circuit in which it is used. This occurs when the resistor generating the noise power is equal to the resistance it sees in the circuit. In Fig. 6-2, an equivalent circuit shows the resistor as a source of noise. The noise-generating resistor is divided into two parts—a voltage, e_{ni}, noise source and a theoretical noiseless resistor R_{NI}—as an aid in the analysis. Term R_G can be the circuit input resistance of a transistor. For the maximum transfer of noise power from R_{NI} to R_G, $R_{NI} = R_G$. Resistance R_{NI} and R_G form a voltage divider. Because $R_{NI} = R_G$, the voltage across R_G and R_{NI} is e_{ni} 2. The power across R_G is $(e_{ni}/2)^2/$ divided by R_G, so that Equation 6-2 becomes

$$P_{ni} = e_{ni}^2/4R_G \qquad \text{(6-3A)}$$

and

$$e_{ni}^2 = 5.49 \times 10^{-23} \, (273° + °C) \, (B) \, (R_G) \qquad \text{(6-3B)}$$

The generated noise voltage is proportional to the square root of the size of the resistor creating it.

Life would be very simple if Equation 6-3 could be used just as it is stated. However, R_G must be modified when it is shunted by some arrangement of capacitors and/or inductors. This is the case in Fig. 6-3 where the transistor impedance is so high that it presents a capacitance, C_{in}, to the input source, rather than presenting only a resistance. The input can also be shunted by the capacitance of a voltage source such as a ceramic microphone or phonograph cartridge, shown as C_s in the figure. The total capacity, C_t, across R_G is $C_s + C_{in}$. Should the reactance of C_t at the noise midfrequency be less than about 10 times the size of R_G in the figure. R_G shown in Fig. 6-3 cannot be used as is in equations 6-3. The entire input impedance of the circuit must be considered and only the resistive component of the entire input impedance is R_G for the equation. This component is derived as follows.

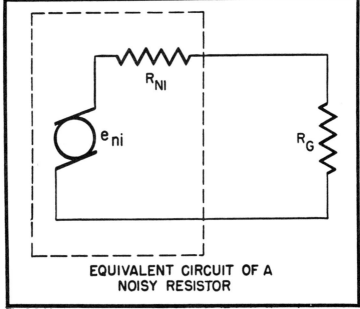

EQUIVALENT CIRCUIT OF A
NOISY RESISTOR

Fig. 6-2. Maximum noise power is transferred from the noise source when $R_{NI} = R_G$.

The reactance due to C_t is $j/\omega\, C_t$, where $\omega = 6.28f$ and f is the frequency (in Hertz) involved. The j notation indicates a 90° reactive phase shift where $j = \sqrt{-1}$. The resistor in parallel with C_t is R_h. The formula used to determine the impedance of the combination is similar to the one used to determine the equivalent resistance of two resistors, R_1 and R_2, in parallel or $R_1 R_2/(R_1 + R_2)$. Here, however, the effect of the j operator must be included. The total impedance is:

$$Z = \frac{-R_G\,(j/\omega\ C_e)}{R_G - j/\omega C_t} \tag{6-4}$$

Multiply the numerator and denominator by $R_G + j/\omega C_t$ and change $j^2 = (\sqrt{-1})\,(\sqrt{-1})$ to -1, and you have:

$$Z = \frac{\dfrac{-R_G^2 j}{\omega C_t} + \dfrac{R_G}{\omega^2 C_t^2}}{R_G^2 + 1/\omega^2 C_t^2} \tag{6-5}$$

Since R_G is assumed to be much greater than $1/\omega\ C_t$, the $1/\omega^2\ C_t^2$ in the denominator of the equation may be ignored when compared in magnitude to R_G^2. Since only the resistive component of the impedance is required, the j term in the numerator can be discarded. Then the R_G for use in equation 6-3 becomes:

$$R_G(\text{for Eq. 6-3}) = \frac{\dfrac{R_G}{\omega^2 C_t^2}}{\dfrac{R_G^2}{1}} = \frac{1}{R_G \omega^2 C_t^2} \tag{6-6}$$

where R_G is the actual resistance shown in Fig. 6-3, R_G (for Eq. 6-3) is the resistance of R_G derived using equation 6-6. This newly derived value for R_G is to be substituted for the R_G now in equation 6-3.

The frequency f (from the $\omega^2 = (2\pi f)^2$) is the geometric center frequency of the noise bandwidth. Thus, if the noise bandwidth B includes all frequencies between the limit of a high one at f_H and a low one at f_L, the frequency to be used for determining R_G is

$$f = \sqrt{f_L\ f_H}.$$

Using the derived formulas, adding a little calculus and making several minor approximations the information can be stated in a new formula similar to that in Equation 6-3B; that is,

$$e_{ni}^2 = (1.37 \times 10^{-24})\,(273° + °C)\left(\frac{B}{f_H\ f_L}\right)\left(\frac{1}{R_G C_t^2}\right) \tag{6-7}$$

where B, R_G and °C are identical to the values used in Equation 6-3. Terms C_t, f_H and f_L have been discussed in the text.

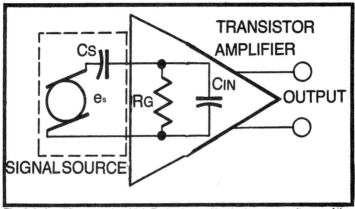

Fig. 6-3. Amplifier stage in which R_G is shunted by the input capacitance of the transistor, C_{in}, and the capacity of the signal source, C_s.

Looking back over the discussion just completed, you recall that we started examining the reasons for the existence of the noise spectrum in Fig. 6-1. We started to discuss white noise, then described the effects of an important white noise generator, the resistor. We also discussed how much of this noise generated by the resistor can be transferred to a circuit in which it is located. Thermal noise is not the only cause of the white noise spectrum. The *shot noise* phenomenon in semiconductor junctions is also a source. It is noise generated by the random passage of charged particles through the junctions. Shot noise increases with the quantity of current flowing through the device.

Emitter current of bipolar devices divides between the base and collector introducing *partition noise*. It is similar in nature to white noise. Obviously the noise is minimized when the beta of the transistor is large and the number of partitions is small.

In Fig. 6-1 the 6 dB per octave increase in noise at the upper frequencies is due to the rolloff of beta at the high end of the band rather than to any phenomenon different from that discussed above. This noise increase is usually noted at some radio frequency and is unimportant when considering audio designs.

Semiconductor noise at low frequencies drops at the *rate* of 3 dB per octave. The term 1/f noise is due to surface phenomena and leakage current. It is minimized when the current flowing through the bipolar transistor and the voltage across the device are low. Minimizing temperature goes a long way in reducing noise from this factor. As for the JFET this noise is least objectionable when the transconductance of the device is high.

121

The effect of $1/f$ noise is quite important in audio devices. While bipolar transistors are subject to this phenomenon up to 1,000 hertz, the effect becomes negligible at about 100 hertz when JFETs are involved. Transistors have been designed where noise due to the $1/f$ effect may be disregarded at frequencies far below those noted.

NOISE FIGURE

The signal-to-noise ratio at the input of an amplifying device is higher than at the output because of the contribution of the stage of gain to the noise at the output. Noise factor F relates the two signal-to-noise ratios.

$$F = \frac{P_{si}/P_{ni}}{P_{so}/P_{no}} \qquad (6\text{-}8)$$

where P_{si} and P_{so} are the input and output signal powers, respectively, and P_{ni} and P_{no} are the input and output noise powers, respectively. The optimum noise factor is unity, for only then will the input and output signal-to-noise ratios be equal, suffering no noise contribution from the amplifying device.

Since the power gain of an amplifier is $G=P_{so}/P_{si}$ the noise factor can be expressed as:

$$F = \frac{P_{no}}{GP_{ni}} \qquad (6\text{-}9)$$

where GP_{ni} is the input noise power multiplied by the power gain of the device, or the output noise power due to noise present at the input.

Using Table 6-1 the number for noise factor F in terms of a decibel ratio can easily be determined. When expressed in decibels the ratio is referred to as *noise figure*, *NF*. For example, the decibel equivalent of a power ratio of 2:1 is 3 dB; hence, a noise factor of two is identical to a noise figure of 3 dB.

The noise figure is specified in one of two ways. The more conventional data sheet indicates the *spot noise figure*. This is a maximum noise figure number at one frequency, usually 1000 hertz for a banawidth of 1 hertz. In an alternate method the noise figure is specified over the entire band. This latter number usually supplies more information covering both the white noise and the $1/f$ regions of the curve.

EQUIVALENT NOISE GENERATORS

Noise associated with the transistor circuit can be analyzed as being caused by three noise generators, one real and two hypothet-

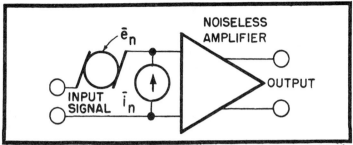

Fig. 6-4. Equivalent circuit to study noise generated in a transistor consists of a voltage noise generator, $\bar{e}_n$, and a current noise generator, $\bar{i}_n$.

ical, at the input to a theoretically noiseless amplifier. The real noise is generated by components connected to the input circuit and transferred to the amplifier stage. The noisy resistor generator discussed previously is an example of this. Two hypothetical noise generators—a voltage generator and a current generator—are within the transistor proper. They are considered as the only sources of noise produced within the amplifier. For analysis, they are drawn in an equivalent circuit in Fig. 6-4, where these two hypothetical noise generators are placed at the input of a noiseless amplifier.

Here we are to mathematically determine the effect of the transistor-generated noise on the circuit. We will use the equivalent circuit in Fig. 6-4 for this purpose. The noise-generating sources, $\bar{e}_n$ and $\bar{i}_n$ are separated from the actual transistor and placed at the input of the noiseless amplifying device. This is the equivalent circuit of an actual condition. The generators will cause the noise at the output of the transistor to be the same as it would be from an actual device in a real circuit.

The output noise is due to $\bar{e}_n$ when the input to the amplifier is shorted and is due to $\bar{i}_n$ when the input is open circuited. $\bar{e}_n$ can be calculated by using data obtained from two measurements—the noise voltage at the output when the input to the amplifier is shorted and the voltage gain, A_v. $\bar{e}_n$ is equal to the noise voltage at the output divided by A_v.

To determine $\bar{i}_n$, compare the output current when the input is an open circuit with the current present at the output with a known current source at the input.

The total noise power at the input, P_{nit}, consists of the actual thermal noise power in Equation 6-2, or $1.37 \times 10^{-23} (273° + °C)$ B (this may be due to a noisy source resistance located at the input to the amplifier), in addition to the noise power due to $\bar{e}_n$ and $\bar{i}_n$ in the

123

transmitter, or $\overline{e}_n{}^2/4R_G + \overline{i}_n{}^2R_G/4$. Here, R_G is the circuit input resistance. As before, it may require modification if the input capacitance is relatively large. All factors must be multiplied by G, the power gain of the transistor, if the result of the calculation is to be the noise at the output.

The actual noise power at the input only is assumed due to a noisy resistor located at the input, or is $1.37 \times 10^{-23} (273° + °C)B$. Substituting all the data in these two paragraphs into Equation 6-9 the noise factor in terms of $\overline{e}_n$ and $\overline{i}_n$ becomes:

$$F = \frac{P_{no}}{GP_{ni}} = \frac{GP_{nit}}{GP_{in}}$$

$$F = G\left[[1.37 \times 10^{-23} (273° + °C)B]\right] + \frac{\overline{e}_n{}^2}{4R_G} + \frac{\overline{i}_n{}^2R_G}{4} \quad (6\text{-}10)$$

$$F = 1 + \frac{\overline{e}_n{}^2/R_G + \overline{i}_n{}^2R_G}{5.49 \times 10^{-23}(273° + °C)B} \quad (6\text{-}11)$$

The noise figure is, of course, equal to the noise factor found in Equation 6-10 and expressed in dB.

From Equation 6-11 it can be determined that the noise factor is at a minimum when $R_G = e_n/i_n$. Substituting this into Equation 6-11, we find that the best noise factor that can be obtained for a particular transistor is about $(1 + \overline{e_n i_n})/2.74 \times 10^{-23} (273° + °C)B$.

Equation 6-10 can be rewritten in the form showing that the total input noise power affecting the output of the transistor is:

$$P_{nit} = P_{ni} F$$
$$= F(1.37 \times 10^{-23})(273° + °C)B$$
$$= \frac{\overline{e}^2_{nit}}{4R_G} \quad (6\text{-}12)$$

so that the total (real and hypothetical) input noise voltage that affects the output is:

$$\overline{e}_{nit} = [4R_GF(1.37 \times 10^{-23}) \times (273° + °C)B]^{1/2} \quad (6\text{-}13)$$

The input signal voltage must be compared with $\overline{e}_{nit}$ to determine the signal-to-noise ratio of a transistor circuit.

NOISE AND THE BIPOLAR TRANSISTOR

The variations of noise figure with collector current and source resistor can be described by the set of contour curves in Fig. 6-5. This is most useful in audio amplifier design. The maximum noise figure stated on data sheets usually specifies the characteristic at a

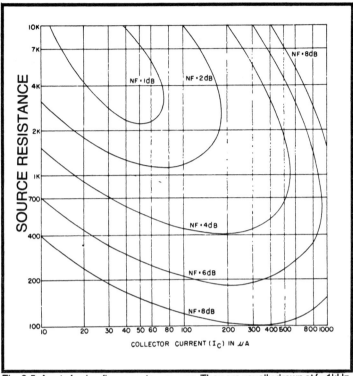

Fig. 6-5. A set of noise-figure contour curves. They are usually drawn at f=1kHz, T_A = 25C. (T_A is the ambient temperature).

specific collector current, collector voltage and frequency when a particular resistor is at the input. Using the curves, you can determine the noise figure for a coincident collector current and input resistor. Operation within the lowest contour assures you that the amplifier will deliver the minimum amount of noise to a load, within its capabilities.

In addition to the contour curves shown, other similar curves may be drawn. Some extremely wideband applications may require a set of contour curves showing how the noise figure is related to the input resistor at specific frequencies rather than at specific collector currents.

The source (input) resistance and I_c relationships can be split into two curves (Figs. 6-6A and B) showing the variation of NF with each of these factors. Another useful curve, in Fig. 6-6C, shows the variation of NF with frequency. All these curves are limited compared to the one in Fig. 6-5 because many factors must be specified before any one variable can be determined. Curves of this type supply information concerning one variable factor, while all others are usually held constant at their optimum values for minimum noise.

The design of an amplifier for low noise can be accomplished in several logical steps, beginning with the selection of the most suitable device. Should the source resistance be determined by circuit requirements, characteristic curves of different transistors should be checked to determine which device will contribute least to the noise when a reasonable amount of collector current is flowing. On the other hand, if only a specific device is available, the circuit should be designed so that operation is within its lowest applicable noise contour curve.

Once the device has been chosen, factors should be substituted into Equation 6-13 to calculate the noise voltage due to the transistor and the circuitry. The average input signal voltage to be fed to the device is compared with the generated noise determined from Equation 6-13, to decide if the signal-to-noise ratio is satisfactory.

As an example, use a magnetic phonograph cartridge to feed a preamplifier stage. The resistance of the cartridge, R_G, may be taken at 3000 ohms. A collector current near the lowest noise contour curve in Fig. 6-5 coincident with $R_G = 3000$ ohms is 50 microamperes. The noise figure is about 1 dB. From Table 6-1, a NF of 1 dB is equivalent is to a noise factor, F, of 1.3.

Assume the amplifier is to reproduce 20 to 20,000 Hz within 1 dB, so that the 3dB power points are at one octave beyond these frequencies, or at 10 and 40,000 Hz. The effective noise bandwidth is about $1.57 \times 40,000 = 63,000$ Hz. Substituting this into Equation 6-13, the noise voltage at 27 °C is:

$$\bar{e}_{nit} = [4(3 \times 10^3) \ (1.3) \ (1.37 \times 10^{-23}) \ (300) \ (6.3 \times 10^4)]^{\frac{1}{2}}$$
$$= 2.01 \times 10^{-6} \text{ volts}$$

Here, the worst case is assumed, where the source resistor is equal to the input resistance of the amplifier and the maximum poise power available is transferred to the transistor circuit.

The average output voltage from a magnetic cartridge may be assumed to be 2×10^{-3} volts. The ratio of signal-to-noise is $2 \times 10^{-3}/2.01 \times 10^{-6}$ which is approximately equal to 10^{-3}. From Table 6-1, a voltage ratio of 10^3:1 is 60 dB. This is a good specification for any amplifier.

The actual audible noise is less than the 2.01×10^{-6} volts multiplied by the voltage gain of the stage. The $2.01 \times 10^{-6}A_v$ is the noise usually measured on test instruments at the output of the

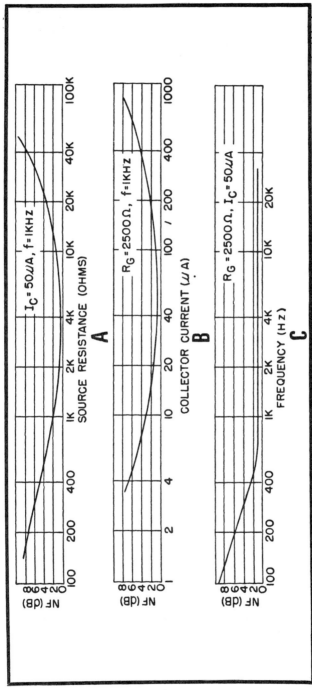

Fig. 6-6. These curves indicate how the noise figure varies with the source resistance, collector current and frequency for a hypothetical bipolar transistor. Curve A is a plot of the noise figure against the source resistance with the collector current and frequency held constant. Curve B is a plot of the noise figure against the collector current with the source resistance and frequency held constant. Curve C is a plot of the noise figure against frequency with the source resistance and collector current held constant.

127

amplfier. This is for a noise bandwidth of 63,000 Hz. As discussed above, a practical audible noise bandwidth is 11,300 Hz. Substituting this into Equation 13 yields:

$$\overline{e}_{nit} = [\, 4 \,(3 \times 10^3) \,(1.3)\,(1.37 \times 10^{-23})\,(300)\,(1.13 \times 10^4)\,]^{\frac{1}{2}}$$
$$= 0.85 \times 10^{-6} \text{ volts}$$

so that the signal-to-noise voltage ratio is $2 \times 10^{-3} / .85 \times 10^{-6} = 2.35 \times 10^3$. Using Table 6-1, we can proceed as we did earlier in the chapter to determine this ratio in dB. 2.35×10^3 can be separated into the product of 2.35 and 10^3. The closest dB figure for the 2.35:1 voltage ratio is 2.2:1 or 7 db. 10^3 is 60 dB. Hence, the signal-to-noise ratio is 60 db + 7 db = 67 db. The actual audible noise is 7 db better than the measured value.

As a general rule, bipolar transistor amplifiers should be designed with a minimum collector current and voltage as well as with the smallest practical source resistor in the base circuit.

NOISE AND THE JFET

In order to conform with convention, the definition of R_G in the following discussion differs from the meaning used previously in this chapter. Here, R_G is a resistor connected to the input of an FET. It is an actual physical resistor. It is not the resistance presented by the transistor to the input circuit. The symbol R_G was used with this definition only when bipolar noise was discussed and does not apply here. Because of the high input impedance of the FET, only a capacitance is assumed to be presented by it at its input terminals to a source of signal or noise.

JFET noise is not specified by using contour curves. Usually, individual curves are used to relate the noise figure to various factors affecting noise. Several typical curves spelling out these relationships are shown in Fig. 6-7.

Another set of curves relate $\overline{e}_n/\sqrt{\Delta f}$ and $\overline{i}_n/\sqrt{\Delta f}$, the noise voltage and current generators at the input to the hypothetical noiseless amplifier, to frequency. The curves are shown in Fig. 6-8. The $\sqrt{\Delta f}$ is the square root of the noise bandwidth of the circuit. The curves in Fig. 6-8 refer to the variations of $\overline{e}_n$ and $\overline{i}_n$ with frequency when the bandwidth is 1 Hz. Should the noise bandwidth be 2 Hz, the $\overline{e}_n/\sqrt{\Delta f}$ or $\overline{i}_n/\sqrt{\Delta f}$ read from the curve is to be multiplied by $\sqrt{2}$. In a similar manner, for a 100-Hz noise bandwidth, both readings are to be multiplied by $\sqrt{100}$ or 10.

Some specifications state $\overline{e}_n/\sqrt{\Delta f}$ (sometimes written $\overline{e}_n/\sqrt{\sim}$ or $\overline{e}_n/\sqrt{hz}$) for bandwidths other than 1 Hz. If, or example, it were specified for a 5-Hz bandwidth, the stated number should be first

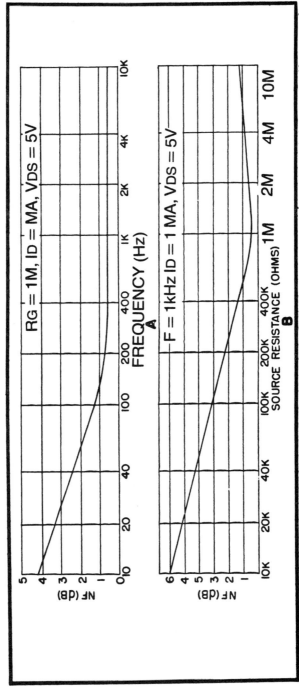

Fig. 6-7. Curves indicate how the noise figure varies with the size of the resistor at the input, drain-to-source voltage, drain current and frequency, for a hypothetical JFET. Curve A is a plot of noise figure against frequency with all other factors held constant at specified values. Curve B is a plot of the noise figure against the size of the resistor at the input, with all of the noise figure against the size of the resistor at the input, with all other factors held constant of the resistor at the input, with all other factors held constant at specified values.

129

divided by $\sqrt{.5}$ before proceeding to find the noise figure for the actual bandwidth involved. Once the correction is made, the procedure outlined in the paragraph above can be used. This also applies to determining $\bar{i}_n$ if a bandwidth other than 1 Hz is specified in the data.

In Fig. 6-3 it is indicated that input capacitors are associated with the transistor. These are important factors when calculating the noise associated with the JFET. It was indicated in Chapter 5 that there are two capacitances associated with transistors, namely C_{GS} and C_{CD}. Capacitance C_{in} in Fig. 6-3 is equal to $C_{gs} + C_{gd}(A_v + 1)$ where, as you recall, C_{gs} is the gate-to-source mode is, of course, approximately equal to the product of the drain resistor, R_D, and the transconductance, g_m. Along with C_{in} the capacity C_s of a transducer feeding the amplifier is important in determining transistor noise characteristics.

Capacitive and resistive inputs to the circuit affect the magnitude of noise and signal voltages applied to the input of the hypothetical amplifier. Quantities $\bar{e}_n$, $\bar{i}_n$ and input signal voltage e_s must be modified before they can be used to calculate the total noise and signal-to-noise ratio at the input of the JFET. The input noise is, of course, directly proportional to all noise at the output.

A circuit showing the various sources of noise referred to the input of the theoretical noiseless amplifier appears in Fig. 6-4. It is redrawn in Fig. 6-9 to include the input impedances along with the capacitance of the signal source C_s and the parallel combination of R_G and C_{in} form a voltage divider. If R_G is much larger than the reactance of $C_{in} + C_s$ the input signal voltage, e_{sa}, appearing at the amplifier proper is:

$$e_{sa} = \frac{e_s\, C_s}{C_{in} + C_s} \qquad (6\text{-}16)$$

while the noise voltage at the input of the noiseless amplifier is

$$\bar{e}_{na} = \frac{\bar{e}_n C_s}{C_{in} + C_s} \qquad (6\text{-}17)$$

Noise voltage at the input of the amplfier proper due to the current noise genertor, $\bar{e}_{nia}$, is the product of $\bar{i}_n$ with all the impedances across the input, or:

$$\bar{e}_{nia} = \frac{\bar{i}_n}{6.28f\,(C_s + C_{in})^2} \qquad (6\text{-}18)$$

where f is the frequency at the center of the noise spectrum and A_v is the voltage gain of the amplifier.

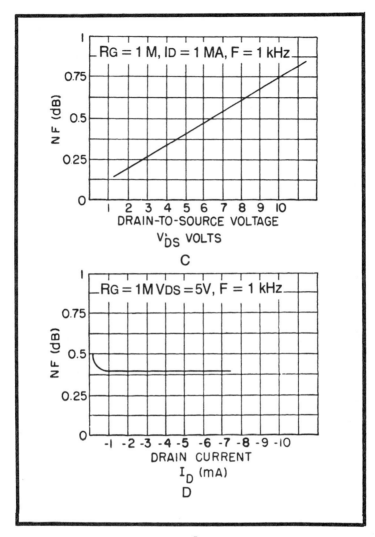

Fig. 6-7 (continued) Curve C is a plot of the noise figure against the drain-to-source voltage with all other factors held constant at specified values. Curve D is a plot of the noise figure against the drain current with all other factors held constant at specified values.

Should R_G not be much larger than the reactance of $C_{in} + C_s$ accuracy dictates that R_G be included in the derivation of $\bar{e}_{sa}$, $\bar{e}_{na}$ and $\bar{e}_{nia}$. As a rule of thumb disregard R_G if it is at least ten times larger than the parallel reactance of C_{in} and C_s. If the reactance of $C_{in} + C_s$ is at least ten times larger than R_G, use $\bar{e}_n$ and $\bar{I}_n$ without any of the modifications shown in the equations. When R_G and the reactance of

131

$C_{in} + C_s$ approach each other the simplest procedure is to calculate noise twice, once assuming R_G is relatively large using the modifications in Equations 6-16, 6-17 and 6-18, and then assuming R_G is relatively small. In the second calculation, use $\overline{e}_n$ and $\overline{I}_n$ from the curves without any modification. The noise is somewhere between the solutions to the two calculations. Estimate the noise by noting whether the capacitive reactance or the resistance dominates the input impedance and by how much.

The total noise voltage due to all sources is the square root of the sum of the squares of the noise voltages due to each individual source or:

$$\overline{e}_{nit} = (\overline{e}_{na}{}^2 + \overline{e}_{nia}{}^2 + e_{ni}{}^2)^{\frac{1}{2}} \qquad (6\text{-}19)$$

Individual noise voltages are defined by Equations 6-17, 6-18 and 6-16 respectively. Noise voltage $\overline{e}_n$ rather than $\overline{e}_{na}$ should be used if R_G is small compared to the reactance $C_{in} + C_s$. Quantity $\overline{e}_{nia}$, the voltage produced by the current generator, would in this case become $i_n R_G$ rather than the value calculated from Equation 6-18. Likewise, e_s rather than e_{sa} will be used when determining the signal at the input of the amplifier if R_G is much less than the reactance $C_{in} + C_s$.

It is now possible to determine the signal-to-noise ratio of an amplifying stage. As an example, assume that a ceramic phonograph cartridge delivers 0.1 volt at 1 kHz to a 5.6-megohm resistor load at the input of a JFET amplifier. The voltage gain of the amplifier is 10 while $C_{gd} = 3$ picofarads and $C_{gs} = 5$ picofarads. It follows then

$$C_{in} = C_{gs} + C_{gd} (A_V + 1).$$

Inserting the known values into the preceding equation shows

$$C_{in} = 5 + 3(10 + 1)$$
$$= 38 \text{ pF}.$$

The 3 dB bandwidth from 10 hertz to 40 kilohertz is the same as in the previous problem so that the noise bandwidth is 1.57×40 kilohertz = 63 kilohertz. The geometric center frequency for this bandwidth is $(10 \times 40{,}000)^{\frac{1}{2}} = 632$ hertz. Use the transistor described by the curves in Figs. 6-7 and 6-8.

Curves in Fig. 6-9 supply us with the information that at 632 hertz

$$\frac{\overline{e}_n}{\sqrt{\Delta f}} \approx \frac{0.085 \ \mu V}{\sqrt{\Delta f}}$$

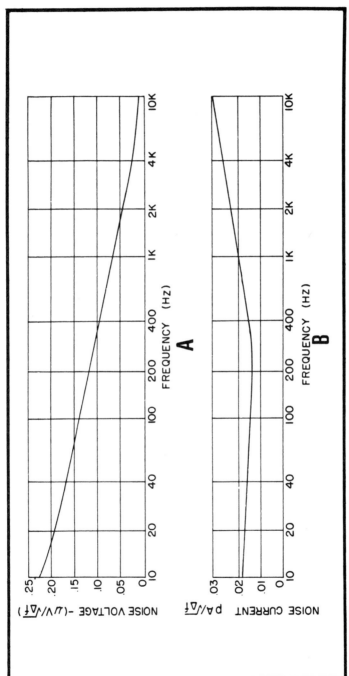

Fig. 6-9. Relationship of the hypothetical noise voltage to frequency (A) and the relationship of hypothetical noise current to frequency (B).

133

and

$$\frac{\overline{i_n}}{\sqrt{\Delta f}} \approx \frac{0.0175 \text{ pA}}{\sqrt{\Delta f}.}$$

Quantity Δf is 63 kilohertz so that $\sqrt{\Delta f}$ is 250 hertz. The actual $\overline{e_n}$ for substitution into Equation 6-17 is

$$\overline{i_n} = (250) (0.0175)$$
$$= 4.4 \text{ pA}$$

or 4.4 picoamperes. Considering that C_{in} was calculated at 38 picofarads and that C_s was stated at 500 picofarads the total reactance at 632 hertz due to the capacitors is

$$Z = \frac{1}{(6.28)(632)(538 \times 10^{-12})}$$
$$= 468318$$

or approximately 500 kilohms. Because this is less than 10% of R_G the modifications dictated by Equations 6-16, 6-17 and 6-18 must be used. That is, from Equation 6-16 we find

$$e_{sa} = \frac{(0.1)(500)}{38 + 500}$$
$$= 0.093 \qquad (6\text{-}20a)$$

from Equation 6-17 we find

$$(6\text{-}20b)$$
$$e_{na} = \frac{(21.2 \times 10^{-6})(500)}{(38 + 500)}$$
$$= 19.7 \times 10^{-6}$$

and from Equation 6-18 we find

$$e_{nis} = \frac{(4.4 \times 10^{-12})}{(6.28)(632)(500 + 38)} \qquad (6\text{-}20c)$$
$$= 2.07 \times 10^{-18}$$

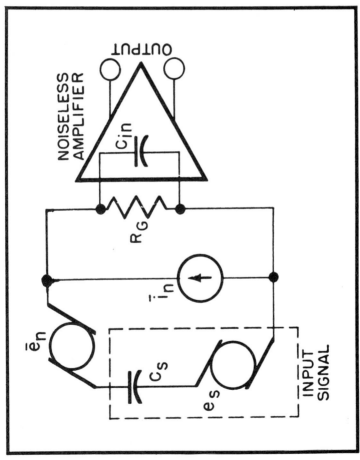

Fig. 6-10. Circuit drawn to include the effect of source and input capacitors in noise voltage and noise current calculations.

135

At 27°C term e_{ni}^2 from Equation 6-7 is

$$e_{ni}^2 = (1.37 \times 10^{-24})\,(300)\,\left(\frac{(63 \times 10^3)}{(10)\,(40 \times 10^3)}\right)$$

$$= 4 \times 10^{-11}\left(\frac{1}{(5.6 \times 10^6)\,(538 \times 10^{-12})}\right)$$

(6-21)

Since $\overline{e}_{nia}$ is negligible compared to all other noise voltage,

$$\overline{e}_{nit} = [(19.7 \times 10^{-6})^2 + (3.9936 \times 10^{-11})]^{1/2}$$

$$= 20.8 \times 10^{-6} \text{ volts.}$$

(6-22)

The signal-to-noise ratio is $0.093/20.68 \times 10^{-6} \approx 4.45 \times 10^3$. Using previously employed methods along with Table 6-1, the decibel figure for the voltage ratio is about 13 dB + 60 dB = 73 dB.

In general, FET noise is primarily due to $\overline{e}_n$ when impedances are high and $\overline{i}_n$ when impedances are low. The contribution from the input resistor is small, but is best when it is equal to $\overline{e}_n/\overline{i}_n$. JFET noise will be at a minimum if the transistor is biased at about $V_{GS} = 0$. Tranconductance g_m must be high if 1/f noise is to be relatively low.

Chapter 7
Power
Amplifiers

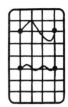

FET and bipolar transistor data sheets present two groups of information. One group provides the designer with the electrical characteristics such as beta and leakage current for the bipolar device and transconductance and pinch-off voltage for the FET. These, a well as other characteristics, have been shown in detailing the designs of various circuits.

The second group presents information concerning the operating limits of the transistor. These ratings indicate, for example, the maximum base, emitter and collector currents that may be permitted to flow through the device. It discloses the maximum voltages that the designer may place across various junctions or combinations of junctions without causing the transistor to break down. The voltage allowed across any junction may vary with voltages applied at other junctions of the device, as well as with temperature. Limits also apply to operating and storage temperatures, as well as to the amount of power a transistor may dissipate.

Maximum ratings were ignored in voltage and current amplifier discussions because these boundaries are seldom exceeded in small-signal preamplifier stages; however, it is essential to take these limits into consideration when choosing a transistor for any application. Economical power amplifier designs cannot be completed without full cognizance of the permissible confines of transistor operation.

Many of the limits apply to both FET and bipolar devices. At this writing, the small JFET is used primarily as a small-signal device. The larger junction VFET is a power field-effect transistor. This discussion of power devices and amplifiers considers arrangements using bipolar transistors as well as VFETs.

POWER RATINGS

Real power is developed across a device when current flows through it while a voltage exists across it. Heat is generated in the

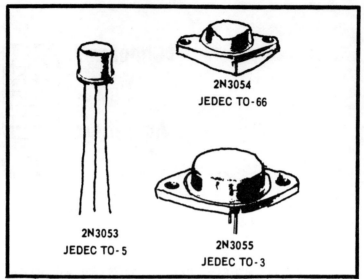

Fig. 7-1. Power transistors come in different case sizes and types. The three most popular case types are shown (courtesy RCA).

device due to the power dissipated. With a transistor the amount of power it can dissipate depends upon the maximum temperature the junction may reach without being damaged. It also depends upon the ability of the finished package to pass generated heat from the junctions to the surrounding air.

Power transistors come in many different types of packages. The three most common ones for bipolar devices are the TO-5, TO-66 and TO-3 shown in Fig. 7-1. The larger TO-3 devices can usually dissipate more power than transistors in the small TO-5 package. Packages for some VFETs are larger than the TO-3 case, and these transistors can dissipate larger amounts of power. Transistors in TO-3 cases, as well as those in the smaller size TO-66 cases, can be conveniently mounted on a large metal surface to facilitate the removal of heat from the junctions.

The amount of power a transistor can dissipate is related to the ambient temperature or to the temperature of the case. The curve in Fig. 7-2 shows this relationship for the popular 2N3055 transistor in a TO-3 case. Up to 25°C, the dissipation is limited to 115 watts. Permissible dissipation drops when the case temperature exceeds 25°C until zero watts may be dissipated at the upper thermal limit of the transistor case at 200°C. Should the design, for example, require that 55 watts be dissipated by the transistor, the case temperature must not exceed 115°C.

Power-limiting information for the bipolar device, should be plotted on the transistor collector characteristic curves. Characteristic curves are supplied by the manufacturer. Points on the power-limiting curve to be superimposed on the collector characteristic curve, can be calculated using the electrical power equation, $I_C = P_{CEM}/V_{CE}$, where I_C is the collector current, P_{CEM} is the maximum power that can be dissipated by the transistor at the stated case temperature, and V_{CE} is the collector-to-emitter voltage.

The following data is derived for plotting the power-limiting curve when a transistor is permitted to dissipate up to 55 watts; hence, for $V_{CE} = 0$,

$$I_C = \frac{55}{0}$$
$$= \infty \; ;$$

for $V_{CE} = 5$ volts,

$$I_C = \frac{55}{5} = 11A;$$

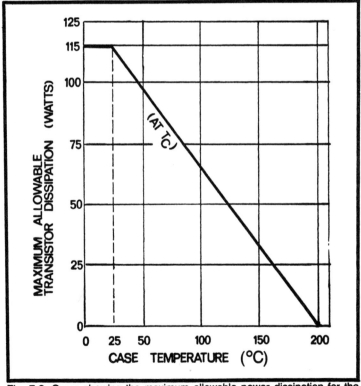

Fig. 7-2. Curve showing the maximum allowable power dissipation for the 2N3055 at various temperatures (courtesy RCA).

for $V_{CE} = 10$ volts,

$$I_C = \frac{55}{10} = 5.5A;$$

for $V_{CE} = 20$ volts,

$$I_C = \frac{55}{20} = 2.75A;$$

for $V_{CE} = 40$ volts,

$$I_C = \frac{55}{40} = 1.38A;$$

and for $V_{CE} = 60$ volts,

$$I_C = \frac{55}{60} = 0.92A.$$

Plot these points on the collector characteristic curves and connect them with a smooth line curve as in Fig. 7-3. The circuit must be designed so that the transistor will operate within the limits set by the curve. Operation above the P$_{CEM}$ curve may cause the device to overheat and be destroyed due to thermal factors. It should be noted that although the P$_{CEM}$ curve is superimposed on the collector characteristics, it is independent of these curves. Wherever possible and in the interest of clarity the actual collector curves are omitted from the drawings that follow.

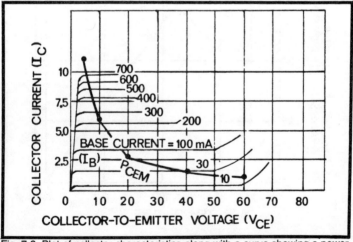

Fig. 7-3. Plot of collector characteristics along with a curve showing a power limitation. Operation is usually below the P$_{CEM}$ curve (courtesy RCA).

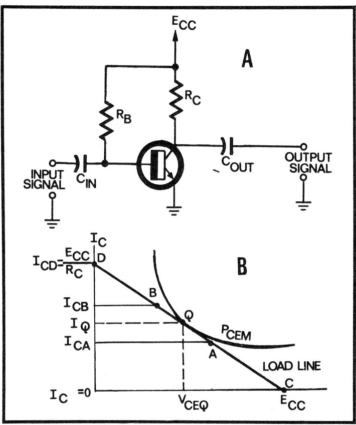

Fig. 7-4. Class A amplifier with load line and maximum power dissipation curve. Collector characteristic curves have been omitted for clarity. Note that the P_{CEM} curve and load line touch only at the center of the load line when it is tangent to the hyperbola.

CLASS A BIPOLAR POWER AMPLIFIER

A class A amplifier is biased so that collector current flows during the entire cycle. Output is limited only by the leakage and saturation characteristics of the transistor. Class A power amplifiers can be differentiated from class A signal-voltage amplifiers by the magnitude of the output signal swing. This can be illustrated using the circuit in Fig. 7-4A and its load line.

You may recall that the DC equation of the output collector circuit of the transistor is:

$$E_{CC} = I_C R_C + V_{CE} \qquad (7\text{-}1)$$

where V_{CE} is the voltage across the device. As was the case with the small-signal circuits the equation defines the load line. One point on

141

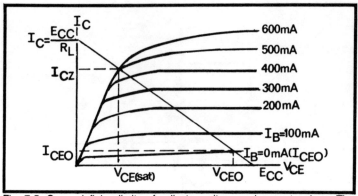

Fig. 7-5. Curve defining limits of collector voltage and current swings. The minimum useful voltage, V_{CE}, in audio applications is about $3V_{CE}$ (sat). It is usually sufficient to subtract a few volts to compensate for V_{CEO}.

the load line is when $V_{CE} = 0$ and $I_C = E_{CC}/R_C$. A second point is when $I_C = 0$ and $V_{CE} = E_{CC}$. Plot the two points as shown in Fig. 7-4B and connect them with a straight line. All coincident collector-to-emitter voltage and collector current conditions under which the transistor may operate must lie on this line.

Assume the transistor is idling at point Q on the load line. Bias current is I_Q while collector-to-emitter voltage is V_{CEQ}. In the absence of a signal the transistor current and voltage are at I_Q and V_{CEQ}, respectively. A small signal may cause the output current to swing from I_{CA} to I_{CB} or from point A to B along the load line; with a large signal at the output the collector current may swing the limits from zero to I_{CD} or from point C to D on the load line. In the former case the amplifier may be designed using the small-signal equivalent circuits discussed in Chapter 4. Amplifier stages which must accommodate the larger swing should be designed using the power amplifier considerations detailed here; however, there is no definite point of demarcation where the signal amplifier stops and the power amplifier begins.

It is obvious from Fig. 7-4B that the collector current swing is limited to a minimum of zero and a maximum of E_{CC}/R_C amperes. Likewise, the collector voltage cannot drop below zero or increase above E_{CC}. Other factors limiting the swing may be observed from the exaggerated collector characteristic curves in Fig. 7-5 and the load line on this drawing.

At the left all curves seem to emanate from a reasonably straight line which starts at the vertex. This line is not coincident with the I_C axis. In this low collector-to-emitter voltage region the transistor

142

behaves as a resistor about equal to $V_{CE(sat)}/I_{CZ}$, known as the saturation resistance. $V_{CE(sat)}$, the saturation voltage, is specified at a specific collector current. In the drawing it is shown at the point of intersection of the characteristic curves and the load line. The saturation voltage is different at other collector currents. It may likewise not agree with the transistor data supplied by the manufacturer for it may specify $V_{CE(sat)}$ at a different collector current than the I_{CZ} in the drawing; however, the saturation voltage shown in the significant saturation voltage in this particular application. There is no amplification of any signal that may swing the base current to the left of the saturation resistance curve.

At the right the load line is limited by the $I_B = 0$ mA curve. The output current may not go below this curve. Considering both limits the actual maximum collector current swing is I_{CZ}-I_{CEO} and the voltage swing is V_{CEO}-$V_{CE(sat)}$. In the initial design work, these limits may be ignored; however, they may be very significant in the final design stages.

In Fig. 7-4B the load line just touches the P_{CEM} curve at point Q. Although Q has been used previously as the quiescent operating

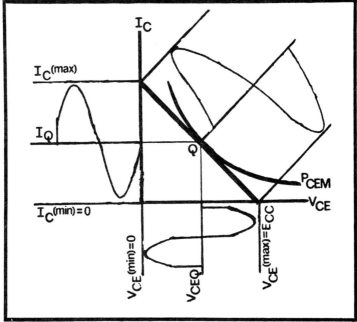

Fig. 7-6. The sine wave travels along the load line and the output current and voltage appear at the axis. The swing here is at a maximum, ignoring the limitations set in Fig. 7-5.

point here it is assumed to be a point of contact between the P_{CEM} curve and the load line. The actual idling condition may be chosen at Q or at any other point along the load line. Point Q is the center of the load line. Significantly, if the load line touches (is tangent to) the P_{CEM} curve at any one point the point of contact is always at the center of the load line.

Should a sinusoidal signal be applied to the input of the transistor after amplification it will travel along the load line at the output as shown in Fig. 7-6. Here it is assumed that point Q is the quiescent bias point at the center of the load line. The transistor will dissipate the maximum power when it is idling at Q or during the instant in the cyclic variations when the collector current is I_Q and the collector-to-emitter voltage is at V_{CEQ}. Since $I_Q = I_{C(max)}/2$ and $V_{CEQ} = E_{CC}/2$ the maximum power dissipated at any instant in the cycle is:

$$P_{C(max)} = \frac{I_{C(max)}E_{CC}}{4} \qquad (7\text{-}2)$$

$$= \frac{I_{C(max)}^2 R_C}{4} \qquad (7\text{-}2a)$$

$$= \frac{E_{CC}^2}{4R_C} \qquad (7\text{-}2b)$$

where R_C, the load resistor in Fig. 7-4A, is equal to $E_{CC}/I_{C(max)}$.

If the load line just touches the maximum dissipation curve $P_{C(max)}$ is also equal to the maximum permissible dissipation of the transistor. The product of $I_{C(max)}/2$ and $E_{CC}/2$ on the load line is always the point in the cycle when the transistor dissipates the maximum power, independent of whether it is the actual quiescent point or whether or not the load line touches the P_{CEM} curve.

As discussed in Chapter 4 the RMS voltage of a sine wave is $V_P/\sqrt{2}$, where V_P is the peak voltage. It is also equal to $V_{P\text{-}P}/2\sqrt{2}$ if we let $V_{P\text{-}P}$ equal the peak-to-peak voltage. It follows that the RMS current is $I_{P\text{-}P}/2\sqrt{2}$. In Fig. 7-6 the peak-to-peak voltage across the load resistor is E_{CC} so that the RMS output voltage is $E_{CC}/2\sqrt{2}$. Similarly, RMS current across R_C is $I_{C(MAX)}/2\sqrt{2}$. Signal power P_{RC} developed across the load is the product of the RMS current and voltage or

$$P_{RC} = \frac{E_{CC}I_{C(max)}}{8} \qquad (7\text{-}3)$$

or

$$P_{RC} = \frac{E_{CC}^2}{8R_C} \qquad (7\text{-}3a)$$

or

$$P_{RC} = \frac{I_{C(max)}^2 \, R_C}{8} \qquad (7\text{-}3b)$$

Comparing Equation 7-2 with Equation 7-3 it should be noted that the transistor can deliver only one-half the maximum power it can dissipate safely.

Assuming a perfect sinusoidal output the quiescent point will not shift from Q. Average power dissipated by the transistor is then equal to the maximum instantaneous power as stated in Equation 7-2, or $E_{CC}^2/4R_C$. Since the average or quiescent voltage across the load resistor is $E_{CC}/2$, the average power dissipated across R_C is $E_{CC}^2/4R_C$. Ignoring the power dissipated by the input circuit, the supply must furnish power equal to the sum of that dissipated by the transistor and that dissipated across the resistor load, or $E_{CC}^2/2R_C$.

Efficiency of the circuit, defined as 100 multiplied by the ratio of the maximum AC power that can be delivered to the load to the power that must be provided by the supply, is 25%. To improve this the wasted DC power across the load resistor must be minimized or entirely eliminated.

A circuit with an output transformer can be used to minimize the DC resistance in the collector circuit, thus diminishing the magnitude of DC power the supply must provide. In Fig. 7-7 an output transformer is shown between the transistor and the load. The effect of the load resistor, R_L, is reflected into the primary circuit. To determine the effect multiply R_L by the square of the turns ratio of the transformer. If N_P is the number of turns in the

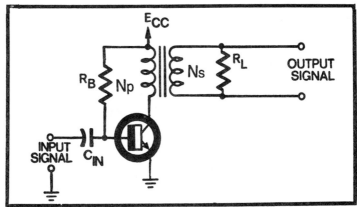

Fig. 7-7. Circuit using an output transformer.

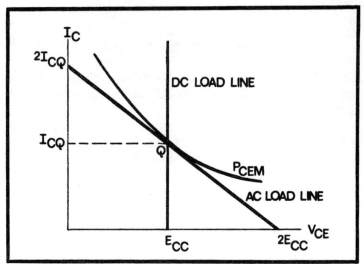

Fig. 7-8. AC and DC load lines for a class A amplifier with transformer output. Zero resistance is assumed for the transformer and power supply. The swing here is at a maximum, ignoring the limitations set in Fig. 7-5.

primary winding and N_S is the number of turns in the secondary, the reflected AC load into the primary is $R'_L = R_L (N_P/N_S)^2$. R'_L is only a factor of the AC load. There is also a DC load on the circuit.

Two load lines—DC and AC—must be drawn for the circuit. Assume zero resistance in the windings. Using the collector relationship $E_{CC} = I_C R_C + V_{CE}$ stated above, one point on the DC load line is at $I_C = 0$ and $V_{CE} = E_{CC}$ while the second point is at $V_{CE} = 0$ and $I_C = \infty$. In Fig. 7-8 this is a vertical line from E_{CC} on the V_{CE} axis. Choose a quiescent point at Q where the DC load line crosses the P_{CEM} hyperbola. Draw an AC load line so that it passes through Q and is at a tangent to the P_{CEM} curve. The AC load line must then pass through two other points as well, namely through $2E_{CC}$ on the horizontal axis and through $2I_{CQ}$ on the collector current vertical axis.

Assume a sine wave across the load causes the collector voltage to swing from zero to $2E_{CC}$, while the collector current swings from $2I_{CQ}$ to zero. The power developed across the load is:

$$P_{R'L} = \frac{(2\ E_{cc})}{2\ \sqrt{2}} \frac{(2\ I_{CQ})}{2\ \sqrt{2}} = \frac{E_{CC}\ I_{CQ}}{2} \qquad (7\text{-}4)$$

The maximum power that can be dissipated by the transistor is:

$$P_{CEM} = P_{C(max)} = E_{CC} I_{CQ} \qquad (7\text{-}5)$$

146

As for the previous class A circuit here too the transistor can deliver but one-half the power it can dissipate safely, or $P_{CEM}/2$. But here little or no power is lost in the resistance of the load.

There are three major advantages in using an output transformer. First, the circuit efficiency is almost doubled to 50%, since the DC supply must provide power only for the transistor. Little power is dissipated by the low DC resistance in the primary winding of the transformer. Next, the transformer can be used to make a low-impedance load, R_L, such as a loudspeaker, appear as a higher impedance in the primary winding where it is most desirable. Finally, it isolates the speaker from the transistor collector current. It is undesirable to let DC flow through the speaker voice coil because it would limit the full and linear travel of the cone.

In most cases the DC resistance in the collector circuit cannot be ignored. Should the resistance in the primary winding of the transformer be significant the DC load line will no longer be perfectly vertical. It will be at an angle with the horizontal axis as in Fig. 7-9. The DC load line can be found using the methods applied to Fig. 7-4B.

The AC load line can be determined using the following logic. The quiescent point on the DC load line is Q. This is also one point on the AC load line. Two points are necessary to define any line. If we let R'_{LT} be the total resistance in the collector circuit (the reflected resistance through the transformer plus all resistance in

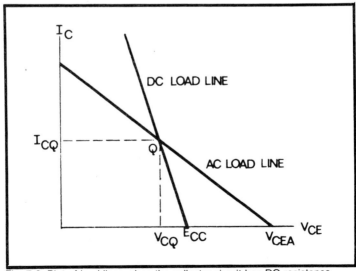

Fig. 7-9. Plot of load lines when the collector circuit has DC resistance.

the AC portion of the collector circuit), the second point, V_{CEA}, can be determined from the equation:

$$R'_{LT} = \frac{V_{CEA} - V_{CQ}}{I_{CQ}} \qquad (7\text{-}6)$$

A PRACTICAL EXAMPLE

Our task is to design an audio amplifier capable of delivering 5 watts to a 3.2-ohm loudspeaker load. The transistor available is the 2N3055. Outline a step-by-step procedure using the 2N3055.

1. Draw a workable circuit. In order to keep direct current out of the speaker winding an output transformer should be used. For improved thermal stability use a resistor in the emitter to provide DC feedback. If desired bypass it with a capacitor to prevent AC degeneration and the reduction of power reaching the loudspeaker. A valid circuit arrangement is shown in Fig. 7-10.

2. Determine the actual power the amplifier must deliver. Although 5 watts is desired at the speaker, the 2N3055 must deliver more than this due to losses in the output transformer. Assuming 75% transformer efficiency the power available from the 2N3055 across the primary of the transformer must be at least $5/0.75 = 6.67$ watts.

3. Choose V_{CEA}, the voltage at which the AC load line crosses the horizontal axis. The following considerations apply. Maximum voltage that may safely be applied between the collector and emitter of a transistor varies with the size of resistor placed between the base and emitter. Breakdown voltages are specified on data sheets for different resistor values. There is no resistor used in the circuit in Fig. 7-10; therefore, the BV_{CEO} rating applies. BV_{CEO} is the voltage that may be applied between the collector and emitter of the transistor without destroying the device when there is no resistor between the base and emitter. BV_{CEO} is the breakdown voltage when the current flowing through the device is very small. As the collector current increases BV_{CEO} is reduced to a more or less constant value, $V_{CEO}(sus)$, referred to as the sustaining voltage. For the 2N3055, V_{CEO} (sus) is 60 volts. V_{CEA} should be equal to or less than 60 volts. Taking various factors into consideration, such as peak voltages due to the primary inductance of the transformer, the possibility of getting transistors at

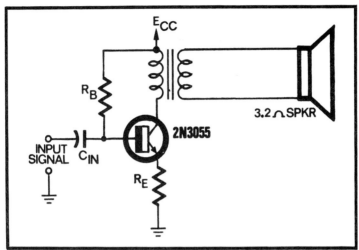

Fig. 7-10. Audio output circuit used in the text problem.

reduced prices when BV_{CEO} (sus) is low, the economy of a low-voltage power supply, etc., choose V_{CEA} at 25 volts.

4. Calculate the power the transistor must dissipate. Because it must deliver 6.67 watts the device must be capable of dissipating at least $2 \times 6.67 = 13.3$ watts. The 2N3055 is capable of dissipating 115 watts at room temperature so 13.3 watts should be no problem. In fact, add 25% to the required dissipation capability to accommodate the limitation of current and voltage swings on the load line as well as signal power losses across the emitter resistor. Required dissipation capability should be $13.3 + (0.25 \times 13.3) = 16.6$ watts.

5. Determine points on the $P_{CEM} = 16.6$ watts parabola and draw a line from $V_{CEA} = 25$ volts to the I_C axis touching the parabola at one point. Several points on the parabola are, for example, where $V_{CE} = 25$ volts,

$$I_C = \frac{16.6W}{25V} = 0.66A;$$

Where $V_{CE} = 20$ volts,

$$I_C = \frac{16.6W}{20V} = 0.83A;$$

where $V_{CE} = 15$ volts,

$$I_C = \frac{16.6W}{15V} = 1.11A;$$

where $V_{CE} = 10$ volts,

$$I_C = \frac{16.6W}{10V} = 1.66A;$$

where $V_{CE} = 5$ volts,

$$I_C = \frac{16.6W}{5V} = 3.32A;$$

and where $V_C = 2$ volts,

$$I_C = \frac{16.6W}{2V} = 8.3A.$$

Draw the parabola using the data just calculated. See Fig. 7-11. Starting from the selected $V_{CEA} = 25$ volts on the V_{CE} axis, draw an AC load line tangent to the parabola at $V_{CEA}/2 = 12.5$ volts and $I_{CQ} = 16.6$ watts/12.5 volts = 1.33 amperes. It will intersect the I_C axis at $2I_{CQ} = 2.66$ amperes. The DC load line will also intersect P_{CEM} curve at point Q.

6. In Fig. 7-10 the voltage across R_E should be between 0.5 and 1 volt. Since the quiescent current has been chosen at 1.33 amperes R_E may assume any value between 0.5 volt/1.33 amperes = 0.375 ohm and 1 volt/1.33 amperes = 0.75 ohm. Choose a relatively standard 0.56-ohm 10% resistor. Power the resistor must be capable of dissipating is $I_{CQ}^2 R_E = (1.33)^2(0.56) \approx 1$ watt. Use a 2-watt component for safety reasons.

7. AC resistance seen by the transistor is equal to the reciprocal of the slope of the AC load line, or

$$\frac{V_{CEA}}{2I_{CQ}} = \frac{25}{2.66} = 9.4\Omega.$$

8. The DC load line is determined by supply voltage E_{CC}, the resistor in the emitter circuit and the resistance of the primary winding of the output transformer. We know that R_E is 0.56 ohm. Choose a transformer so that the sum of R_E and the resistance in the transformer winding will be small—let us say about 1.5 ohms. The slope of the reciprocal of the DC load line is equal to this resistance, so that

$$1.5 = \frac{E_{CC} - V_{CQ}}{I_{CQ}} = \frac{E_{CC} - 12.5}{1.33}.$$

V_{CQ} is set to 12.5 volts because at the center of the load line V_{CQ} is equal to $V_{CEA}/2$. E_{CC} must then be 14.5 volts. Plot this point on the

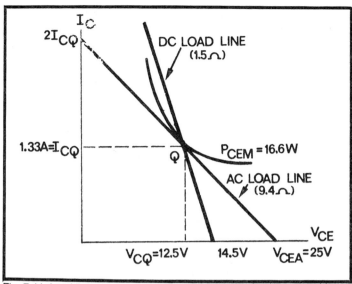

Fig. 7-11. Load lines and power limiting curves drawn for the text problem.

V_{CE} axis. Draw a line connecting the 14.5 volt point on the horizontal axis with Q on the AC load line. This is the DC load line.

9. Total AC resistance in the collector circuit is equal to the sum of the primary resistance of the transformer (1.5 ohms − 0.56 ohm = 0.94 ohm), the 0.56-ohm resistor in the emitter and resistance reflected from the secondary into the primary winding due to the 3.2-ohm speaker in the secondary. If the resistance of the secondary winding is not small compared to the 3.2-ohm load, R'_L is due to the reflection of the sum of the speaker resistance plus the resistance of the secondary winding. In step 7 it was determined that the total AC resistance the transistor must see is 9.4 ohms. Assuming the DC resistance of the secondary winding is low the reflected resistance into the primary of the transformer is 9.4 − 0.56 − 0.94 = 7.9 ohms.

10. The impedance ratio of the transformer is 7.9:3.2 ohms. Since this is equal to the square of the turns ratio of 7.9/3.2 = $(N_P/N_S)^2$, where N_P is the number of turns in the primary winding and N_S is the number of turns in the secondary, the turns ratio from the primary to the secondary must be about 1.6:1.

11. Check if sufficient power can be delivered to the load. Transistor characteristics set limits to the possible out-

151

put current and voltage swings. At one end the saturation voltage of the transistor is stated in the specifications as 1.1 volt at 4 amperes. Since our maximum current is 2.66 amperes, the saturation voltage is somewhat less. Let us assume that the minimum voltage across the transistor due to saturation is 0.75 volt. Let us also assume a 1-volt loss in swing at the other end of the load line due to leakage current limits; thus, the signal voltage swing is limited to

$$25 - 0.75 - 1 = 23.25 \text{ volts}.$$

Power the transistor can deliver is

$$\frac{(23.25)^2}{8(9.4)} = 7.2 \text{W}.$$

AC power developed across the emitter resistor is

$$\frac{(2I_{CQ})^2 R_E}{8} = \frac{(2.66)^2(0.56)}{8} = 0.5 \text{W}.$$

Total power across the output transformer is $7.2 - 0.5 = 6.7$ watts. If the transformer is 75% efficient, the power reaching the load is $0.75 \times 6.7 = 5$ watts.

12. DC bias conditions must now be established. The emitter resistor is 0.56 ohm. When reflected into the base circuit, it appears as a DC resistor equal to the beta of the transistor multiplied by R_E. The DC beta curve, reproduced in Fig. 7-12, shows the average beta is about 50 when $I_{CQ} = 1.33$ amperes; thus, the resistance at the input is $0.56 \times 50 = 28$ ohms.

13. Quiescent base current, I_B, must be $I_{CQ}/\beta = 1.33\text{A}/50 = 0.027$ ampere.

14. Using the data from steps 12 and 13 we can calculate R_B, for $E_{CC} = I_B (R_B + \beta R_E) = 14.5 = 0.027 (R_B + 28 \text{ ohms})$. R_B is equal to 509 ohms. Use a standard 510-ohm resistor. Power dissipated by R_B is $I_B^2 R_B = (0.027)^2 (510) = 0.37$ watts. A ½-watt resistor can be used here, although a 1-watt component is more desirable.

15. AC resistance reflected into the base circuit from the emitter circuit is $\beta (R_E + r_e)$, where r_e is the AC emitter resistance of the transistor. In step 12 the DC emitter resistance was ignored since it is negligible; however, the AC emitter resistance was specified as equal to $26/I_Q$ in Chapter 4, where I_Q is expressed in milliamperes. In

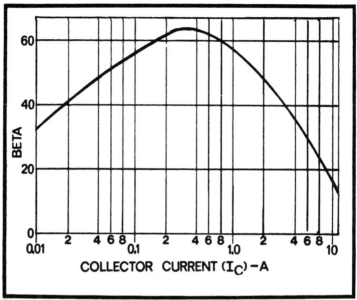

Fig. 7-12. Curve shows how DC beta of the 2N3055 varies with collector current when $V_{CE} = 4$ volts (courtesy RCA).

this problem r_e will be very small if calculated from the formula. In reality it is seldom less than 1 ohm. We will assume it to be 1 ohm. AC emitter resistance reflected into the base circuit is then $50(0.56 + 1) = 78$ ohms. It is assumed the AC beta is equal to the DC beta.

The input impedance is essentially this 78 ohms in parallel with the 510-ohm resistor calculated in step 14, or 67 ohms. If this amplifier is designed to have a good frequency response down to 20 hertz, C_{IN} must be at least equal to $1/6.28(20)(67) = 120$ microfarads. This assumes that the impedance of the input signal source is zero. Calculations of this type will be elaborated upon in Chapter 9.

In this problem the transistor will deliver 5 watts only if the collector current and voltage will swing over its maximum capabilities. Because of nonlinearity of the collector characteristics, it is most desirable to limit the swing to the minimum. This is especially true near the saturation voltage lines as well as near the I_{CEO} curve where I_B is zero. A good rule of thumb is to make the minimum collector voltage equal to three times the saturation voltage. Subtract another 2 volts due to the leakage current.

The above solution to the problem is marginal. In the laboratory it will probably be found that more power output capability is necessary and improved circuit efficiency will be required. Some measures of improving efficiency include bypassing the 0.56-ohm emitter resistor with a large capacitor, using a more efficient output transformer, increasing Ecc, etc.

CLASS AB POWER AMPLIFIERS

The quantity of power that can be delivered by a class A amplifier is extremely limited. A transistor can dissipate a specific amount of power. Should the transistor conduct current over the entire cycle as well as when it is idling, a considerable amount of power is wasted just keeping the device operating at its predetermined quiescent bias. This state of affairs exists in the class A mode of operation.

On the other hand class B power amplifiers are biased so that no collector current will flow when the transistor is idling. The transistor does not conduct until the applied signal is of a sufficient magnitude and polarity to put the device into its active region. Silicon bipolar transistors, for example, do not conduct until the signal applied to the base relative to the emitter is positive and greater in magnitude than the 0.6 or 0.7 volt necessary to turn on the base-emitter junction.

Even though the amount of power a transistor is capable of dissipating in class B remains identical to its capabilities in class A, in the former mode it will dissipate this power only when conducting useful audio currents. The portion of power wasted in maintaining class A bias is applied here to enable class B amplifiers to deliver more useful signal output.

Only one-half of a pure AC sinusoidal cycle will turn on a transistor biased in the class B mode. In order to reproduce the alternate half of the cycle the circuit must use a second transistor which conducts during this latter portion of the cycle. Two transistors are required to reproduce a full cycle in class B biased amplifier circuits.

Class B Statistics

A push-pull class B amplifier circuit is shown in Fig. 7-13 using two NPN transistors. Should a sine wave be fed to the input the various waveforms shown can be found at the specific points in the circuit when they are measured with respect to ground. Dots next to the ends of the input transformer windings indicate that the

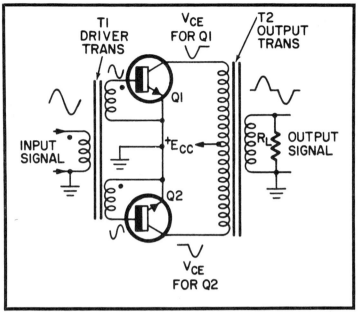

Fig. 7-13. Transformer coupled class B push-pull circuit. Significant waveforms are shown.

corresponding leads or terminals are identical in polarity with respect to those at the unmarked ends. The base of Q1 is in the same phase with respect to its emitter as is the hot lead of the input signal with respect to ground. To establish the proper status for push-pull operation the polarity of the signal at the base of Q2 is 180° out of phase with that at the base of Q1.

During the first half-cycle the base of Q1 is positive with respect to the emitter; so this transistor will conduct. Q1 will not conduct during the second half-cycle because during this interval the base-emitter junction is reversed in polarity. The collector voltage is as shown, for the voltage across the transistor and the upper half of the transformer winding is reduced as the transistor goes into conduction.

The second half of the cycle turns Q2 on, since only then does the signal bias that base positive with respect to its emitter. The waveform of the output voltage at the bottom of the output transformer with respect to the center tap, as well as across the transistor, is as shown. The voltage across the entire primary is relatively sinusodial, as is the output signal across load R_L. Ideally, the output signal is a power-magnified version of the input signal.

As discussed for class A amplifier the two transistors see the actual load R_L reflected as a resistor, R_L, into the entire primary winding of output transformer T2. $R'_L = R_L (N_P/N_S)^2$ is an equation describing the relationship. In this formula N_P is the number of turns in the entire primary winding and N_S is the number of turns in the secondary. Either one of the transistors sees a resistance, R''_L, across one-half of the transformer winding. The number of turns each transistor sees is $N_P/2$. Then

$$R''_L = R_L \left(\frac{\frac{1}{2}N_P}{N_S} \right)^2 \qquad (7\text{-}7)$$

$$= \left(\frac{R_L}{4} \right) \left(\frac{N_p}{N_S} \right)^2 \qquad (7\text{-}7a)$$

Comparing the equation for R'_L with the equation for R''_L we arrive at the important conclusion that R''_L is equal to $\frac{1}{4}R'_L$ or that the AC load seen by either one transistor appearing across half the primary winding of the transformer is equal to one-fourth that seen by both transistors across the entire transformer.

Each transistor delivers power to the load. To determine the power delivered by the two transistors we need only determine the power one transistor delivers and multiply this number by two. Using one transistor draw the P_{CEM} maximum power dissipation hyperbola on the collector characteristic curves of the transistor, as shown in Fig. 7-14. As is our practice we omit the actual transistor curves to avoid cluttering the drawing. Assuming half the primary winding of transformer T2 has zero resistance, the DC load line, defined by the equation $V_{CE} = E_{CC} - I_C R_P$, is a vertical line up from the E_{CC} voltage point on the V_{CE} axis. R_P in the equation is the resistance of one-half of the primary winding of transformer T2.

The AC load resistance is $R''_L = (R_L/4) (N_P/N_S)^2$. Assume that at its maximum the load line is tangent to the P_{CEM} curve. We will deviate from the concept of not working above the P_{CEM} curve later on. Here we assume the load line cannot cross this hyperbola. If a sinusoidal signal is at the input, a half-cycle of voltage and current will appear at the output due to one transistor. For the maximum output the collector-to-emitter voltage will swing from E_{CC} to zero and the collector current will swing from its I_{CM} maximum to zero. Since the RMS values of a half-sine wave are the peak voltage or current divided by two, the signal power delivered to the AC load, R''_L, is:

$$P''_{RL} = \left(\frac{I_{CM}}{2} \right) \left(\frac{E_{CC}}{2} \right)$$

$$= \frac{E_{CC}^2}{4R''_L} = \frac{I_{CM}^2 R''_L}{4} \qquad (7\text{-}8)$$

This equation is valid regardless of where the AC load line is with respect to the P$_{CEM}$ hyperbola. Maximum power is dissipated by the transistor at the instant the swing is at the center of travel or:

$$P_{C(max)} = \left(\frac{I_{CM}}{2} \right) \left(\frac{E_{CC}}{2} \right) \qquad (7\text{-}9)$$

This equation is also independent of the P$_{CEM}$ curve.

It should be emphasized that P$_{C(max)}$ is not the average power the transistor will dissipate. It is the power the transistor will dissipate only at the instant the swing is at I$_{CM}$/2 and E$_{CC}$/2. This is the maximum power it will dissipate at any point in the swing. If the load line is tangent to the maximum allowable power dissipation hyperbola, P$_{C(max)}$ = P$_{CEM}$. Power dissipated when averaged over the entire cycle is less than P$_{C(max)}$ for it is P$_{C(max)}$ for only two instants in the half-cycle swing on the load line.

Comparing Equations 7-8 and 7-9 we notice that the transistor can deliver as much power as the maximum instantaneous power it

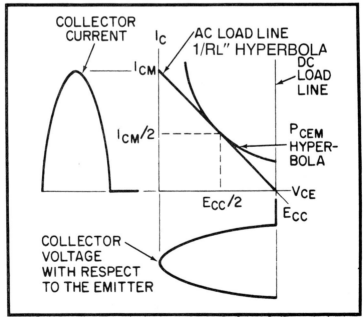

Fig. 7-14. Plot of load lines for class B amplifier. A sinusoidal input and output signal is assumed.

will dissipate in the half-cycle. This is double the power the same transistor was capable of delivering in class A.

Average or direct current in a half-sine wave of collector current is I_{CM}/π. This is discussed in Chapter 4. The power supply must provide this direct current. It must provide $P_{ECC} = E_{CC}(I_{CM}/\pi)$ watts to the transistor. Comparing this with the power delivered to the load the efficiency percentage of the circuit is

$$\frac{100P''_{RL}}{P_{ECC}} = \frac{100\pi}{4} = 78.5\%$$

which is a decided improvement over the class A case.

The transistor dissipates power during one-half the cycle only, for it does not conduct during the alternate half-cycle. Over a complete cycle one transistor (Q_1 for example) of the push-pull pair will dissipate:

$$P_{Q1} = \frac{0.068E_{CC}^2}{R''_L} \qquad (7\text{-}10)$$

if the signal swings the output from zero to its E_{CC} maximum limit. Average power the device will dissipate over the cycle is higher if the swing is less than the maximum. Should the transistor deliver about 40% of the P''_{RL} in Equation 7-8, it will dissipate more power than it will dissipate with any other degree of signal swing. Power it will dissipate is:

$$P_{M(av)} = E_{CC}^2/\pi^2 R''_L \qquad (7\text{-}11)$$

if the power it delivers to the load is 40% of the maximum. Comparing this with Equation 7-8 the transistor can deliver about 2½ times the power it may dissipate.

Averaged over a complete cycle the transistor may dissipate P_{CEM} watts. It will cross the P_{CEM} hyperbola and yet be within the power dissipation rating of the transistor when the dissipation is averaged over the 360°. This differs from the class A case because here the idling and average power over the cycle were at P_{CEM} when the transistor was biased for minimum distortion. Since the power during idling (and hence the average during the cycle) was not permitted to exceed P_{CEM} the load line was not permitted above the maximum power dissipation hyperbola.

Bipolar Class B Design Procedure

Assume you are called upon to design a 60-watt push-pull amplifier which will drive an 8-ohm loudspeaker system. How would

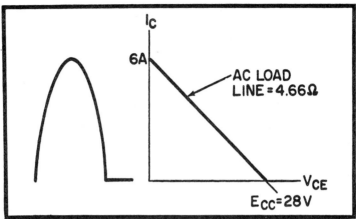

Fig. 7-15. Curves for class B design procedure.

you proceed to specify the output transistors and transformer? Use the circuit in Fig. 7-13.

If the two transistors are to deliver 60 watts, each one must be capable of delivering half the power or 30 watts to the load. If the transformer is 25% efficient, the transistors must deliver 30 watts + 25% of 30 watts = 37.5 watts to half the ouput transformer primary. Add about 10% to compensate for losses due to saturation voltage and leakage current; therefore, the circuit should be designed to be capable of providing about 42 watts.

A good power transistor for this application is the 2N3055. Maximum collector current that can safely flow through this transistor is 10 amperes. Adding some leeway use 6 amperes as the maximum collector current. Since the RMS current of the half-sine wave (see Fig. 7-15) is $6/2 = 3$ amperes, the load the transistor must see at the primary of the transformer is

$$R''_L = \frac{P''_{RL}}{I_{RMS}^2} = \frac{42}{9}$$

$$= 4.66.$$

The supply voltage from Equation 7-8 is

$$E_{CC} = (4R''_L P''_{RL})^{\frac{1}{2}}$$
$$= [(4)(4.66)(42)]^{\frac{1}{2}}$$
$$= 28V.$$

Maximum power is dissipated by the transistor when the power delivered to the load is about 40% of 42 watts, or 16.8 watts.

When delivering this power the transistor will dissipate

$$\frac{E_{CC}^2}{\pi^2 R''_L} = \frac{783}{(9.9)(4.66)} = 17W$$

The 2N3055 can easily cope with this power dissipation requirement. It is interesting to stop for a moment and observe several things here. For the full swing the transistor will dissipate

$$\frac{0.068 E_{CC}^2}{R''_L} = \frac{(0.068)(783)}{4.66} = 11.4W.$$

This is less than the power dissipated when 40 % of the maximum power is delivered to the load.

The power a transistor will dissipate is equal to the power taken from the supply less the power delivered to the load. Power furnished by the supply can be calculated as follows. Based on Equation 7-8 and defining $I_{C(40\%)}$ and $P''_{RL(40\%)}$ as the collector current and output power respectively, when the transistor delivers 40% below its maximum capabilities the square of the collector current swing is

$$I_{C(40\%)}^2 = \frac{4P''_{RL(40\%)}}{R''_L}$$

Hence,

$$I_{C(40\%)}^2 = \frac{(4)(16.8)}{4.66}$$

$$= 14.4.$$

Therefore

$$I_{C(40\%)} = 3.79A.$$

The power from the supply is $P_{ECC} = \dfrac{E_{CC} I_{C(40\%)}}{\pi}$

$$= 28 \left(\frac{3.79}{3.14}\right)$$

$$= 33.79W.$$

Subtract the 16.8 watts delivered to the output at 40% of the maximum output power from the 33.79 watts supplied by the power source, and the transistor must dissipate 16.99 watts. This is very close to the 17-watt solution from the $E_{CC}^2/\pi^2 R''_L$ equation above.

Since the impedance across one-half the primary of the output transformer is 4.66 ohms, the impedance from collector to collector (across the entire primary) is 4 × 4.66 ohms, or 18.64 ohms. The impedance ratio of the entire primary to the secondary is 18.64:8 or 2.33:1. Turns ratio is the square root of the impedance ratio, or 1.51:1.

Class AB

A typical set of collector characteristic curves appear in Fig. 7-3 for the 2N3055. Notice that they are not evenly spaced. Should

160

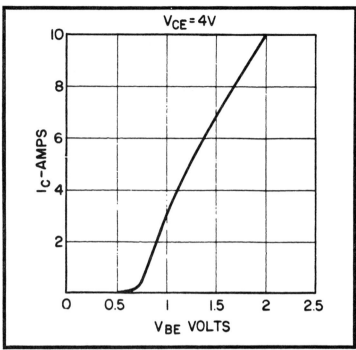

Fig. 7-16. Transfer characteristic curve for a 2N3055 (courtesy RCA).

the collector current swing the full 10 amperes for the half-cycle the current gain differs at various points of the cycle. For example, at the point in the cycle where 2 amperes collector current is required, the base current at the input is about 40mA. At the 4-ampere collector current point in the cycle the base current is about 120 mA, while for 6 amperes it is about 250 mA. In the portion of the output curve where there is a 2-ampere collector current rise from 2 to 4 amperes the equivalent base current increase about 120 – 40 = 80 millamperes, while for the same 2-ampere collector current increment from 4 to 6 amperes the equivalent base current increase is 250 – 120 = 130 milliamperes. Even though the increase in collector current remains at 2 amperes in both cases the base current drive required is greater at higher collector currents. This information could, of course, have been derived from the beta curves in Fig. 7-12, which show that beta varies considerably with collector current. The AC and DC gain is nonlinear, resulting in distortion.

Another curve, shown in Fig. 7-16, is a plot of the collector current against the base-emitter voltage. You may recognize this as a transconductance curve, where the definition of transconductance is not unlike that applied to the JFET. Note that this curve, after the first 0.6 or 0.7 volt, is a relatively straight line. The slope of this line is the AC transconductance. It is equal to $\Delta I_C/\Delta V_{BE}$, where the Δ indicates a change or difference. The AC transconductance is relatively constant with changes in collector current. Should the half-cycle of 10 ampere collector current be at the output, the required input base-emitter voltage at the 2-ampere collector current point in the cycle is 0.9 volt, at the 4-ampere point it is 1.1 volts, and at 6 amperes it is 1.3 volts. While the collector current increase is in increments of 2 amperes the base-to-emitter voltage increase in one case is $1.1-0.9 = 0.2$ volt, and in the second case it is $1.3-1.1 = 0.2$ volt; hence, equal changes in base-emitter voltages produce equal changes in collector current. This is a linear situation favorable to the cause of low distortion.

Good power amplifiers are driven from low-impedance voltage sources where transconductance is the controlling factor, rather than from high-impedance current sources where the varying beta determines the relatively distorted output. In Fig. 7-17A we apply half a sine wave of voltage to the input between the base and emitter. Collector current at the output appears next to the I_C axis. Note that there are portions in the cycle where there is little or no output current. This is known as the crossover region. For the two-transistor push-pull circuit in Fig. 7-13 the output across load, R_L would appear as in Fig. 7-17B, rather than be perfectly sinusoidal. This signal has a considerable amount of odd harmonics in the distortion and intermodulation distortion. Even worse, in conjunction with transformer and speaker inductance this abrupt crossover can cause sharp voltage peaks in the circuit which may damage or destroy the transistor.

Crossover distortion can be minimized if the transistor is biased so that it is always conducting some minimal amount of collector current. A normal procedure to determine the minimum base-emitter voltage for this type of operation is to extend the straight line of the transconductance curve to the V_{BE} axis. The curve in Fig. 7-16 crosses this axis at 0.75 volt; so the transistor should be biased at this voltage. It is true that some power will be dissipated due to the idling collector current (about 40 mA at 0.75 volt), but the reduction in crossover distortion is well worth this minor expenditure of power. Some manufacturers allow the transistors to idle at much higher current to insure that the collector current will never be completely cut off. This type of biasing puts the transistor into what is referred to as class AB operation.

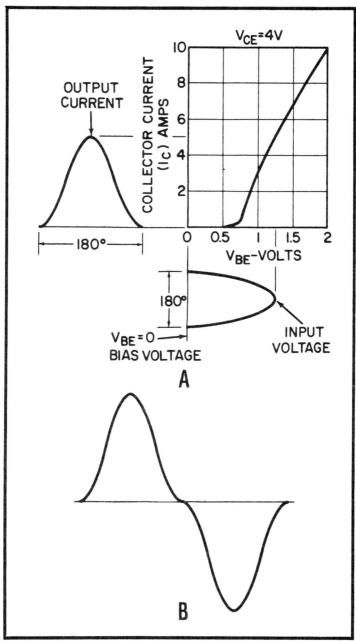

Fig. 7-17. Derivation of output curve. Curve A is the collector current with half a sine-wave input. Curve B is the collector current as it appears for a full cycle. Notice the crossover distortion (courtesy RCA).

163

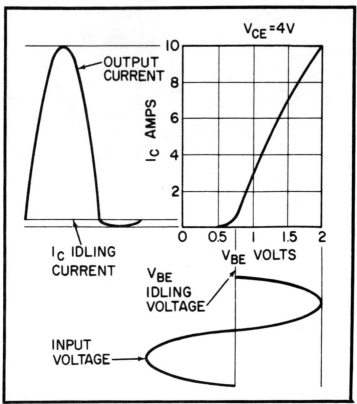

Fig. 7-18. Collector current signal when the transistor is biased for class AB operation (courtesy RCA).

A drawing of the output current when the transistor is biased at 0.75 volt is shown in Fig 7-18. There is no portion of the half-cycle during which there is an absence of collector current. Distortion is relatively low when compared to the distortion in class B mode of operation. The output over the full cycle is a fairly good sine wave.

Should the circuit in Fig. 7-13 be biased for class AB operation it could take the form shown in Fig. 7-19. Bias voltage is developed across Rx, which is applied between the transistor bases and emitters. RB and Rx form a voltage divider with EBB as the source of the base bias supply voltage. Quiescent base current can be determined using Thevenin's equivalent circuit procedure described in Chapter 2. Do not forget to include the DC resistance of the driver transformer's secondary winding in series with the base circuit.

The design procedure in all other facets is identical to that described for class B operation. A 10% factor was added for contingencies such as saturation voltage and leakage current. Perhaps in class AB this factor should be increased to 15 or 20%.

Only one type of push-pull circuit the type using transformers, is described here. It was used only for convenience. Modern designs obviate the need for this type of component at the input or at the output. Design considerations do not change in this type of circuit. Transformerless output circuits are described in detail in Chapter 11.

Transformerless class AB push-pull circuits are, at the moment, primarily designed around bipolar transistors. Junction type power FETs, that is VFETs, are now coming into wide usage. Because of their desirable characteristics, these VFETs will eventually be used more frequently in higher power amplifiers than their bipolar counterparts. A set of curves which may be used to describe the drain characteristics of these VFETs is shown in Fig. 7-20. These curves do not represent any particular device but can be used as a basis for understanding the desirable characteristics of the power FET. Compare these curves drawn here with those of a typical bipolar transistor, as shown in Fig. 7-3.

The first thing to note in Fig. 7-20 is that the curves for the VFET are relatively vertical, while those of the bipolar device are essentially horizontal; hence, the output resistance of the VFET is much lower than that of the bipolar transistor. While the collector

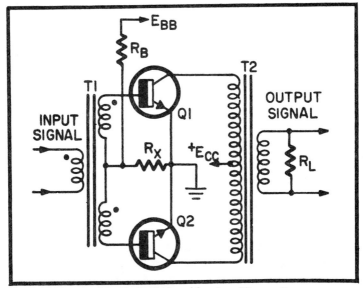

Fig. 7-19. The circuit in Fig. 7-13 biased for class AB operation.

resistance of the bipolar device is as high as several hundred ohms, the drain resistance of the VFET can be as low as 10 ohms— sometimes even lower. This gives the VFET a big advantage when feeding a loudspeaker directly without an intervening transformer. The loudspeaker sees a low impedance so that an extremely large amount of negative feedback is not necessary around the circuit to reduce the output impedance and thereby improve the damping factor. There is also the advantage that, at all frequencies, the relative voltages across the output circuit will be delivered in the proper proportions to the loudspeaker despite the usual variations of speaker impedance with the applied frequency.

Other advantages can be summarized from the evenly spaced curves in the characteristic drawing. The output is more linear than that of the bipolar device: hence, distortion due to the transistor is lower here. The excellent distortion characteristic is further enhanced when you consider that there is no such thing as thermal runaway in an FET. The transistor can consequently be biased to idle at up to 0.5 ampere. With this much idling current, crossover distortion is virtually eliminated. Large idling current is also permissible because of the basic design of the VFET. In this device there is no concentration of large amounts of current in one portion of the chip; hence, there is no possibility of second breakdown (see Chapter 8). Nevertheless, caution must be exercised in order that excessive current does not flow through the device so that it will not dissipate more power than it can handle. This is especially important when it is remembered that because breakdown voltage can be as high as 300 volts, the power limitations can be exceeded when a relatively small amount of current is flowing.

An advantage not derivable from the drain characteristics is that the storage time of the VFET is very low. This means that it will not retain a charge after the supply of that current or charge has been turned off. At high audio frequencies crossover distortion is present in bipolar amplifiers because of this storage effect. There is no such problem with the VFET. Basic circuits using VFETs in output transformerless arrangements are discussed in Chapter 11.

CLASS D AMPLIFIERS

Class A, B and AB amplifies increase the gain of the audio input signal, preferably without altering its shape in the process. Not so with the class D circuits.Here, the input audio signal is transformed into pulses. The width or time duration of each pulse depends upon the instantaneous amplitude of the audio input signal. There must be

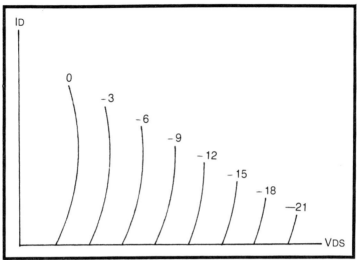

Fig. 7-20. Drain characteristic curves for a hypothetical VFET.

a large number of pulses present during each audio cycle if the cycle is to be represented accurately by these pulses. For example, if one cycle of the top audio frequency of 20 kilohertz is to be represented by pulses there must be a sufficient number of pulses of varying widths to supply detailed information of the various segments of the audio cycle. Each cycle should be split into at least ten parts so that the frequency of the pulse is 200 kilohertz or more. Generally, 500 kilohertz is used so that a more accurate representation of the audible signal is possible.

How is all this accomplished? A method can be described with the help of Fig. 7-21. It shows a sawtooth waveform being used to pulse-modulate one-half of a sinusoidal-shaped cycle. The audio sine wave and sawtooth wave are mixed in a circuit. Output from that circuit is the pulse-length modulated sine wave. Width of each pulse is determined by the instantaneous amplitude of the audio signal that it represents. A circuit such as the one in Fig. 7-22 can be used to form these pulses. This is a differential amplifier circuit to be discussed in a later chapter. In the circuit the sawtooth wave is fed to Q_1 and the sawtooth output appears across R_E. It is added to the sine wave at the input of Q2. The sum of the two signals turns transistor Q2 on and off. Due to the on and off cycle of Q2 pulses appear in the collector circuit of Q2. Width of these pulses are governed by the base-emitter voltage at Q2. This, in turn, is determined by the high and low sum voltage formed by the presence of the sine wave and sawtooth wave across this junction. When the total voltage at the base-emitter junction of Q2 is zero, Q2 is turned off and the output voltage at the collector of Q2 is Ecc. When the total voltage is positive, Q2 is turned on and the collector voltage approaches zero due to the voltage drop across Rc.

Output from the differential amplifier can be applied to a class B circuit. A large capacitor should be placed across the loudspeaker output load to reconstruct these pulses into enlarged variations of the orignal audio input. A circuit using the efficient class B arrangement is shown in Chapter 11.

CLASS G AND CLASS H AMPLIFIERS

Another efficient mode of providing high audio power output uses the class G amplifier system developed by Hitachi. Here, two sets of output transistors are used—one set of working at a low voltage and one set working at a high voltage. The transistors in the low-voltage circuit are turned on at all times and behave as any other class AB pair of output transistors. When the signal fed to the top circuit exceeds a preset level the transistors in the high-voltage circuit are turned on. The amplifier is then capable of delivering the high-output signal to the load. As these large signals usually do not last for long periods of time, the high-voltage circuit is on for but a short interval. The overall circuit is efficient.

The Variproportional class H amplifier developed by Sound-craft uses an idea similar to that of the class G arrangement. In class H as in class G there are two levels of power supplies. In the class H

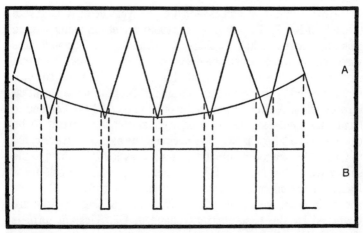

Fig. 7-21. Sawtooth mixed with half-sine wave in A to form pulse-modulated representation of half-sine wave in B.

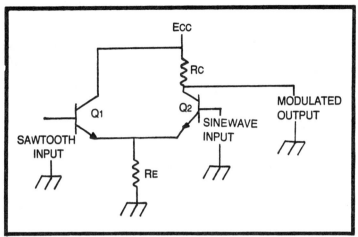

Fig. 7-22. Circuit used to generate the pulse-modulated representation of the sine wave.

arrangement one voltage is about two-thirds that of the other. Here is where the similarity ends between the two classes of operation. In class H, all output transistors are always on. Low voltage is applied to these transistors. When the signal exceeds a predetermined level, a logic circuit applies the high voltage across the output devices. This high voltage is turned on before clipping can occur at the output due to the low voltage normally applied across these stages. As was true of the class G arrangement, class' H is an efficient mode of operation. Representative circuits of both arrangements are shown and described in Chapter 11.

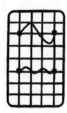# Chapter 8
Boundaries
of Operation

Many transistor characteristics and the methods of utilizing these characteristics have been discussed in preceding chapters. Here the discussion centers on information concerning the maximum ratings that define the various limits of the device.

BIPOLAR TRANSISTORS

In Chapter 1 we learned that if a diode is reverse biased (the anode negative with respect to the cathode) it will break down and start conducting large amounts of current if the applied voltage exceeds a specific level. This level varies from type to type. The same is true for transistor junctions.

The collector-base junction of a transistor is reverse-biased in normal audio amplifier circuit applications. The junction will break down if the applied voltage is above an avalanche voltage, $V_{(BR)CBO}$ = BV_{CBO}. (Here and in the discussion below, the first symbol shown is the preferred JEDEC notation for a limiting value. Subsequent symbols are frequently used in the literature to indicate the same characteristic. No voltage applied to any pair of terminals or leads of a transistor should exceed the $V_{(BR)\,CBO}$ rating.

A tighter limit imposed on the transistor is the breakdown voltage between the collector and emitter. The voltage is at its maximum when a reverse bias is applied between the base and emitter terminals. Here the symbols for the breakdown voltage are $V_{(BR)CEV}$ = BV_{CEV}. Starting with $V_{(BR)CEV}$, the highest collector-to-emitter breakdown voltage, other collector-to-emitter breakdown voltages in descending order of magnitude are:

- $V_{(BR)CES}$ = BV_{CES} when the base-emitter junction is short circuited.
- $V_{(BR)CER}$ = BV_{CER} when a resistor, R, is connected between the base and emitter
- $V_{(BR)CEO}$ = BV_{CEO} when the base-emitter junction is open circuited

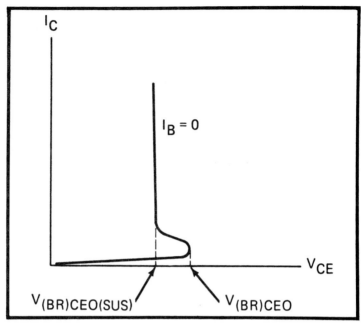

Fig. 8-1. Collector characteristic curve showing breakdown and sustaining voltage for a condition when the base is left open.

It is obvious that the smaller the resistor placed across the base-emitter junction the higher the breakdown voltage will be. The voltage may even be specified for the presence of a particular circuit that may be placed between the base and emitter. In this case the symbol is $V_{(BR)CEX} = BV_{CEX}$.

Various breakdown voltages defined here occur at low collector currents. At high current the breakdown voltage is reduced and is referred to as a sustaining voltage. It is simple noted by placing the symbol (sus) after the particular breakdown voltage notation. Sustaining voltage should be specified at the specific current used in a circuit. A hypothetical collector characteristic curve showing $V_{(BR)CEO}$ and $V_{(BR)CEO(sus)}$ is in Fig. 8-1.

The base-emitter junction forms a diode subject to breakdown when reverse biased. This voltage, $V_{(BR)EBO} = BV_{EBO}$, should not be exceeded at any time. Special precautions must be taken when operating in a push-pull class AB or class B mode because a reverse signal is applied to this junction during a significant portion of the cycle.

Other maximum ratings which must not be exceeded are the collector and base current limits, power dissipation at specific

171

operating temperatures and the specific maximum temperatures when storing, operating and soldering a device into the circuit.

LIMITING VOLTAGES FOR JFETS

Similar to bipolar devices, JFETs are encumbered by limiting factors. The obvious limiting voltages are:

- $V_{(BR)GSS} = BV_{GSS}$, the gate-to-source breakdown voltage with the drain connected to the source
- $V_{(BR)DGS} = BV_{DGS}$, the drain-to-gate voltage with the source connected to the gate.
- $V_{(BR)DSS} = BV_{DSS}$, the drain-to-source voltage with the gate connected to the source
- $V_{(BR)DSX} = BV_{DSX}$, the drain-to-source voltage with the gate at a specified voltage with respect to the source

The maximum allowable drain power dissipation, drain current and the various temperatures are normally stated on data sheets and should, of course, not be exceeded in any design.

SECOND BREAKDOWN

JFETs and small-signal bipolar transistors should not be forced to operate outside the limits set by the maximum power dissipation hyperbola discussed in Chapter 7. More stringent restrictions are placed on medium- and high-power bipolar devices by a phenomenon known as second breakdown.

A transistor is subject to second breakdown when there is a substantial amount of collector current flowing while the collector-emitter voltage, although within all ratings, is relatively high. This phenomenon may occur even if the transistor is operating well within its maximum power dissipation rating. At one specific combination of I_C and V_{CE} the collector-emitter voltage will suddenly drop and the collector current will rise rapidly. A curve illustrating this is shown in Fig. 8-2, where at $V_{(BR)(sus)}$ and I_{SEC}, the transistor goes into a second breakdown state. The voltage across the device in this state is V_{SEC}.

Second breakdown is usually explained by stating that when large amounts of current flow through a tiny area of semiconductor material, it will cause local overheating and breakdown. Once a device is in second breakdown, the transistor is usually destroyed. Several precautions should be taken to minimize the chances of second breakdown:

- Keep the collector-emitter voltage to the minimum consistent with circuit design requirements.

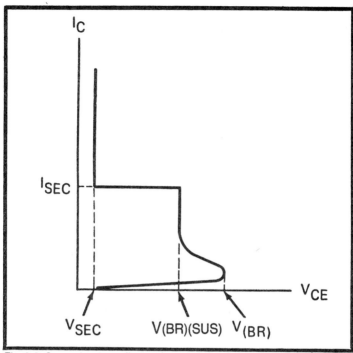

Fig. 8-2. Curve showing collector characteristics during a second breakdown.

- Use single diffused rather than double or triple diffused devices if this limitation is at all compatible with the circuit.
- Check the frequency requirements of the circuit carefully. Use the transistor with the lowest high-frequency cutoff specification that will satisfy a design. Frequency characteristics of a transistor are discussed in the next two chapters.
- Watch for inductive loads. When a transistor is reverse biased during a portion of a cycle, it will theoretically not conduct current; however, when the voltage across the transistor is high, an inductive load will discharge current through the transistor. Current will flow through a small area of the semiconductor while V_{CE} is large—the perfect situation to initiate second breakdown. In this case the proper precaution is to keep the reverse base-emitter voltage as small as practical and make sure the resistor in the circuit is comparatively high in value.

Once transistors have been designed into an audio output circuit they can be checked against safe operating area curves to

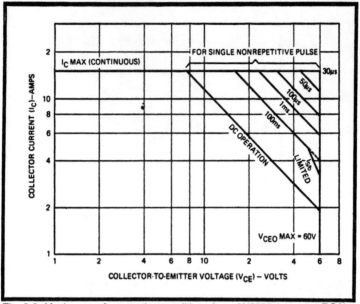

Fig. 8-3. Maximum safe operating conditions for a 2N3055 (courtesy RCA).

ascertain if they are operating within the boundaries necessary to avoid second breakdown. These safe operating curves are provided by the manufacturer of the device. Curves of this type for the 2N3055 transistor are shown in Fig. 8-3.

A circuit should be established and tests performed to ascertain if the load line for a transistor is within the limits set by the curves; thus, if there is a 100-millisecond pulse flowing through the transistor, the load line for the transistor should be below the curve marked 100 ms. Similarly, if there is a 100-microsecond pulse in the collector circuit, the load line for the transistor should fall below the curve marked 100μs. As the pulses get longer, limiting curves get more severe. For intermediate size pulses not shown on the curves, the limits can be determined by interpolation. It is obvious that for a pulse of any duration a safe load line will fall below the curve marked DC operation; however, this severe load-line limit is not required should shorter pulses be reproduced.

The question may arise as to how the load line may vary with the duration time of the pulse. Previously we drew the DC and AC load lines and disregarded their dependence on frequency. It should be obvious that an inductive load line, due to a transformer or speaker load, is frequency sensitive and will vary in shape and size with the pulse width.

174

To test a circuit sine waves rather than pulses may be used. Here the duration time indicated on the curve can be considered safe if the load falls below the limit curve of ½f seconds, where f is the frequency of the sine wave.

The circuit may also be tested by using the actual haphazard signal, such as music or speech, normally present at the output of an audio amplifier. In this case the continuously varying load lines should fall below the DC operation curve in Fig. 8-3. This is a severe test and a better indicator of transistor safety in operation than is a test performed with any other type of signal.

To perform the test the transistor in the output circuit can be connected to a calibrated scope as shown in Fig. 8-4. The collector current flows through R_E. Voltage across R_E is then proportional to I_C, the collector current. This voltage is plotted on the vertical axis of the scope in terms of collector current. At the same time the collector-emitter voltage is applied to the horizontal input of the calibrated scope. The V_{CE}-I_C plot on the scope is the load line of the transistor. Vary the frequency fed to the amplifier or change

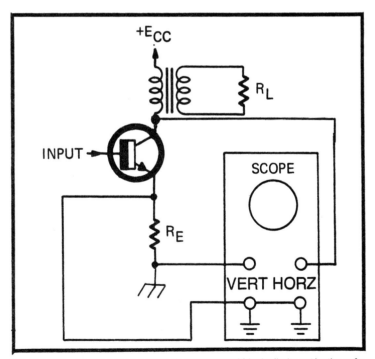

Fig. 8-4. Setup to check if a transistor is operating within the limits set by the safe operating curves.

the type of load, and the load line plot on the scope will be altered. To attain a safe operating condition no point on the load line is to be above the limits set by the curves in Fig. 8-3 at any frequency of operation for any load and at any power output level. Identical test arrangements can be made for transistors in push-pull and output-transformerless circuits. Quantities I_C and V_{CE} are measured across one output device at a time.

THERMAL CIRCUITS AND LIMITS

The primary source of heat in a bipolar transistor is the power dissipated at the collector junction. The contribution of heat generated at the base-emitter junction to the overall temperature of the device is relatively negligible. Maximum operating junction temperature for silicon transistors is usually specified at 200 °C, while for germanium devices it is limited to 100 °C.

Heat within a transistor must be removed from the junction as it is being generated if the transistor is not to become too hot and break down. There is a thermal resistance, θ (units are degrees Celsius per watt), which resists the flow of heat from the junction. Thermal resistance between the junction and the case of the transistor is Θ_{jc}. The case is cooled by the surrounding air, which is normally at a lower temperature than the case. There is a thermal resistance between the case and the air, assigned the symbol Θ_{CA}.

Because the surface area of the case is small, very little air can flow over it within a specified period of time; therefore, the case is usually mounted on a large metal surface or sink. It has a large area exposed to the ambient temperature; however, there is a thermal resistance between the case and the sink, Θ_{CS} and between the heat sink and the air, Θ_{SA}. It is obvious that $\Theta_{CA} = \Theta_{CS} + \Theta_{SA}$, but it should be noted that Θ_{CA} is smaller when a heat sink is present than when only the case is exposed to the air. Thermal resistance between the case and sink, Θ_{CS}, can be relatively sizable, but may be reduced if silicone grease is used between the case and sink to insure good contact between the surfaces.

Electronic circuits frequently require that the case (usually connected to the collector of the transistor) be insulated from the grounded heat sink. A mica insulator is usually placed between the case and heat sink to fulfill this function. Thermal resistance between the case and heat sink is increased when the mica is used, but this is unavoidable. Once again, the situation can be alleviated by applying silicone grease to both sides of the mica washer. Typically, Θ_{CS} when a plain mica washer is used about 0.8°C/W, while the

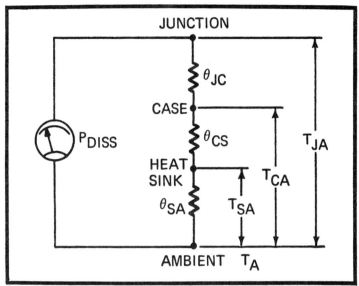

Fig. 8-5. Thermal equivalent circuit.

addition of silicone grease will reduce Θ_{CS} to approximately 0.4 °C/W. Compare this with the thermal resistance when no washer is used. Here Θ_{CS} can be $0.2°C\mu$ without the silicone grease and 0.1°C/W with the use of the silicone grease between the contacting surfaces.

Thermal resistance can be put into a thermal equivalent circuit and treated as an ordinary resistor in an electric circuit. The equivalent to the electric current is the power, P_{diss}, dissipated by the semiconductor. P_{diss} flows through the thermal circuit in a manner similar to the flow of current through an electric circuit.

When current flows through an electric circuit a voltage is developed across a resistor in the circuit. Heat, measured in degrees Celsius is developed across a thermal resistor when power flows through the thermal circuit. We can thus write an equation relating thermal resistance, power and temperature:

$$P_{diss} = \frac{T_J - T_A}{\theta_{JA}} = \frac{T_J - T_A}{\theta_{JC} + \theta_{CS} + \theta_{SA}} \qquad (8\text{-}1)$$

where T_J of the temperature at the junction and T_A is the ambient temperature. This is an important equation to remember. A schematic diagram presenting the information described by the equation is shown in Fig.8-5. Quantities T_{JA}, T_{CA} and T_{SA} are temperatures at the junction, case and heat sink, respectively, with respect to the ambient. Temperatures are developed across ther-

177

mal resistors shown in the drawing. These temperatures represent the heat rise above the ambient, which is treated as if it were the circuit ground.

Using Equation 8-1 the temperature at the heat sink is $T_S = \theta_{SA}P_{diss} + T_A$. Similarily, if the case temperature is $T_{CA} + T_A$, the junction temperature is $T_{JA} + T_A = T_{CA} + T_A + \theta_{JC}P_{diss}$. It is evident that the junction temperature is directly related to the case temperature. It is further evident that if the junction temperature is limited to some maximum, such as 200° C, the maximum allowable case temperature will decrease as the power dissipated by the semiconductor rises. For example, if θ_{JC} is 1.5°C/W as it is for the 2N3055, and 50 watts is dissipated by the transistor, the maximum allowable case temperature is 200° C - (1.5 °C/W) (50 watts) = 125° C.

A curve can be drawn relating the maximum allowable power dissipation by the device to the temperature of the case. Since the maximum rated dissipation of the transistor is 115 watts, the curve for the 2N3055 is as shown in Fig. 7-2. Note that at 125 °C the maximum allowable dissipation as noted on the curve is 50 watts, substantiating our calculation from the data.

If the transistor temperature rises faster than its ability to dispose of the excess heat, the device will obviously overheat. The elevated temperature will force the current flow to increase. This is due primarily to I_{CBO}, the collector-base leakage current. In turn more heat is produced. The cycle will repeat itself, building up additional heat until the transistor is destroyed. This is known as thermal runway. To avoid thermal runaway, the following inequality must be satisfied.

$$< \frac{T_{JA}}{\theta_{JA} \left[I_c + SI_{CBO}' \right] \left[E_{cc} - I_c (R_c + R_E) \right]} \qquad (8\text{-}2)$$

where:

- T_{JA} is the junction temperature less than the ambient temperature.
- I_c is the idling collector current.
- S is the stability factor discussed in Chapter 2 and equal to $\Delta I_c / \Delta I_{CBO}$.
- I_{CBO}' is the maximum leakage current (collector-to-base with the emitter open) for the maximum temperature at which the semiconductor device can be used. As you recall, for conservative estimates, it doubles for every 6°C rise in the junction temperature of silicon devices and for

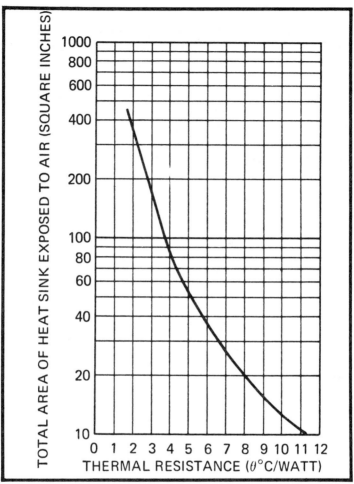

Fig. 8-6. Approximate thermal resistance of a heat sink made of ⅛-inch thick bright aluminum.

every 10 °C rise in the junction temperature of germanium transistors.

- ■ E_{CC} is the collector supply voltage.
- ■ R_C is the DC resistance in the collector circuit.
- ■ R_E is the DC resistance in the emitter circuit.
- ■ Heat sinks used to help maintain safe temperatures are rated by their thermal resistance. They are best used vertically with all surfaces exposed to the air in a type of chimney effect. Once θ_{SA} has been calculated, the size of a non-standard heat sink may be estimated from Fig. 8-6.

THERMAL FATIGUE

It is well known that if a piece of sheet metal were bent back and forth along one line, it will eventually break. Some types of metal can be flexed more often than other types before cracking. So it is with transistors. They can be brought up to a specific high temperature and then cooled. This can be repeated only a specific number of times before the transistor will break down. The graph drawn in Fig. 8-7 shows the number of these heating and cooling cycles that a 2N6099 transistor can endure before breaking down. This **thermal-cycling** rating is related to both the power dissipated by the transistor and to the change of the case temperature during each thermal cycle.

At an average, audio amplifiers can be assumed to go through 1000 of these thermal cycles each year. If you expect the equipment to last five years (another average figure), the transistors must last for at least 5000 cycles. Equipment designed and built by the hobbyist can be made to last through many more cycles, if desired.

In the practical situation, the 2N6099 may be required to dissipate 20 watts. If the minimum number of thermal cycles should be 5000, the case temperature should not change by more than 50 °C. This can be determined from the curves in Fig. 8-7. Used at an

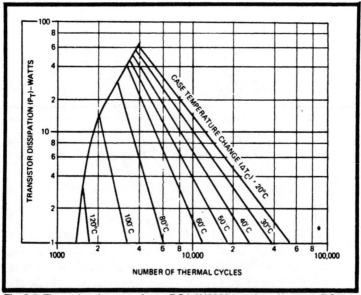

Fig. 8-7. Thermal cycle curves for an RCA 2N6099 transistor (courtesy RCA).

ambient temperature of 20°C, the design should be such as to limit the case temperature to 70°C when power is applied to the amplifier.

A Class AB amplifier dissipates different amounts of power when operating at different volume levels. As an example, assume that one transistor of a push-pull pair dissipates 4 watts when operating at low volume levels and 20 watts when producing loud music. Furthermore, assume that it is anticipated that the transistor in the amplifier will be dissipating 4 watts for 10,000 cycles and that the case temperture will increase 30°C. At the 20-watt level, the case temperature may change by 80°C, but it is required to go through only 2000 cycles. The problem is to determine if the device is being used within its thermal cycling rating.

At the 4-watt level, the number of cycles permitted with a temperature change of 30°C is 17,500, as determined from the curves. Since only 10,000 cycles are required, 10,000/17,500 = 0.57 of the maximum permissible number of cycles are permitted. Only 2000/3000 or 0.67 is 1.24. The transistor is used within is thermal-cycling rating if the sum of the two decimals is equal to or less than 1. Obviously, operation of the above circuit is beyond the rating of the device.

If the number of cycles at the 4-watt level is fixed so that the decimal is 0.57, the number should not exceed 1 - 0.57 = 0.43 at the 20-watt level. Since 3,000 cycles are permitted when used exclusively at $\Delta T_c = 80°C$, the number, N, of actual permitted cycles at the 20-watt level, can be calculated from N/3000 = 0.43. Hence, N = 1290 cycles.

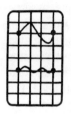

Chapter 9
Multistage
Amplifiers

The gain of an individual transistor circuit is limited primarily by device parameters, by the load it must feed, by the impedance of the input signal, and by the bias and bias stabilization components. Both JFET and bipolar devices are affected by all these factors, but to differing degrees. While the impedance of the input signal will probably have a severe effect on the gain of a circuit using a bipolar transistor as the input device, it will be relatively insignificant when facing the high input impedance of an FET.

Three arrangements are commonly used to couple several transistors into circuits designed to provide more gain than is possible with one device. All methods use the signal derived from one stage of amplification to drive a second stage of gain. The output from the second transistor, may, in turn, drive a third device, and so on. The overall gain is the product of the gains of each individual amplifier circuit, remembering, of course, that the gain of each circuit is affected by the circuit and components preceding and following the one being analyzed.

Of the three types of coupling circuits, capacitive coupling is probably most frequently used. Here, a capacitor conducts the signal from the output of one stage to the input of the next, while all DC voltages are isolated within the individual stages. Although adequate in very many applications, capacitive coupling components discriminate against DC and the low frequencies of the signal being reproduced. There is also a frequency-dependent phase shift which many audio purists find objectionable.

The disadvantages are overcome by omitting the capacitor and using direct coupling. But circuits of this type are not free of drawbacks. Drain or collector current buildup due to instability in one stage is multiplied by the gain of succeeding stages. The current may build up to such proportions as to upset the quiescent conditions in the final stage of amplification. Furthermore, drift due to thermal causes can upset the balance of pushpull output stages, allowing DC current to flow through loudspeaker loads.

Transformer coupling, although frequently used due to convenience and circuit matching advantages, has many of the drawbacks exhibited by the capacitor coupling method. The characteristics of this arrangement are the first to be detailed here.

TRANSFORMER COUPLING

As you recall from Chapter 7, a transformer consists of two or more windings placed in a common magnetic field. The signal appearing in one winding is coupled to the second or whatever number of additional windings may exist. Transformers with a single tapped winding (autotransformers) are seldom used in audio applications because there is no DC isolation possible between coupled stages.

The impedance or resistance placed across the secondary winding is reflected into the pimary winding. To determine the exact effect, multiply the impedance of the secondary load by the square of the turns ratio of the two windings. In Fig. 9-1, R_L is the load placed across the secondary winding of the transformer and the R_S is the DC resistance of that winding. With N_P turns in the primary winding and N_S in the secondary, the resistance reflected into the primary, R_L' due to the resistance in the secondary, is:

$$R_L' = \left(\frac{N_P}{N_S}\right)^2 (R_L + R_S) \qquad (9\text{-}1)$$

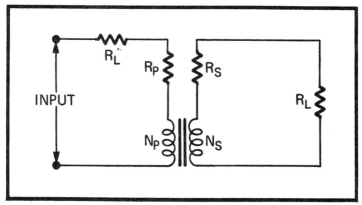

Fig. 9-1. Output load, R_L, is reflected into the primary winding of the transformer as R_L'.

A signal fed to the primary of the transformer sees R_L' in series with the DC resistance of the primary winding, R_P. R_P as well as R_S, the DC resistance of the secondary winding, are wasteful losses in the transformer. Good transformers are designed so that the resistances in the windings are negligible compared to the actual load placed across the winding. Consequently, R_S is made much smaller than R_L. In Equation 9-1, R_S is usually assumed to be zero.

A 25% loss factor is usually included in designs to compensate or account for all inefficiencies of the transformer. The primary factor affecting efficiency is the copper used for the windings. The percent copper efficiency can be readily determined from the equation:

$$\% \text{ Efficiency } = \frac{\text{Power output}}{\text{Power input}}$$

$$= \frac{100}{1 + \left(\dfrac{R_p + n^2 R_S}{n^2 R_L}\right)} \%$$

(9-2)

where $n = N_P/N_S$, the turns ratio of the transformer. Being directly proportional to the voltage ratio, the turns ratio can be determined experimentally by placing a known 400-Hz voltage, V_p across the primary and reading the voltage, V_S, across the secondary winding with an accurate meter. The ratio $V_P : V_S = n$.

The frequency range of a circuit may be limited by the presence of a transformer in that circuit. The circuit in Fig. 9-2A can be used to measure the frequency response of a transformer. A curve similar to that in Fig. 9-2B can be derived from the measurements. It shows the gain of a transformer circuit over a range of frequencies. The low-frequency rolloff is due to the incremental inductance of the primary winding of the transformer, while the high-frequency rolloff is due to the leakage inductance. The jagged characteristics of the curve at the high end are caused by various winding and stray capacitances.

The basic low-frequency equivalent of a circuit using a transformer is a resistor in series with an inductor, as shown in Fig. 9-3. If the secondary of the transformer is open, R may simply be the primary winding resistance, R_p. It should be added to the collector or drain resistance of a transistor, usually r_d, if it is in the primary circuit of the transformer. Load the secondary with R_L and R_{in} becomes $R_p + r_d$ in parallel with the value of the load resistor when reflected into the prmary. Reflected into the primary winding, the

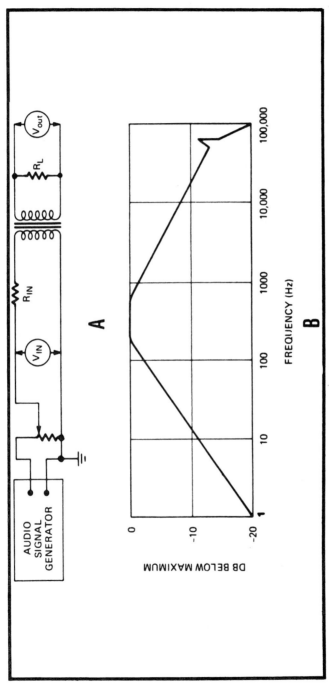

Fig. 9-2. Frequency characteristic of a transformer and the measuring procedure. The test setup (A) is used to measure the frequency response of an output transformer. R_{IN} is the impedance or resistance of the circuit feeding the primary of the transformer. B shows a possible frequency response curve of a transformer. The ratio of the output to the input, expressed in dB, is measured and plotted on the curve.

185

resistance, $R_L' = n^2 R_L$. L in the circuit is not simply the inductance of the primary winding of the transformer, L_p. It is the *incremental inductance*, or the inductance of the primary winding when DC is present in the winding along with the audio signal.

The incremental inductance should be determined for a specific direct current in the winding while there is a 60-Hz AC voltage across the transformer. A bridge can be used for the measurement. The approximate inductance (not incremental) can be determined using a bridge or using the circuit in Fig. 9-4. Here, a 60-Hz AC voltage is fed from the AC lines across a series R-L circuit. A voltmeter is used to measure the voltages across R and across L_p. R is adjusted until both voltages are equal. Then $L_p = R/377$. (Note that when voltages across both components are equal, the voltmeter will indicate more than one half the voltage of the supply due to phase shift in the R-L_p circuit.)

A similar procedure can be used to measure the incremental inductance. Use the circuit in Fig. 9-4, with the addition of a DC supply placed across L_p. This supply must be connected across the winding through a large resistor so that the DC circuit will have no effect on the measurement of the incremental inductance, other than that due to the DC current flowing through L_p. Adjust the DC voltage so that the DC current in the primary of the transformer will be equal to the current expected to flow in the actual transistor circuit. Proceed as before to compare the voltage across R with that across L_p. When the voltages are equal, the incremental inductance is R/377.

The low-frequency response characteristics of the circuit in Fig. 9-3 is shown as curve B in the figure, with an approximation of the exact curve drawn as curve C. Frequency f_0 is known as the corner frequency and can be determined from:

$$f_0 = \frac{R}{6.28L} \tag{9-3}$$

At f_0, the gain has decreased 3 dB from its mid-frequency value. Other important approximate points on the curve are at $2f_0$ where the gain has dropped 1 dB from that at mid-frequency, at $f_0/2$ where the rolloff is 7 dB, and the loss of gain at $f_0/4$ is 12 dB. Below $f_0/4$, the gain decreases at the rate of 6 dB/octave. The straight-line approximation to the curve has a 0 dB rolloff at f_0 and the gain decreases at the the rate of 6 dB/octave below the corner frequency. It should be noted that when the gain drops at the rate of 6 dB octave, it is identical to a 20 dB/decade rolloff.

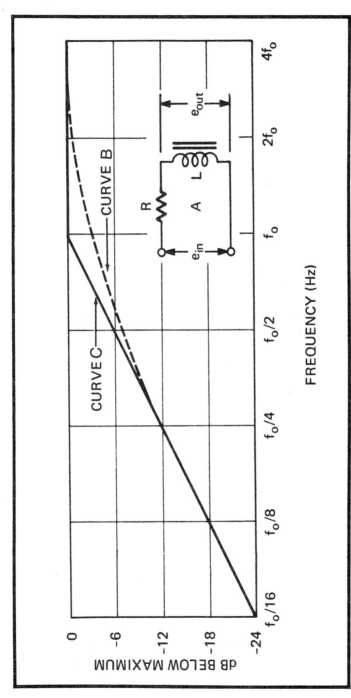

Fig. 9-3. High-pass R-L filter circuit (A). Also shown is the frequency response curve (B) and an approximation (C) to the curve B.

187

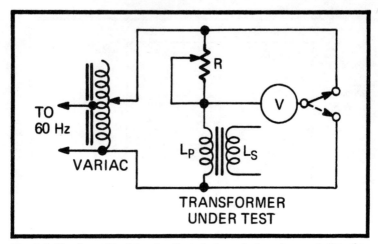

Fig. 9-4. Circuit used to determine the inductance in the primary winding of a transformer. It is determined by equating the resistance of the potentiometer to the impedance of the transformer. The resistance is equal to the impedance when the voltages across both components are equal.

At the high frequencies, the equivalent circuit of the transformer is shown in A of Fig. 9-5. It is a resistor in series with an inductor. Here, R is the sum of primary resistance of the transformer, R_p, the load resistor reflected from the secondary winding into the primary R_L', and the collector (or drain) resistance of the transistor, usually r_d. The leakage inductance, L_{leak}, is the L in the circuit.

Leakage inductance is a stray considered to be in series with the primary winding of the transformer. It is measured on a bridge by applying a 1000-Hz signal at 1 volt across the primary of the transformer while the secondary winding is shorted.

Leakage inductance can also be measured using the circuit in Fig. 9-6. The secondary winding is shorted and a variable resistor is placed in series with the primary winding. About 1.4 volts at 1 kHz is impressed across the series combination formed by the resistor and the primary of the transformer. The variable resistor is adjusted until the AC voltmeter reads the same voltage across the transformer and across the resistor. At this resistance, $L_{leak} = R/6.28 \times 10^3$.

The actual high-frequency response of the circuit is curve B in Fig. 9-5 and the approximation is curve C. As was the case for the low-frequency characteristic, the rolloff of the approximate curve is at the rate of 6 dB/octave or 20 dB/decade, starting at f_0. f_0 is once again defined by Equation 9-3. At f_0, the actual gain is 3 dB down

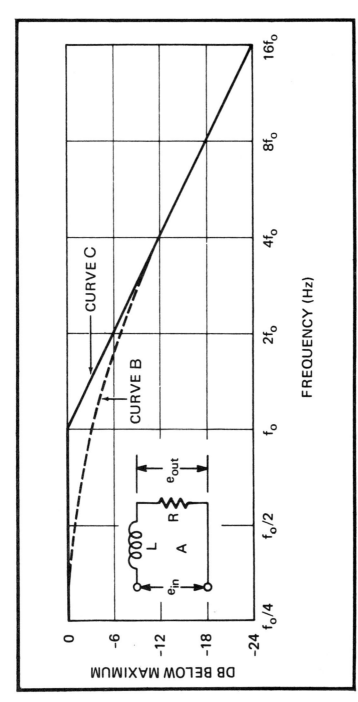

Fig. 9-5. Low-pass R-L filter circuit (A). The curve at B represents the frequency response of the filter and C is an approximation to the curve at B.

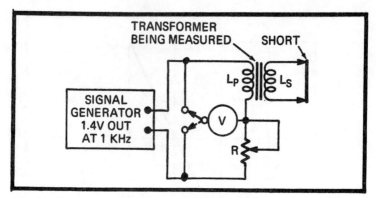

Fig. 9-6. Setup to measure leakage inductance. The secondary winding is shorted and potentiometer R is adjusted until the voltage across the primary winding of the transformer is identical to that across R.

from the gain at the mid-frequency. Gain is 1 dB down at $f_0/2$, 7 dB down at $2f_0$, 12 dB down at $4f_0$ and it rolls off at the rate of 6 dB per octave thereafter.

Due to various stray capacities, the high-frequency rolloff is not as smooth as depicted by the ideal situation described. There are various peaks in the response which cause bumps in the curve. Rolloff can proceed at the rate of 12 dB/octave. The winding capacity responsible for the peaks can be found using the circuit in Fig. 9-7. Here, a few thousand ohms resistor, R, is placed in series with the primary winding of the transformer while the secondary is shorted. The frequency of the signal generator is varied until there is a peak voltage across the primary winding as read on the meter, V. Frequency f_1 is one of the frequencies at which a bump will occur on the response curve. The winding capacity is $C = 1/(6.28f_1)^2 L_{leak}$. Several peaks may be noted for the various capacitances which are characteristic of transformers. Some peaks will be more pronounced than others.

USING COUPLING TRANSFORMERS

In Chapter 7, we indicated that transformers are used to convert the low output impedance of a speaker load across the secondary to a high impedance in the primary winding. This relatively high impedance is to serve as the load for a transistor. In a similar manner, a transformer can be used to couple a high-impedance input source to the low-impedance at the input of a bipolar transistor. This impedance conversion is not generally required when feeding the high-input impedance of a JFET.

The audio input to an amplifier may originate at a microphone. Because of long lines, it is frequently desirable that a balanced input be used, as shown in Fig. 9-8. While a low-impedance long line is less susceptible to hum and noise pickup than a high-impedance line, the use of a transformer with the centertap connected to ground is an important asset in cancelling the in-phase hum and noise induced in the two "hot" leads of the connecting cable.

The signal fed through a low-impedance line may be applied directly to the input of an amplifier, or it may first be transformed so that it will appear as a higher impedance. Voltage gain is added as a fringe benefit. The transformer must be of the proper quality so as not to adversely affect the characteristics of the signal.

Interstage transformer coupling is commonly used in amplifiers. Although these components limit bandwidth and the flexibility of putting large amounts of feedback around the overall circuit due to stability problems (discussed in the next chapter) many excellent designs still do include driver transformers. However, they are found primarily in public address and low-price high fidelity equipment.

Let us now turn our attention to the circuit in Fig 9-9, which uses a considerable amount of transformer coupling, and see just what the circuit component values and arrangements can be. More transformers than are normally used in any one design are shown here. The paper design should be checked in a laboratory for accuracy and reproducibility. On an actual chassis, care must be exercised to avoid magnetic coupling between transformers. Returns to B- and ground should be made in the proper sequence (see Chapter 12) to avoid coupling between stages due to resistance in the leads.

A 50,000-ohm dynamic microphone with 15 mV average output is the signal source. The signal is amplified by three stages of

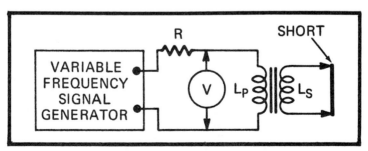

Fig. 9-7. Setup to measure winding capacities. The secondary winding is shorted.

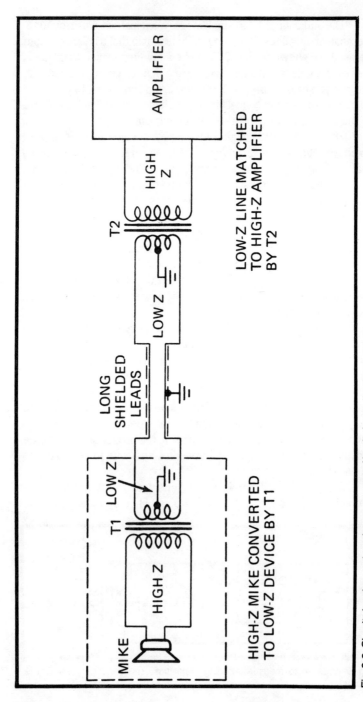

Fig. 9-8. Circuit showing a microphone connected in a balance-line input circuit.

192

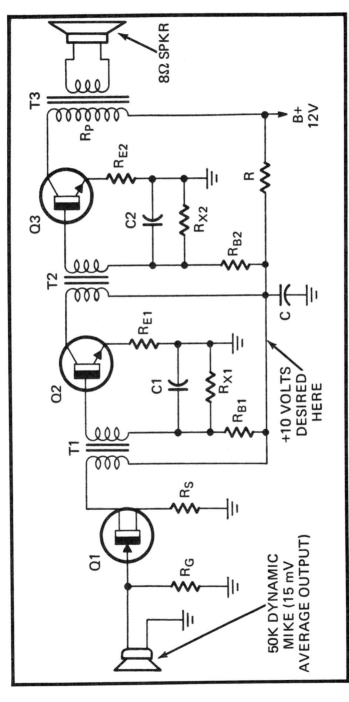

Fig. 9-9. Transformer-coupled amplifier used in the text design problem.

193

gain consisting of an N-channel JFET and two NPN bipolar devices. Each stage is transformer-coupled to the preceding and succeeding transistor. The required output is 1 watt delivered to an 8-ohm speaker. A 12-volt automobile battery is the source of power used directly as the B+ supply for the output stage, and applied through a decoupling R-C network to feed the first two transistors. It is assumed that the first two devices require 10 volts B+. This voltage is present at the junction of R and C.

Starting with the final stage, let us assume the output transformer is 75 percent efficient so that for 1 watt output, 1/0.75=1.33 watts is required at the primary of the transformer. Sufficient leeway can be built into the design if it is assumed that about 3 volts is lost across the output transistor due to leakage current and saturation voltage. About 2 volts of this can be attributed to saturation voltage. Adding this to power loss across R_{E2}, we can expect an additional 25% loss of power at Q3. The total power the output stage must be capable of delivering becomes $1.33 + (0.25 \times 1.33) = 1.66$ watts. We must now determine if the relatively inexpensive 2N3053 transistor in a TO-5 package can deliver this power.

Since 1.66 watts is required across the primary winding, the transistor in the Class A circuit must dissipate 3.32 watts or twice the power the device must deliver. If we assume 2 volts will be developed across the DC resistance in the emitter circuit and the primary winding of transformer T3, 10 volts will be across the transistor in the quiescent state. The quiescent collector current is 3.32 watts/10 volts = 332 mA. The peak current, $I_{max} = 2 \times 332$ mA = 664 mA, which is within the 700 mA rating of the 2N3053.

Draw AC and DC load lines as in Fig. 9-10. From the curve in the figure, the DC load resistance is (12-10) volts/332 mA = 6 ohms. The AC resistance is 20 volts/664 mA = 30 ohms. The resistance that is to be reflected from the secondary of the transformer to the primary is 30 ohms -6 ohms = 24 ohms, so that the impedance ratio of T3 is 24 ohms to 8 ohms = 3:1, and the turns ratio = $(24/8)^{\frac{1}{2}} = 1.73:1$. This assumes the DC resistance in the secondary winding is negligible when compared to the resistance of the 8-ohm load.

If we wish to design the transformer for a minimum of 25% efficiency, the maximum resistance of the primary winding can be determined (from Equation 9-2):

$$25 = \frac{100}{1 + \frac{R_p + 3R_s}{3R_L}}$$

$$= \frac{100}{1 + \dfrac{R_p + 0}{24}}$$

$$(9\text{-}4)$$

And $R_p = 72$ ohms. Since the DC design allows for a maximum of 6 ohms for the sum of the primary winding DC resistance and R_{E2}, the efficiency requirement will automatically be met in a proper design.

The voltage gain of an output stage is relatively unimportant when compared to its performance in delivering output power. Let us assume we would like a voltage gain of about 10 from this stage. Since the AC output impedance in the collector circuit is 24 ohms, the resistor in the emitter should be about one-tenth this value. Use a standard 2.7-ohm resistor for R_{E2}. This will also conform with another rule of thumb stating that about 1 volt should be across the emitter resistor of a power transistor when it is idling. Here the voltage is (2.7 ohms) (332 ma) = 0.9 volt, a value close enough to 1 volt. The DC resistance of the primary winding, R_P, can then be specified at less than 6 ohms-2.7 ohms = 3.3 ohms.

1.33 watts must be delivered to the 24-ohm AC impedance across the primary of T3 if 1 watt is to be delivered to the load. For this output, the RMS voltage across the primary of the transformer is $V = (R_L'P)^{½} = [(24)(1.33)]^{½} = 5.7$ volts.

The emitter resistance, r_e, of the transistor is usually taken at $26/I_E$, where I_E is the quiescent emitter current expressed in ma.

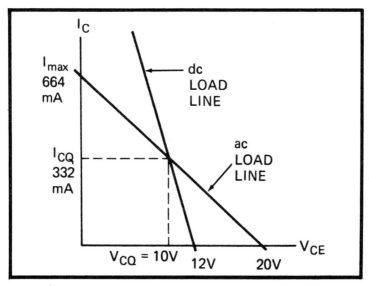

Fig. 9-10. Loadlines used in the design of the output stage in Fig. 9-9.

195

For a current of 332 ma, this figure becomes too small to be reasonable. We assume a minimum DC emitter resistance of 1 ohm for most transistors. The total AC resistance in the emitter circuit is $r_e = 1$ ohm added to the $R_{E2} = 2.7$ ohms, amounting to a total of 3.7 ohms. The calculated voltage gain of the output stage is the ratio of the 24 ohms at the primary of the output transformer to the 3.7 ohms just calculated, or 6.5. This differs from the approximate gain of 10 sought after above. More gain can be designed into the earlier stages. The signal voltage at the input to the transistor must be the 5.7 volts across the primary of the output transformer divided by the gain of 6.5, or 0.88 volt.

The output transformer usually represents the limiting factor on the frequency response. Assume our amplifier is to have an output from 20 Hz to 20 kHz, with the gain down 3 dB from center at these extreme frequencies. To fulfill these goals, the minimum inductance and maximum leakage inductance tolerable in the transformer can be determined with the help of Figs. 9-3 and 9-5.

Since R in Fig. 9-3A is essentially $R_L' = 24$ ohms (for it is R_L' in parallel with $r_d + R_p$), the incremental inductance of the primary winding of the transformer must be somewhat more than $L = R_L'/6.28f_0$ from Equation 9-3. Letting $f_0 = 20$ Hz, L must then be more than $24/6.28 (20) = 0.19$ henry.

At the high-frequency end of the band, from Fig. 9-5A, $R = r_d + R_p + R_L'$. Substituting numbers, $R_p + R_L' = 3.3$ ohms + 24 ohms = 27.3 ohms. The collector resistance, r_d, at 10 volts and 332 mA can be determined from the slope of the 2N3053 output characteristic curves in Fig. 9-11. It is about 180 ohms. R is thus 180 ohms + 27.3 ohms = 207.3 ohms. Using Equation 9-3, the maximum leakage current is $L = R/6.28f_0 = 207.3/6.28 (2 \times 10^4) = 1.65$ millihenrys.

The bias circuit is the next item to be designed. R_{X2} should be specified at about 10 times the size of R_{E2} for stability purposes, or at less than 27 ohms. Since there is about 0.7 volt across the base-emitter junction and 0.9 volt across R_{E2}, the sum of these voltages, or 1.6 volts, is across R_{X2}. The current flowing through R_{X2} is 1.6 volts/27 ohms = 59 mA.

From the characteristic curves in Fig. 9-11, it can be seen that about a 6 mA base current is required to get the 332 mA of current in the collector. The 59 ma flowing through R_{X2} and the 6 mA base current, both flow through R_{B2} for a total of 65 mA. Since the circuit is designed for 10 volts at the junction of R and C, $R_{B2} = (10-1.6)$ volts/65 mA = 129 ohms.

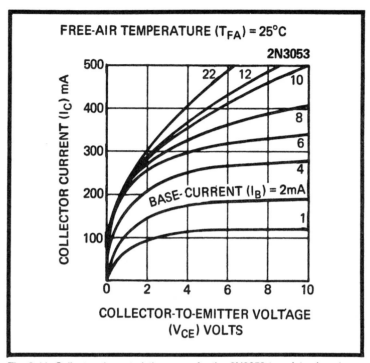

Fig. 9-11. Collector characteristic curves for the 2N3053 transistor (courtesy RCA).

The impedance across the secondary of T2 is $(R_{E2} + r_{e2})$ reflected into the base circuit. Since beta is 332 mA/6 mA = 55, the reflected impedance is $(2.7 + 1) \times 55 = 204$ ohms. Capacitor C_2 must be a short circuit compared to the 204 ohms at 20 Hz (the lowest frequency to be amplified) in order to effectively bypass the bottom end of the transformer to ground. If it is made one one-hundreth of 204 ohms, or about 2 ohms at 20 Hz, the capacitor will be $C_2 = 1/ (6.28) (20) (2) = 4000$ mfd.

The 0.88 volt signal determined above and required at the input to Q3 must be developed across the 204 ohms at the input of the base circuit. Hence, $e^2/ R = (0.88)^2/204 = 3.8$ milliwatts must be present at the output of T2.

Repeating the above procedure to design the circuit for Q2, 3.8 milliwatts/0.75 = 5 milliwatts must be present at the primary of T2 if the transformer is 75 % efficient. Additional power was required previously from the large signal transistor due to the limitations set on the load line by the saturation voltage and leakage current. These boundaries can usually be disregarded when small signal voltage-amplifier-type devices are involved.

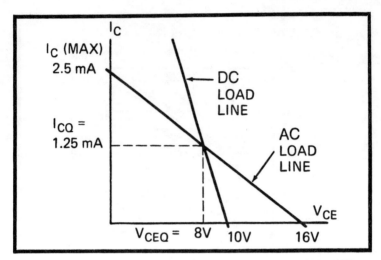

Fig. 9-12. Load lines used to design the proper quiescent condition of Q2.

Since the transistor must be able to deliver 5 milliwatts, it must be capable of dissipating 10 milliwatts. A 2N3391 transistor can do this easily and, therefore, can be used here.

Curves drawn in Fig. 9-12 are for AC and DC loads. Using the 10 volts at the junction of R and C as the supply and assuming that 2 volts is developed across R_{E1} and the DC resistance of the primary of the transformer, the quiescent voltage across Q2 is 8 volts and the quiescent current is 10 mw/8 volts = 1.25. The DC load resistance is 2 volts/1.25×10^{-3} amps = 1600 ohms. The AC load resistance is 16 volts/2.5×10^{-3} amps = 6400 ohms. The AC impedance across the primary of T2 is 6400 - 1600 = 4800 ohms. We can easily let R_{E1} = 470 ohms so that the gain of Q2 is 4800/470 = 10.2. The remaining DC resistance can be in the transformer winding.

The impedance ratio of the transformer is 4800:204, so the turns ratio and voltage ratio is about 4.9:1. Hence, the gain of the transformer is 1/4.9. Multiplying this by the gain of Q2, the overall gain of this part of the circuit is (10.2) (1/4.9) = 2.1. The signal voltage at the input to Q2 and across the secondary of T1 should thus be 0.88 volt/2.1 or 0.42 volt. Since the emitter resistance, r_e, of Q2 is about $26/I_E = 26 / 1.25 = 20.7$ ohms, and R_{E1} = 470 ohms, the total resistance in the emitter circuit is 470 ohms + 20.7 ohms = 490.7 ohms. From the specifications of the 2N3391, the average beta is 350, so the resistance of the emitter circuit when reflected into the base is (350) (490.7) = 1.74×10^5 ohms.

As for the basic circuit, make R_{X1} equal to 10 times the resistor in the emitter circuit or 4700 ohms. The voltage across this resistor is $V_{BE} = 0.7$ volt $+ (1.25$ mA$) (470$ ohms$) = 0.7$ volt $+ 0.59$ volt for a total of 1.29 volts, so the current flowing through R_{X1} is $1.29/4.7 \times 10^3 = 0.27$ mA. The average base current is the collector current divided by beta, or $1.25 \times 10^{-3}/350 = 0.0036$ mA. Add the base current to the current flowing through R_{X1} to determine the current in R_{B1}. It is 0.2736 mA. With 10 volts $- 1.29$ volts across R_{B1}, the resistor should be specified at about 8.71 volts$/0.2736 \times 10^{-3}$ mA $= 32,000$ ohms.

Returning to the AC circuit, the impedance of C1 should be one-hundredth that across the secondary of the transformer, or 1.74×10^3 ohms at 20 Hz. C1 $= 1/(6.28) (20) (1.74 \times 10^3) = 4.5$ mfd.

To deliver the required power, 0.42 volt must be developed across the 1.74×10^5 ohms at the base of Q2 and across the secondary of T2. The power required here is very small, and is $(0.42)^2/ 1.74 \times 10^{-5} \approx 1$ milliwatt. This power can easily be delivered by Q1, the JFET. The efficiency of the transformer approaches 100 % as R_L in Equation 9-2 becomes extremely large. We can now use the turns ratio of the transformer to supply gain and not be excessively concerned about losses and frequency characteristics of the component.

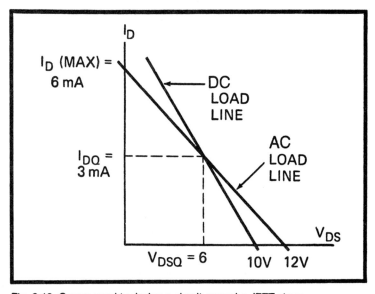

Fig. 9-13. Curves used to design a circuit around a JFET stage.

Select a 2N4303 N-channel JFET. Draw the AC and DC load lines for the 2N4303 JFET as shown in Fig. 9-13. Since the transformer winding can now have a large resistance without radically affecting performance, assume there is 6 volts across the transistor in the quiescent state. This leaves 4 volts to be dropped across the DC resistance of the primary winding of the transformer and across Rs, the resistor in the source lead. For low noise, which is an important consideration in the first stage of amplification, assume the quiescent drain current, I_{DQ}, is near I_{DSS}. The I_{DSS} for the 2N4303 is specified to be between 4 and 10 mA. Make the quiescent current, I_{DQ}, equal to 3 mA, so the AC load line can theoretically swing from 0 to 6 mA and the AC impedance in the drain circuit is 12 volts/6 mA = 2000 ohms.

The DC resistance—the sum of the resistance in the source circuit and the resistance of the primary winding of transformer T1—is (10—6) volts/3 mA = 1,333 ohms; therefore, the impedance R_L reflected into the primary of the transformer is 2000 ohms—1333 ohms = 667 ohms. The impedance ratio of the transformer is $667:1.74 \times 10^5 = 0.0038$. The turns ratio is $(0.0038)^{1/2} = 0.062$, so the voltage gain of the transformer is 1/0.062 = 16. Thus, 0.42 volt/16 = 0.026 volt (26 millivolts) is required at the drain of the 2N4303 if the amplifier is to deliver 1 watt across the 8-ohm load at the output. (As you recall, 0.42 volt is the signal voltage required across the secondary of transformer T1).

The microphone delivers 15 mv. The gain of the JFET must be at least 26 mv/15 mv = 1.73. Using a gain of three to compensate for variations in the actual semiconductor device and microphone, the source resistor, Rs, can be calculated from the equation:

$$A_V = \frac{g_m R_D}{1 + g_m R_S} = 3 \qquad (9\text{-}5)$$

where A_V is the voltage gain of the JFET, and g_m is the transconductance at the quiescent current (3 mA). R_D is the resistance in the drain circuit, and R_S is the source resistor.

The minimum transconductance at I_{DSS}, when the gate-to-source voltage is zero, is $g_{mo} = 2000$ micromhos. Using the maximum value of $I_{DSS} = 10$ mA and an idling current, $I_D = 3$ mA, we can find the minimum transconductance of the circuit at the operating point from the equation:

$$g_m = g_{mo} \left(\frac{I_D}{I_{DSS}} \right)^{1/2} = 2000 \left(\frac{3}{10} \right)^{1/2} = 1100 \qquad (9\text{-}6)$$

200

Substituting this into Equation 9-5:

$$3 = \frac{1100 \ (667)}{1 + 1100 \ R_s} \qquad (9-7)$$

Solving the equation, $R_s = 223$ ohms.

If conditions were such that the circuit could not supply sufficient gain, a "stepup" transformer can be used between the microphone and the input to the JFET for this purpose.

It must be noted that the microphone is not loaded with its characteristic impedance. If it were, the voltage delivered to the load at the input of the JFET would be half the voltage delivered when the microphone is feeding the extremely high input impedance at the transistor. The load on the microphone would become a factor if the input transistor were of the bipolar variety.

RESISTOR-CAPACITOR COUPLING

The limits inherent in R-C or resistor-capacitor coupled circuits are similar to those of transformer-coupled circuits. Capacitive reactance is inversely related to the frequency of the voltage across the capacitor. In the formula:

$$X_c = \frac{1}{6.28fC} \qquad (9-8)$$

X_c is the reactance of the capacitor in ohms, f is the frequency of the applied signal in Hertz, and C is the capacity in farads. Include the

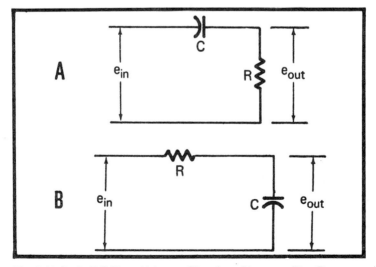

Fig. 9-14. Basic R-C filters: high-pass filter, A, and low-pass filter, B.

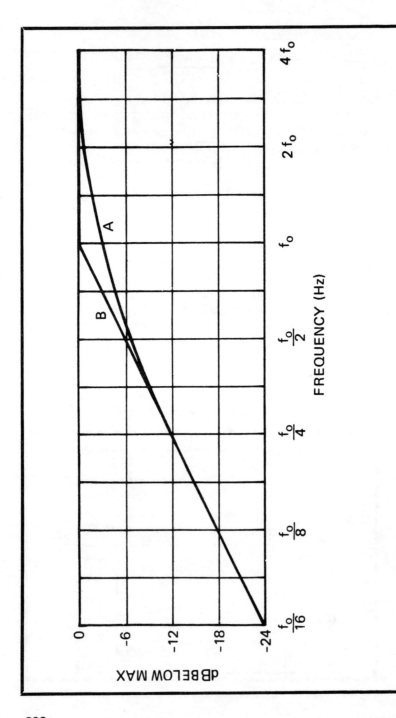

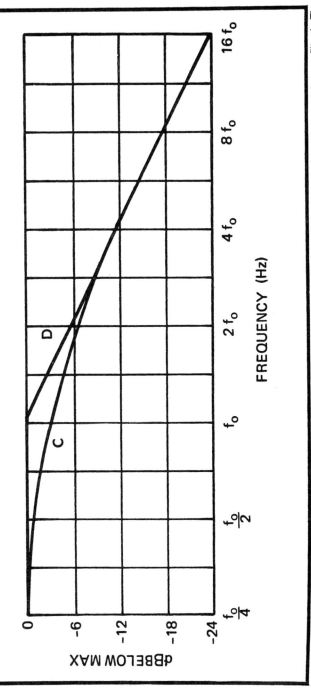

Fig. 9-15. Curves showing the frequency characteristics of the R-C filters in Fig. 9-14. The exact frequency response of the high-pass filter in Fig. 9-14A is illustrated by Curve A. Curve B is an approximate curve for the filter in Fig. 9-14A. Curve C represents the exact frequency response of the low-pass filter in Fig. 9-14B. An approximate curve for the filter in Fig. 9-14C is shown as D.

203

capacitor in a circuit with a resistor and you have a frequency-dependent R-C filter. These filters are part and parcel of the R-C coupled transistor circuit.

R-C Filters

Two basic filter circuits using one resistor and one capacitor in each are shown in Fig. 9-14. The high-pass filter in Fig. 9-14A discriminates against the low frequencies and freely passes the upper end of the spectrum. The exact and approximate frequency characteristic for this filter are shown as curves A & B, respectively, in Fig. 9-15. Note the 6 dB/octave or 20 dB/decade rolloff which makes these curves identical to those applied to the R-L filters. The corresponding curves for the low-pass filter of Fig. 9-14B are shown as curves C and D. The corner frequency, f_0, can be determined from the equation:

$$f_0 = \frac{1}{6.28RC} \tag{9-9}$$

where R is the resistance in ohms and C is the capacitance in farads.

Two or more such filters can be connected into the circuit to increase the rate of the rolloff beyond 6 dB/octave. At any particular frequency, the reduction in gain below maximum is equal to the sum of the reduction in gains of each of the individual filter sections at the frequency in question. Five such sums are performed graphically in Fig. 9-16.

The circuit in Fig. 9-16A consists of two low-pass 6 db/octave filters; one is composed of R1-C1 and the second is R2-C2. The corner frequency of the R1-C1 combination is f_{01} and that of the R2-C2 section is f_{02}. Should f_{02} be higher than f_{01}, the approximate frequency characteristic curve of the total filter is the heavy line drawn in Fig. 9-16B.

In the drawing, the low-frequency end of each curve is flat with 0 dB attenuation. At f_{01}, one curve starts to roll off at the rate of 6 dB/octave and beginning at f_{02} the second curve rolls off at the same rate. The heavy line is the sum of the two curves. Up to f_{01}, neither R-C combination attenuates the signal, so the heavy curve is flat with 0 dB attenuation. Between f_{01} and f_{02} the rolloff is affected only by R1-C1, so that this portion of the curve rolls off only at the rate of 6 dB/octave. From f_{02} on up to an ideally infinite frequency, the slope due to the rolloff characteristic of the R2-C2 section must be added to the slope due to R1-C1. Since both 6 dB/octave circuits

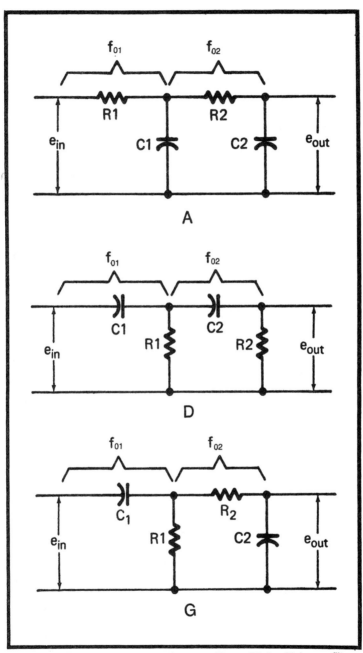

Figs. 9-16A, D and G. A shows two low-pass filters. D is two high-pass filters. G depicts one high-pass and one low-pass filter forming a bandpass filter.

are involved, the heavy curve is characterized by a 12 dB/octave rolloff.

Another way of plotting the effect of the total filter is to add the curves of each section vectorially, point by point. Up to f_{o1}, the attenuation of both curves is zero, so $0 + 0$ is 0 dB. At $2f_{o1}$, or at f_{o2}, the attenuation of one curve is 6 dB and that of the second curve is still zero. The point on the heavy line curve is thus $6 \text{ dB} + 0 \text{ dB} = 6$ dB. Continuing this, at $4f_{o1} = 2f_{o2}$, one curve shows an attenuation of 12 dB while the other is 6 dB down. Since the total is 18 dB, this is another point on the heavy line curve.

All points can be connected by a straight line, with the resulting heavy-line curve being the approximation to the complete filter. The characteristics differ somewhat from the ideal due to the effect of the loading of one filter section on the other. The procedure outlined is more accurate when the two filter sections are isolated from each other. This isolation can be accomplished by placing a high-impedance transistor stage between the two R-C sections.

Should f_{o1} and f_{o2} coincide, the rolloff is 12 dB/octave, beginning at the coincident corner frequency. This is shown in the plot in Fig. 9-16C. Similar plots for the high-pass filter in Fig. 9-16D are in Figs. 9-16E and 9-16F.

Characteristic curves of the bandpass filter in Fig. 9-16G are drawn in Fig. 9-16H. The vector additions producing the sum curve defining the response of the total filter are performed as before.

An equivalent to the input circuit of a transistor can take the form shown in Fig. 9-17. While R can be the Thevenin equivalent resistance of the output of a preceding circuit, R_p may represent the input resistance of a transistor or may be the resistor placed at the input of a transistor circuit. C could be the input capacitance of a JFET or bipolar device. The actual and approximate attenuation curves of this circuit are shown in Figs. 9-15C and 9-15D. However, it is displaced from the 0 dB maximum level by a number of dB determined by the resistive components in the circuit.

The horizontal portion of this curve from 0 Hz to f_o Hz, is not at 0 dB, as was the case when the curve in Fig. 9-15 was drawn for the circuit in Fig. 9-14B. Here there is already some attenuation at the low frequencies. At these frequencies, the attenuation is determined by the resistive voltage divider formed by R and R_p, because up to f_o, C is effectively an open circuit. Up to f_o:

$$e_{out} = \left(\frac{R_p}{R + R_p} \right) e_{in} \qquad (9\text{-}10)$$

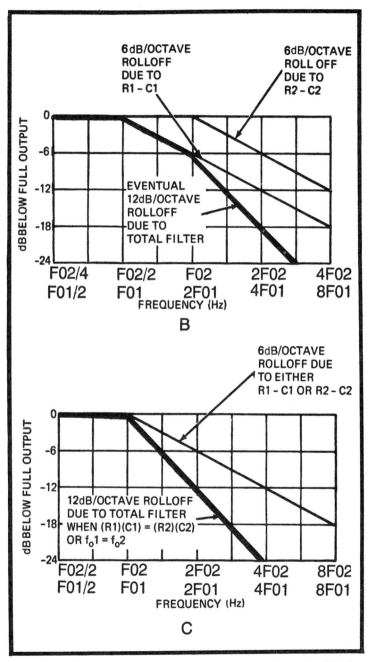

Figs. 9-16B and C. B is the response of Circuit A when $f_{o1} \neq f_{o2}$. C is the response of Circuit A when $f_{o1} = f_{o2}$.

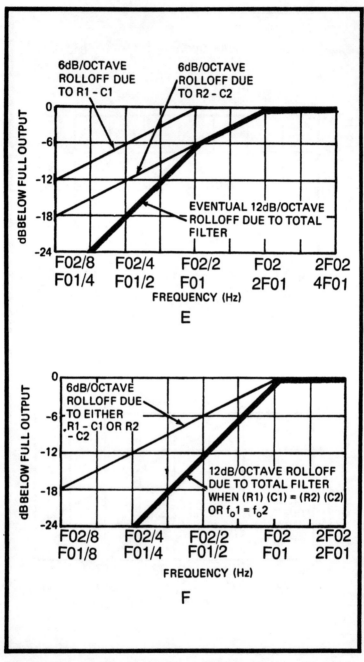

Figs. 9-16E and F. E is the response of Circuit D when f01 ≠ f02. F is the response of Circuit D when f01 = f02.

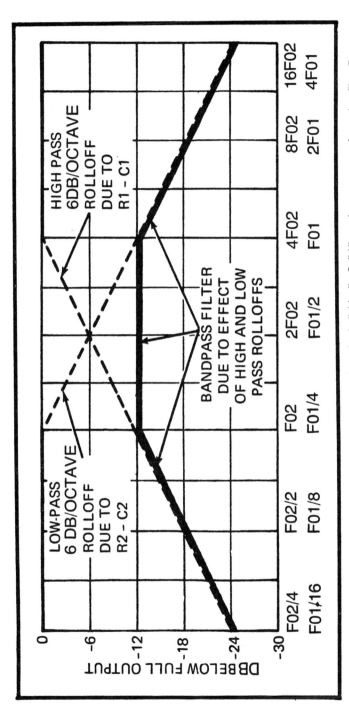

Fig. 9-16H. Response of Circuit G. Dotted lines show response of each section individually. Solid lines show response of complete filter. Response is when $f_{01} \neq f_{02}$.

209

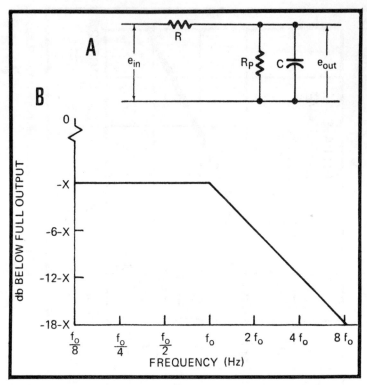

Fig. 9-17. Practical form (A) of the equivalent circuit at the input to a transistor. B is the frequency response curve for the circuit.

so that the dB attenuation at these frequencies can be determined from the equation:

$$\text{dB attention} = 20 \log_{10} \left(\frac{e_{out}}{e_{in}} \right) = 20 \log_{10} \left(\frac{R_p}{R + R_p} \right) \quad (9\text{-}11)$$

The corner frequency can be determined by shorting the input voltage, e_{in}, while the output circuit at e_{out} is left open. Then note the effective resistance shunting the capacitor, C. For this circuit, R is in parallel with R_P across C. Using the symbol $R \parallel R_p$ to represent the parallel resistor combination:

$$f_o = \frac{1}{2\pi \ (R \parallel R_p)C} \quad (9\text{-}12)$$

This equation is identical in form to Equation 9-9, where $2\pi = 6.28$.

A high-pass filter circuit frequently encountered is shown in Fig. 9-18A. In a practical circuit, R_p can be the input resistance of a

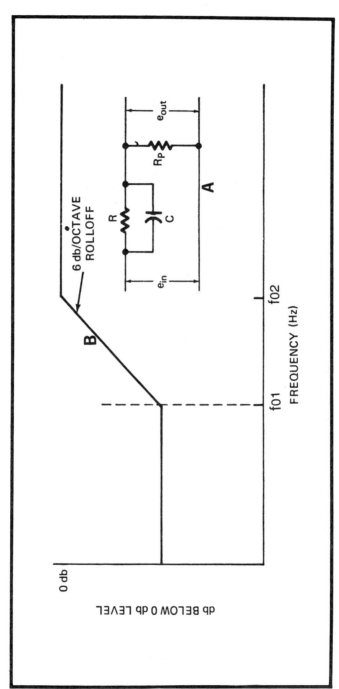

Fig. 9-18. Practical high-pass filter (A) used as the equivalent of a coupling circuit for a transistor amplifier. B is the frequency characteristic curve for the circuit.

211

transistor circuit, while C may be a coupling capacitor shunted by a resistor, R. R may be the resistance due to the leakage of an electrolytic coupling capacitor. The frequency characteristic curve for this circuit is also shown in Fig. 9-18.

As was the case with the circuit in Fig. 9-17, the output from 0 Hz to f_{o1} Hz is dependent only upon the resistive voltage divider formed by R and R_p and can be determined using Equation 9-11. The lower corner frequency can be calculated from the parallel RC circuit when e_{in} is open circuited and the output is shorted at e_{out}. It is simply equal to $1/6.28RC$ as stated in Equation 9-9. The curve from f_{o1} to f_{o2} has a 6 dB/octave slope. Equation 9-12 can be used to determine f_{o2}. As before, e_{in} is shorted to determine the resistance across the capacitor, $R \parallel R_p$, while e_{out} remains open.

$$f_{o2} = 1/6.28(R \| R_p)C \qquad (9\text{-}13)$$

The curve in Fig. 9-18 is actually the sum of two curves, for there are two corner frequencies. The addition is performed in a manner similar to that described for Figs. 9-16 and detailed in Fig. 9-19.

Let us now see just what we did to determine the corner frequencies. One corner frequency, f_{o2}, is determined from the parallel R-C circuit when e_{in} is shorted and e_{out} is left open circuited. For the high-pass filter, the low frequency rolls off or **decreases** below f_{o2}. The second corner frequency, f_{o1}, is determined from the parallel R-C circuit when e_{in} is open circuited and e_{out} is short-circuited. In this case, the output **increases** at the rate of 6 dB/octave from the corner frequency.

One more coincidence is evident with respect to the low-pass filter in Fig. 9-17 and the representative curve in Fig. 9-15C. The corner frequency was determined by shorting e_{in} while e_{out} was left open. The curve above f_o rolled off or **decreased** at the rate of 6 dB/octave. This rolloff was common to both the high- and low-pass filters when the corner frequency was determined after e_{in} is shorted while e_{out} is left untouched. We can now write two rules.

1. Determine one corner frequency by shorting the input while the output remains open. Substitute the equivalent resistance of all resistors in parallel with C into Equation 9-9. The curve will roll off or **decrease** at the rate of 6 dB/octave from this frequency. The direction of the rolloff will depend upon whether the circuit is a high- or low-pass type of filter.
2. Determine a second corner frequency by opening the input circuit while shorting the components at e_{out}. Substi-

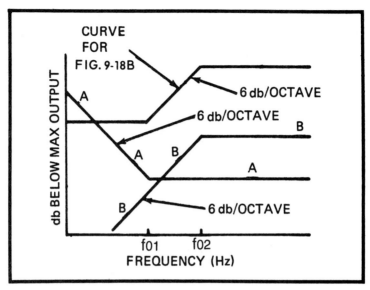

Fig. 9-19. Curves A and B are used to generate the sum curve in Fig. 9-18B. f_{01} and f_{02} must be determined for Curves A and B.

tute the equivalent resistance of all resistors in parallel with C. The curve will **rise** at the rate of 6 dB/octave from the frequency determined by using all resistance across C. If the parallel R-C combination is in series with the signal, the output will rise to 0 Hz as shown on curve A in Fig. 9-19. If a parallel R-C network is a component at the output terminals of the filter, the curve will rise to ∞ Hz beginning at the corner frequency.

Let us apply these two rules to the circuit in Fig. 9-20A. Since C is across a portion of the output, it is essentially a low-pass filter circuit. Determine f_{01} by shorting the input e_{in}. The equivalent resistance is $(R + R_s)$ in parallel with R_p, written $(R + R_s) \parallel R_p$. Thus, f_{01}, the frequency at which the rolloff starts is $1/[6.28][(R + R_s) \parallel R_p][C]$. Leaving e_{in} open and shorting the component at e_{out}, the second corner frequency, $f_{02} = 1/(6.28)(R_p \parallel R)(C)$, can be determined. The individual curves and the sum of the curves are shown in Fig. 9-20B. The number of dB the horizontal section of the curve is below the 0 dB reference can be determined from the resistor components and is equal to:

$$\text{dB below zero} = 20 \log_{10} \left(\frac{R_p + R}{R_p + R + R_s} \right) \qquad (9\text{-}14)$$

213

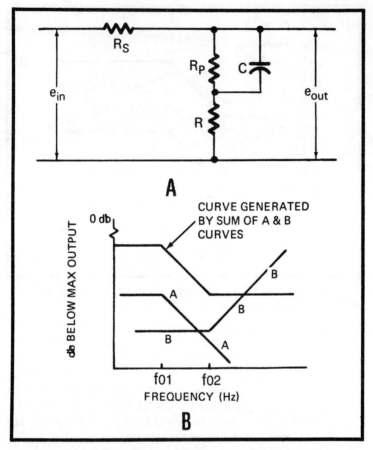

Fig. 9-20. Analysis of the circuit and the final curve generated by adding Curves A and B.

Frequency Characteristics of an R-C Stage

The circuits discussed can be applied to practical R-C and direct-coupled stages. A possible circuit is shown in Fig. 9-21. The input signal is fed through capacitor C1 to the gate of a JFET. The voltage developed across R_D is coupled through capacitor C2 to the base of a bipolar transistor. R_{in} is the resistance seen when looking into the base of Q2. The output of the 2-stage amplifier, appearing across R_C, is fed to load resistor R_L through capacitor C3.

Should e_{in} be a voltage source, the corner frequency for the circuit consisting of R_G and C1 is $1/6.28R_GC1$. The curve picturing the frequency characteristic of the signal across R_G is shown in Fig. 9-15A. The identical curve is used for the circuit involving R_D-C_2-R_{in}

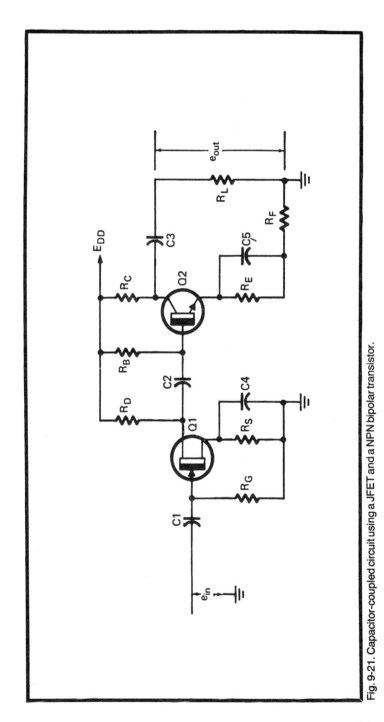

Fig. 9-21. Capacitor-coupled circuit using a JFET and a NPN bipolar transistor.

215

(assuming R_B is much larger than R_{in}; R_{in} is the input resistance of the bipolar transistor circuit) where the corner frequency is $1/6.28C_2(R_D + R_{in})$ as well as for the circuit including R_C-C_3-R_L with a corner frequency at $1/6.28C_3(R_C + R_L)$.

Corner frequencies are also affected by the capacitor-resistor combination in the source and emitter circuits. Due to these combinations, the gain rises at the rate of 6 dB/octave from the corner frequency up to ∞ Hz. For the JFET the corner frequency is $1/6.28C_4R_S$, while for the bipolar device it is $1/6.28C_5R_E$.

The unbypassed resistor, R_F, in the emitter, in conjunction with C5 and the balance of the circuit, comprise a circuit with the frequency characteristic shown in Fig. 9-15C. The corner frequency here is:

$$\frac{1}{6.28\ C_5}\left(\frac{R_E + R_Q}{R_E\ R_Q}\right) \tag{9-15}$$

where R_Q is $R_F + r_e +$ (resistance in the base circuit) divided by β. R_Q is the resistance seen by R_E looking back into the emitter circuit of the transistor.

Response curves are all approximate due to stray and component capacitance and resistance ignored in the calculations. All calculations should be checked in the laboratory.

The load lines for the input transistor in this circuit (the JFET) are drawn in Fig. 9-22. The DC load line involves all resistors in the drain circuit and is the sum of resistors R_D and R_S. If, for this discussion, R_S is negligible compared to R_D, the maximum drain current shown in the drawing is $I_{D(max)} = E_{DD}/R_D$. The quiescent current and voltage point is normally chosen at the center of the load line when the transistor is operated in Class A.

At the mid-frequencies, all capacitors are considered as short circuits. The mid-frequency AC load line, therefore, is determined by R_D shunted by R_B, while this combination is in turn shunted by the impedance, R_{in}, looking into the base circuit of the bipolar transistor or $r_b + \beta\ (r_e + R_F)$. If R_B is large compared to R_{in}, R_{in} is the resistance shunting R_D when the AC load line is considered. The effective AC load line is then determined by R_{in} in parallel with R_D. It passes through the quiescent point on the DC load line.

Note that the possible voltage swing across the DC load resistance ranges from 0 to E_{DD}. Shunting resistor R_D with R_{in}, as is required to determine the AC load line, the possible output voltage swing is limited from V_{D1} to V_{D2}. It is obvious that the larger R_{in} is made with respect to R_D, the larger the voltage swing of the output signal can be. R_{in} is normally designed to be at least equal to R_D,

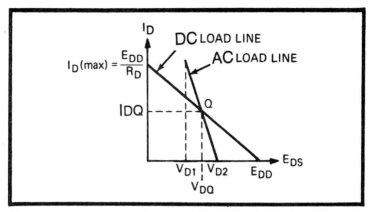

Fig. 9-22. Load lines of the input transistor. In Fig. 9-21, it is an FET. The construction also applies to a bipolar transistor circuit.

although it is most desirable that its resistance be more than ten times that of the resistor in the drain circuit.

Should the input transistor be of the bipolar variety rather than an FET the identical considerations are involved when the resistor in the collector circuit is shunted by other resistors capacitively coupled to it to compose the AC load line. Regardless of the input transistor, R_{ac}, the AC load on the first transistor, depends at least partially upon the loading of the second device on the output circuit of the first transistor. If the second transistor is a JFET, the gate resistor of the second amplifier stage must be considered. Should the second device be a bipolar transistor, as in Fig. 9-21, $R_{ac} = R_D \| R_B \| R_{in}$.

As in the case of all coupled circuits, the mid-frequency gain is the product of the AC gains of each stage when the gains are calculated using the proper AC load at each output. The **proper** AC load includes all components at the input to, and the loading effect of, the succeeding stage.

Coupling Without Capacitors

Capacitor C2 in Fig. 9-21 is vital in keeping the DC at the first stage out of the input circuit of the next stage. Improper DC voltage appearing at the input of the second transistor will upset the quiescent bias conditions of the device.

Capacitors in coupling circuits introduce several disadvantages. They are frequency selective. They limit the swing of the output voltage. They may cause noise pulses to be produced at the output while the capacitors are charging. They may cause a delay in

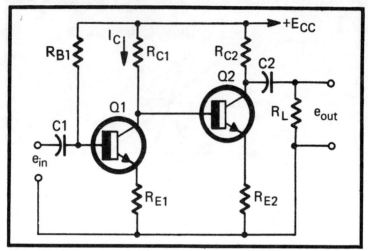

Fig. 9-23. Direct-coupled amplifier circuit.

the establishment of the final stable bias conditions and a delay before the transistor begins to amplify. They may cause the transistor to conduct heavily while charging the capacitor, causing the semiconductor to break down. These drawbacks can be overcome by using direct-coupled circuits.

DIRECT-COUPLED CIRCUITS

Of all methods used to couple one transistor to another, the direct-coupled circuit is the most versatile. Its importance is further enhanced by its ability to accept considerable amounts of feedback (discussed in the next chapter) around the circuit without unduly subjecting the amplifier to low-frequency instability problems. However, quiescent bias point stability problems are much more stubborn than those encountered when using other methods of coupling.

Bias and Stability

A typical direct-coupled amplifier circuit using bipolar devices, is shown in Fig. 9-23. A signal, e_{in}, is fed to the base of Q1 through C1, amplified by the direct coupled stages, Q1 and Q2, and fed to the load through C2.

The quiescent base current flowing through the first transistor is established by R_{B1} and R_{E1}, as well as by the DC beta, β_{1DC} of Q1. As you may recall, the base current of Q1 is $I_{B1} = E_{CC}/(R_{B1} + \beta_{1DC}R_{E1})$. The collector current is beta times the base current.

218

It is a more complex task to determine the base current, I_{B2}, of Q2. The circuit can be analyzed using Thevenin's equivalent methods, as follows. First, disconnect the collector circuit of Q1 from the base circuit of Q2. This means disconnecting the base lead of Q2 from the collector of Q1 as well as disconnecting the ground leads between R_{E1} and R_{E2}. Stage 1 is now isolated from amplifier stage 2. Find the voltage at the collector of Q1 under these conditions.

I_{B1} was determined above. I_{C1} is β_{1DC} I_{B1}. Only I_{C1} flows through R_{C1} when the base of Q2 is not in the circuit. The voltage at the collector, therefore, is $V_{C1}(TH) = E_{CC} - I_{C1}R_{C1}$. This is the Thevenin equivalent voltage of the circuit. The Thevenin resistance of the circuit can be found by connecting the supply, E_{CC}, to ground. Resistor R_{C1} is essentially in parallel with r_{d1}, the collector resistance of transistor Q1. In most cases, r_{d1} is much larger than R_{C1}, so that the Thevenin resistance is only $R_{C1} = R_{C1}(TH)$.

The Thevenin equivalent circuit consists of $V_{C1}(TH)$ in series with $R_{C1}(TH)$. The base and ground leads of Q2 can now be connected to the Thevenin equivalent of the output circuit of Q1. The DC resistance at the base of Q2 is the DC beta, β_{2DC} of Q2 multiplied by the resistors in the emitter circuit òr $\beta_{2DC}R_{E2}$. In Fig. 9-24, the

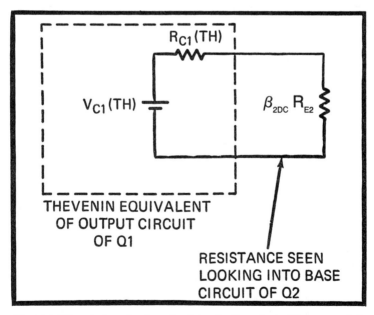

THEVENIN EQUIVALENT
OF OUTPUT CIRCUIT
OF Q1

RESISTANCE SEEN
LOOKING INTO BASE
CIRCUIT OF Q2

Fig. 9-24. DC equivalent circuit used to determine the quiescent base current of Q2.

Thevenin equivalent is shown connected to the equivalent resistance in the base circuit. Ohm's Law can be applied to determine that the base current of Q2 is $V_{C1}(TH)/(R_{C1}(TH) + \beta_{2DC}R_{E2})$.

Voltage gain of the second stage is highly dependent upon the resistor in that emitter circuit. It is a simple matter to make R_{E2} small and get a large amount of gain. But since this resistor is an important factor in setting the base bias current, a small R_{E2} may produce improper bias conditions for Q2. The problem may be overcome by placing a parallel R-C combination in series with a small R_{E2}. Capacitor C is made so large as to make the impedance of the R-C combination completely negligible at the lowest frequency to be reproduced by the amplifier. While the gain remains a function only of R_{E2}, the base current is dependent upon β_{2DC} multiplied by the sum of R_{E2} and the R in the parallel resistor-capacitor circuit.

Direct-coupled circuits such as shown in Fig. 9-23 suffer from bias drift problems. In R-C coupled circuits, one stage is isolated DC-wise from the other by the coupling capacitor. Each circuit in this type of amplifier must be stabilized within itself. As far as bias stability is concerned, one stage does not affect the preceding or succeeding ones.

As for DC-coupled circuits, any drift in collector current in one stage is passed on to the succeeding amplifier and multiplied in magnitude. The stability factor, S, for the overall circuit in Fig. 9-23 is:

$$S = S_1 \left(\frac{\beta_{2DC} \, R_{C1}}{\beta_{2DC} \, R_{E2} + R_{C1}} \right) \qquad (9\text{-}16)$$

S_1 is the stability factor of the first transistor stage. This can be determined using methods described in Chapter 2.

Three or more stages can be coupled, thus extending the circuit in Fig. 9-23 to include more transistors. For a 3-stage amplifier, the stability factor is as stated in Equation 9-16, multiplied by:

$$\left(\frac{\beta_{3DC} \, R_{C2}}{\beta_{3DC} \, R_{E3} + R_{C2}} \right) \qquad (9\text{-}17)$$

where the factors with the subscript 3 refer to components in and characteristics of the third stage. Additional similar multiplying factors are used in the equation for each additional stage of amplification that may be added to the circuit.

Stability problems are also emphasized in direct-coupled JFET circuits. They must be designed to assure the maximum stability in each amplifier stage, with the primary emphasis being placed on the stability of the first stage of amplification. The stability problem may be alleviated by using a balanced circuit in a differential amplifier arrangement. Popular circuits of this type are used in high quality power amplifiers.

Bipolar Differential Amplifier

Two useful differential amplifier circuits are shown in Fig. 9-25. Although both circuits have many similar qualities, each has its own advantages and disadvantages.

Both differential amplifiers amplify the difference between the two signals at their inputs. The voltage, e_{o1}—e_{o2}, appearing between the two collectors in Fig. 9-25A is related linearly to the difference of the input signals, e_{s1}-e_{s2}. Voltage e_o across R_C in Fig. 9-25B is similarly related to e_{s1}-e_{s2}.

Two identical signals, when applied in phase to the inputs of a differential amplifier, should produce zero volts at the output. This type of signal can be applied in series with R_E, as is normally the case with noise voltages rather than at e_{s1} and e_{s2}. It is referred to as common-mode operation. A figure of merit to determine how well this signal is rejected by the circuit is known as the common-mode rejection ratio, CMRR, and is defined by the equation:

$$CMRR = \frac{A_V \text{ (Differential Mode)}}{A_V \text{ (Common Mode)}} \qquad (9\text{-}18)$$

A_V (differential mode) is the voltage gain when the input voltages are equal but with opposing phase (applied at e_{s1} and e_{s2}). A_V (common mode) is defined as the differential voltage gain when the input signals are equal and in phase. When the ratio is expressed in dB, it is known as the common mode rejection (CMR). CMR = 20 $\log_{10}$ CMRR.

It is desirable that the CMR be very large. This is accomplished by making R_E large. Being common to the emitter circuits of the two transistors, in the differential mode two identical but out-of-phase audio signals flow through R_E. The gain is thus not affected by its presence or size. However, the sum of the quiescent emitter currents of Q1 and Q2, I_{EQ1} + I_{EQ2}, also flow through R_E. A large DC voltage is developed across R_E. This dictates that the -E_{EE} supply be very large.

To overcome this drawback, R_E can be replaced by a circuit simulating a large resistor. The circuit is a constant-current source. The desirable characteristic is that the AC impedance of this type of

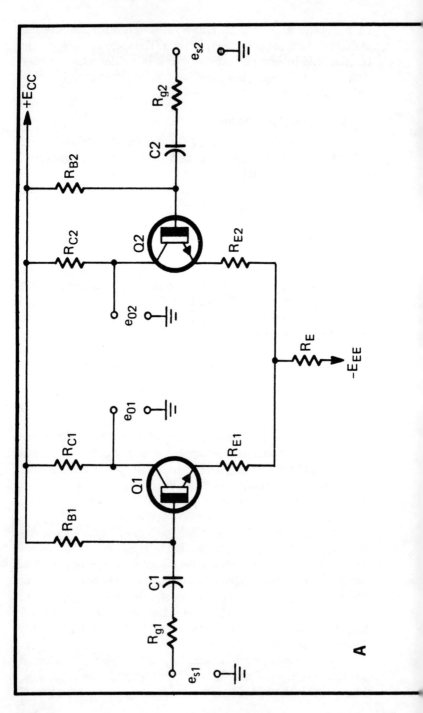

A

222

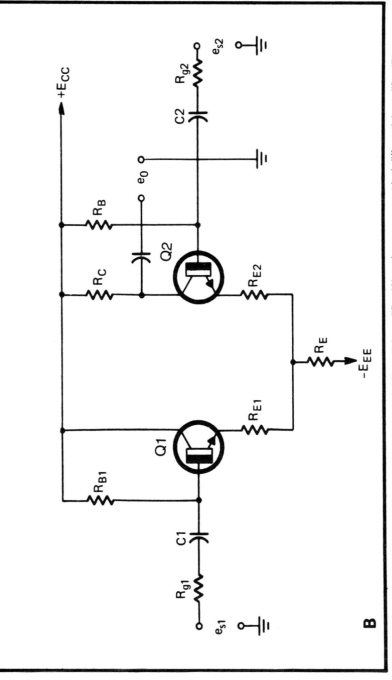

Fig. 9-25. Two versions of differential amplifiers: balanced differential amplifier (A) and an unsymmetrical differential amplifier (B).

223

circuit is large, while the DC voltage drop across the semiconductor device in the circuit is small. A basic circuit to accomplish this is shown in Fig. 9-26.

The divider network in the base circuit is supplied by a fixed voltage. A reasonably stable voltage is developed across R_X. Consequently, the same stable voltage is also across the series circuit in parallel with this resistor, namely R_E and the base-emitter diode of the transistor. Because the voltage across the base-emitter junction is relatively constant regardless of the current flowing through the junction (over a limited current range), the voltage across R_E is constant. Using Ohm's Law, current flowing through R_E is the voltage across that resistor divided by the size of the resistor. As this is also the emitter current of the transistor, it is just about equal to the collector current as well.

The AC output impedance of the circuit is equal to the ratio of the change in collector-to-emitter voltage to the change in collector current. Since the change in current is just about equal to zero (for it is constant), the impedance is high.

Improvements in this circuit are possible. R_X may be replaced by two series-connected forward-biased diodes where the cathodes of both devices are oriented toward ground. The diode current is held relatively constant by virtue of the fact that the magnitude of this current is determined by a current flowing through a large resistor, R_B. The voltages across the diodes vary little with changes in current flowing through the devices.

Because the diodes are in parallel with the base-emitter junction and R_E, the voltage across one diode is identical (when matched properly) to the voltage across the base-emitter junction, and the voltage across the second diode is identical with that across R_E. Since the voltage across a forward-biased diode is relatively constant with minor changes in diode current, the voltage across and hence the current flowing through R_E, are both stable. Since the change in emitter and hence the collector currents are zero, the requirement of establishing a constant current source has been met!

The quality of the circuit is further enhanced when R_X in Fig. 9-26 is replaced by a zener diode with the anode lead closest to ground. Because of its low impednace when in the breakdown region, the voltage across the zener can, within any reasonable boundaries of operation, be considered a constant.

The AC impedance seen at the collector of the circuit is the same as the output impedance of a common-emitter circuit. It is:

$$Z_{out} = \frac{r_d[\beta(R_E + r_e) + (R_G + r_b)]}{R_E + r_e + R_G + r_b} \qquad (9\text{-}19)$$

where r_d is the collector impedance of the device in the common-emitter mode of operation, equal to r_c/β; r_e is the emitter resistance equal to $26/I_E$ when I_E is the collector current expressed in milliamperes; R_G is the resistance of R_X or the impedance of the semiconductors substituting for R_X; and r_b is the base resistance, usually assumed to be about 500 ohms.

FETs can be used effectively as constant-current sources. When operated in the pinch-off region, the drain current is relatively independent of the drain-source voltage. All that is required is to establish the gate-source bias, and the fixed drain current can be determined from the equation:

$$I_D = I_{DSS} \left(1 - \frac{|V_{GS}|}{|V_P|} \right)^2 \qquad (9\text{-}20)$$

discussed in Chapter 3. When the gate-source voltage is zero, the drain current is obviously constant at I_{DSS}.

More generally, the circuit in Fig. 9-27 should be considered. Here, the bias voltage is developed across R_S and the gate-source

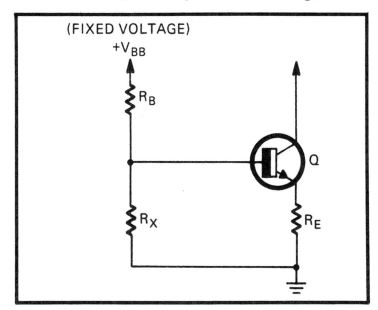

Fig. 9-26. Basic constant-current source circuit. A high impedance exists at the collector of Q.

voltage is the drain (and source) current, I_D, multiplied by the resistor, R_S. Once the desired drain current has been established, R_S can be determined from the equation below. It was stated in Chapter 3 in another form.

$$R_s = \frac{V_p}{I_D} \left[1 - \left(\frac{I_D}{I_{DSS}} \right)^{\frac{1}{2}} \right] \tag{9-21}$$

where I_D is the desired drain current, I_{DSS} is the drain current when $V_{GS} = 0$, and V_p is the pinch-off voltage of the FET in question. The impedance at the drain is equal to the common-drain output impedance of the device:

$$Z_{out} = r_{ds} (1 + g_m R_S) + R_S \tag{9-22}$$

where r_{ds} is the drain-to-source resistance of the FET , and g_m is the transconductance at the point of operation.

Any of the constant-current circuits or simply a large resistor common to the two emitters can be used for the differential amplifiers in Fig. 9-25. The emitter circuit, common to both transistors, is designed to maintain constant the sum of the collector currents flowing through both amplifier circuits, regardless of the input signal. The resistors in the individual emitters do cause degeneration of the signal, but are required to stabilize the difference in the relative emitter currents. In some cases, R_{E1} and R_{E2} are combined into a potentiometer or variable resistor with the wiper arm connected to R_E. It is adjusted for equal current to flow through both amplifiers.

The overall circuit may drift and become unbalanced due to several factors:

1. The leakage current and the base-emitter voltages of the two devices may change because the ambient temperature change at one device is not identical to the change at the second device. While the unsymmetrical circuit in Fig. 9-25B will alleviate the drift problem due to V_{BE} variations, the balanced circuit in Fig. 9-25A will also compensate for I_{CBO} variations.

2. Large temperature changes can cause a shift in the relative output voltages, because the two transistors may not have identical V_{BE} and I_{CEO} characteristics even at normal room temperature.

3. One transistor may be heated more by the signal than the other device in the differential amplifier circuit.

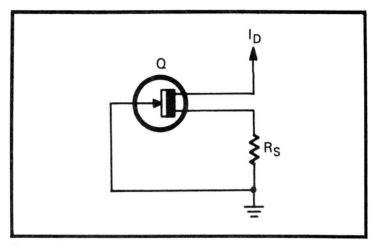

Fig. 9-27. FET constant-current circuit. A high impedance exists at the drain of Q.

The drift is never entirely eliminated, but for identical devices this drawback is negligible when the output is taken from between the two collectors. The effect can be minimized by using low-leakage silicon transistors. Further improvement can be realized if both devices are imbedded in one heat sink, or if the power dissipated due to the signal swing is small when compared to the quiescent power dissipated by each device.

The stability factor, S, of each individual section is identical to the S of one half the circuit when it is isolated from the second half. The S for specific circuits is discussed in Chapter 2. To determine the S from the equations discussed previously, do not substitute the large emitter resistor value into the equation. Instead, substitute $2R_E$, or two times the size of the resistor. All other components in the equation are defined as before.

As with all other amplifiers, the ultimate purpose of this amplifier is to provide gain. For the circuit in Fig. 9-25B, the voltage gain is:

$$A_v = \frac{\beta R_c}{2[(R_g + r_b) + \beta (R_{E1} + r_e)]} \qquad (9\text{-}23)$$

when the output is taken across R_c from the collector to ground. Should the output be taken between the collectors in the circuit in Fig. 9-25A, the voltage gain is:

$$A_v = \frac{\beta R_c}{R_g + r_b + \beta (R_{E1} + r_e)} \qquad (9\text{-}24)$$

227

As far as the input impedance of the circuit is concerned, it is normally double that of each section taken individually (R_E is not involved in this calculation) while the output impedance is essentially equal to the collector resistor. It may be reduced by adding emitter followers at the output.

In audio applications, the input signal is normally fed to the base of Q1 while a feedback signal is fed to the base of Q2. Two out-of-phase outputs appear at the collectors of Q1 and Q2 in Fig. 9-25A to feed a push-pull output circuit. If there is insufficient gain, additional differential amplifier stages may be added as shown in Fig. 9-28. Should the circuit in Fig. 9-25B be used, additional phase inversion circuitry must be added to feed a push-pull output stage.

We will now look at the considerations involved in the design of a balanced differential amplifier commonly used in audio circuits. See the circuit in Fig. 9-29. Q1 and Q2 are components in the differential amplifier while Q3 is a constant-current source. In a balanced circuit, Q1 is matched to Q2 for beta, leakage and the V_{BE} characteristic. The equivalent resistors in the circuit are all made equal. As an example, $R_{C1} = R_{C2}$.

Once the desired quiescent current, I_{CQ}, flowing through each device has been determined, the current flowing through Q3 must be established at $2I_{CQ}$. Assuming that the voltage, V_D, across one diode in the base circuit of Q3 is equal to that across R_E (since the voltage across the second diode is equal to V_{BE} of Q3), R_E is made equal to $V_D/2I_{CQ}$. The current flowing through the diode is usually made equal to the collector current of the constant-current device, so that R_B will be approximately $(E_{CC} - E_{EE})/2I_{CQ}$. (Notice that E_{EE} is negative so that $(E_{CC} - E_{EE})$ is the sum of two voltages.) This assumes the usual case when the voltage across the diodes is negligible compared to a voltage equal to the sum of the two supply voltages. The AC impedance at the collector of Q3 can be determined from Equation 9-19 if we let R_G equal the impedance of the diodes.

The DC quiescent voltages at the collectors of Q1 and Q2 are usually equal to $E_{CC}/2$ so that R_{C1} and R_{C2} can each be made equal to $E_{CC}/2I_{CQ}$.

The voltage at the emitters of Q1 and Q2 can be placed at ground or zero potential. The current flowing through the base resistors may be equated to I_{CQ} so that $R_{B1} = R_{B2} = (E_{CC} - V_{BE})/I_{CQ}$, where V_{BE} is the base-emitter voltage of Q1 and Q2. Letting $R_{x1} = R_{x2} = R_x$, R_x is then equal to about $(E_{EE} - V_{BE})/I_{CQ}$. (Since E_{EE} is negative, $(E_{EE} - V_{BE})$ is the sum of two voltages. Although this sum is

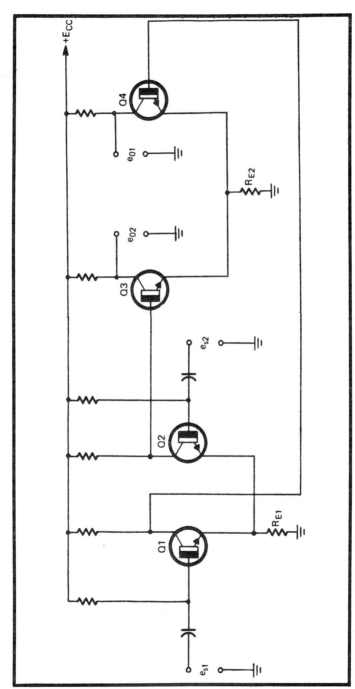

Fig. 9-28. Cascaded differential amplifier circuit using two differential amplifier stages coupled to each other.

229

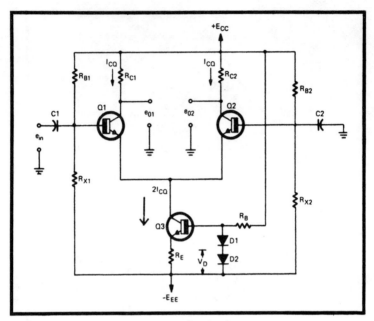

Fig. 9-29. A practical differential amplifier circuit.

negative, R_x is positive as the direction of the current flow is reversed and hence negative in this equation.) This assumes the base current to be negligible when compared to the currents in the base resistors.

The gain of the circuit, the ratio of $(e_{o1}-e_{o2})/e_{in}$, can be determined from Equation 9-24. Here, R_{E1} and R_g equals 0 while $r_e = 26/I_{CQ}$, when I_{CQ} is expressed in milliamperes. The gain of each individual section, e_{o1}/e_{in} or e_{o2}/e_{in}, is half the gain calculated from the equation.

FET Differential Amplifier

An example of a differential amplifier using JFETs and a constant-current source, is shown in Fig. 9-30. Q3 may be replaced with a large resistor to keep the sum of the drain currents through Q1 and Q2 constant, but it would then require a large $-E_{SS}$ supply. As for the equivalent bipolar circuit, the total current flowing through FETs Q1 and Q2 is established by Q3 (here it is the I_{DSS} of Q3) while the AC impedance in the source leads of Q1 and Q2 can be calculated from Equation 9-22. Q3 is in the constant current source for the circuit.

The voltage gain or the ratio of the signal developed between the two drains to the input signal, is $R_D g_m$, where g_m is the transcon-

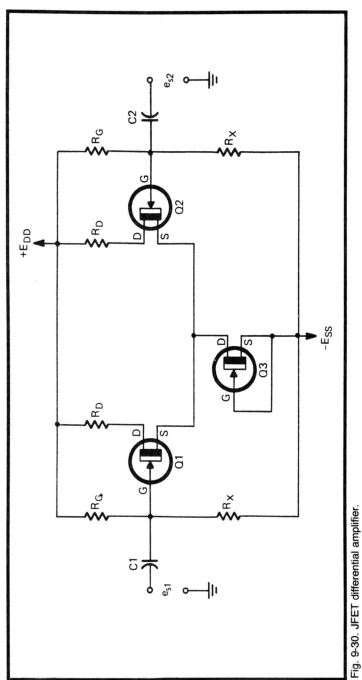

Fig. 9-30. JFET differential amplifier.

231

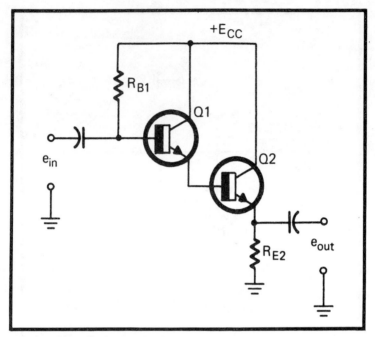

Fig. 9-31. Basic Darlington circuit.

ductance of either device. The gain from the input to the voltage developed across one R_D resistor is $R_{Dgm}/2$. For FET circuits, the common-mode rejection ratio, CMRR, is equal to $2g_m r_{ds}$, where r_{ds} is the drain-to-source resistance of the device.

Darlington Circuit

Different DC-coupled transistor arrangements are used to isolate the output circuit from the input or to provide a circuit with a high input impedance and a low output impedance. One such circuit is the FET source follower discussed in Chapter 5. The bipolar counterpart, the emitter follower, was likewise detailed in a previous chapter.

As you know, the emitter follower has a voltage gain of somewhat less than 1 and a current gain equal to beta. Take two emitter followers and connect them in series. Known as the Darlington circuit, it is shown in Fig. 9-31. The voltage gain remains at somewhat less than 1, while the current and power gains are the product of the betas of the two transistors.

We must pause here to recall that the beta to be used in determining impedances and the current gain is not merely the AC beta as stated on specification sheets. It must always be modified to include the effect of r_d, the collector-emitter resistance of the device. As you know, the effective beta is the transistor beta multiplied by $r_d/(r_d + R_L)$, where R_L is the load resistor regardless of whether it is placed in the collector circuit or the emitter circuit. Although not frequently applied, errors are compounded when this factor is ignored. It is negligible, however, when R_L is much smaller than r_d. The effective beta should be used when evaluating the gain and various impedances of the Darlington circuit if accuracy is an important factor in a specific problem.

There are many variations of the Darlington circuit in Fig. 9-31. For one very common modification, a small resistor is placed from the base of Q2 to ground. The function of this resistor is to increase the collector-emitter breakdown voltage point of the second device. Don't make this resistor too small because it may cause the input impedance of the circuit to be reduced below an optimum level as well as divert excess signal from the base of Q2, reducing the current gain.

A second and useful variation is shown in Fig. 9-32. The circuit is designed so that diode D1 has the same forward characteristics as

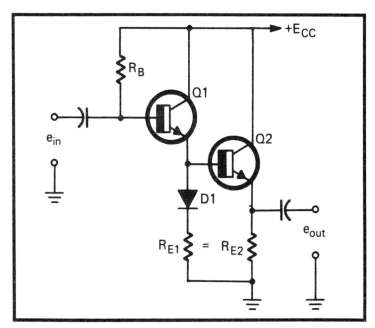

Fig. 9-32. Darlington circuit arranged to make the emitter current through Q1 equal to the emitter current through Q2.

the base-emitter diode of Q2. Also, let $R_{E1} = R_{E2}$. Since the D_1-R_{E1} circuit is in parallel or across the series combination of the base-emitter diode of Q2 and R_{E2}, the voltages across the two combinations are equal. Since the voltages across D1 and the base-emitter junction of Q2 are equal, the voltage and, hence the currents flowing through R_{E1} and R_{E2} (as well as through Q2) are identical. Hence, the collector current flowing through Q2 is equal to that flowing through Q1 if the base current flowing through Q2 is considered negligible in comparison. (This circuit is used in Chapter 11 in a transformerless power amplifier.)

Complementary Circuits

Another circuit with a total beta equal to the product of the betas of two transistors is shown in Fig. 9-33. An NPN transistor is used at the input, and the output is a PNP device. (An identical circuit can be drawn with the roles of the NPN and PNP devices reversed.) The input signal is fed to the base of Q1, and the amplified output appears across R_{C1}. It is in turn fed to the input of Q2. The output signal from the circuit, appearing across R_{C2}, is fed back (feedback is discussed in the next chapter) to the emitter of Q1 through R_F. The various equations describing this circuit are:

$$A_v = \frac{R_F + R_{E1}}{R_{E1}} = R_F/R_{E1} + 1 \qquad (9\text{-}25)$$

$$A_i = \beta_1\,\beta_2 \qquad (9\text{-}26)$$

$$G = A_v\,A_i \qquad (9\text{-}27)$$

$$R_{in} = \frac{R_{B1}\,R_x}{R_{B1} + R_x} \qquad (9\text{-}28)$$

$$R_{out} = \frac{R_{c2} + R_F}{\beta_2\,R_{c2}\,R_F} \qquad (9\text{-}29)$$

Different components can be omitted from the circuit and the appropriate substitutions made in the equations. Some of the variations are shown in Fig. 9-34.

For Fig. 9-34A, $R_{x1} = \infty$, $R_{E1} = 0$, $R_F = \infty$ and $R_{E2} = 0$. Substituting these into Equations 9-25 through 9-29, $A_v = 1$, $G = A_i$, $R_{in} = R_{B1}$ and $R_{out} = R_{c2}$. The circuit in Fig. 9-34B is identical to the one in Fig. 9-34A, with the exception that R_{C1} has been omitted, making it infinite. The impedance and gain characteristics of both circuits are identical.

As for Fig. 9-34C, $R_{x1} = \infty$, $R_{E1} = \infty$, $R_{E2} = 0$, R_F, $= 0$ and $R_{C1} = \infty$. Substituting this information into Equations 9-25 through 9-29, the characteristics of the circuit are $A_v = 1$, $G = A_i$, $R_{in} = R_{B1}$ and $R_{out} = 0$. Note the big advantage of this circuit over the ones in Figs.

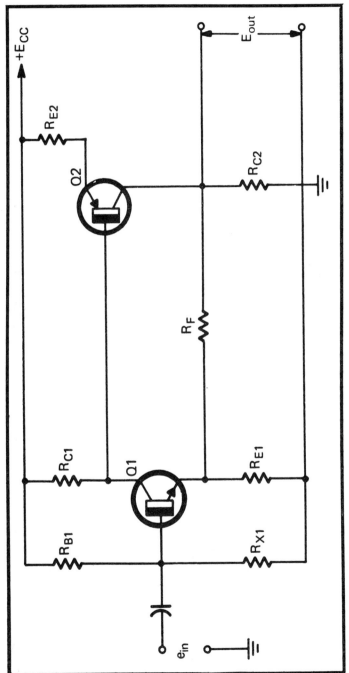

Fig. 9-33. Basic complementary circuit.

235

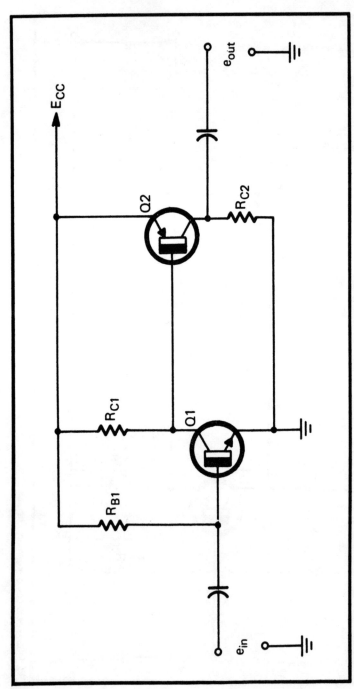

Fig. 9-34A. Variation of the circuit in Fig. 9-33. R_{X1} is ∞, R_{E1} is 0, R_F is ∞, and R_{E2} is 0.

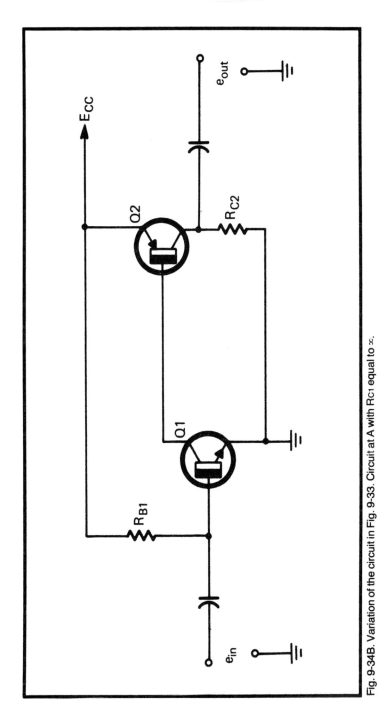

Fig. 9-34B. Variation of the circuit in Fig. 9-33. Circuit at A with R_{C1} equal to ∞.

237

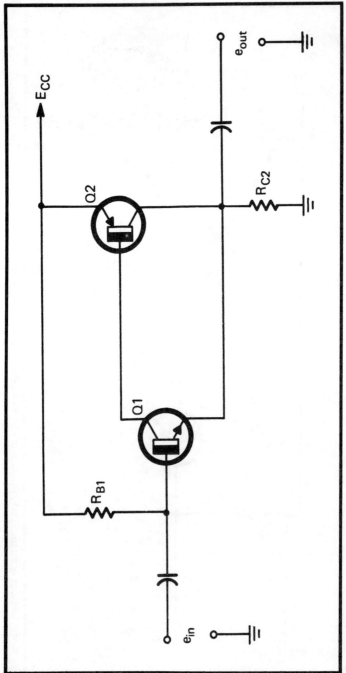

Fig. 9-34C. Circuit in Fig. 9-33 in which R_{x1} is ∞, R_{C1} is ∞, R_{E1} is ∞, R_F is 0 and R_{E2} is 0.

238

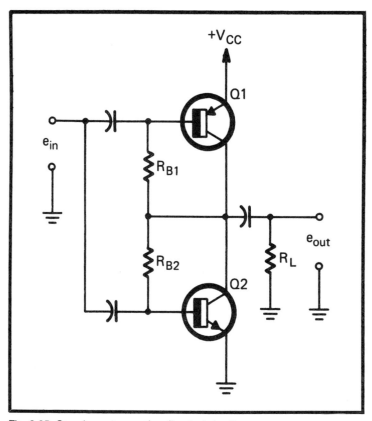

Fig. 9-35. Complementary push-pull output circuit.

9-34A and 9-34B. The output impedance here is very low and equal to zero. Since $R_F = 0$, there is an extremely large amount of feedback. Distortion is thus extremely low. The circuit in Fig. 9-34C is well worth remembering.

Other complementary circuits are frequently used as the power output stages in push-pull amplifiers. A commonly used one is drawn in Fig. 9-35. The input signal, e_{in}, is fed to the bases of the two transistors. The positive half cycles are amplified by Q2 and the negative halves are amplified by Q1. The composite signal is re-created as e_{out}. As in all direct-coupled circuits, here too, bias stabilization is difficult due to DC drift with temperature. DC feedback is an important factor in alleviating the problem.

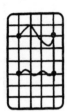

Chapter 10
Audio
Feedback

In a circuit using bipolar transistors, the voltage gain can vary considerably with the beta, emitter resistance and collector resistance of the devices. As for the JFET circuit, the voltage gain is directly dependent upon the transconductance. Consequently, a design may be limited to a few devices only. The circuit will then operate properly with only a narrow group of transistors categorized by a specific range of characteristics.

It would be ideal if the gains and impedances in a circuit were independent of device parameters. Goals of this type can be approached when the designer applies judicial amounts of feedback around his circuit or around the individual device.

A system including feedback uses some method of sensing the output voltage, output current, or both, and feeding the derived information back to an earlier stage, or to the input of a single stage. For audio applications, the phase is arranged so that the gain of the overall circuit is usually reduced when feedback is applied (negative feedback). Because the amount of gain is a function of the feedback, the gain of a circuit tends to remain relatively constant regardless of the amplification in the forward circuit before feedback is applied. (The forward circuit amplification is the gain of an amplifier from the input to the output before any feeding loop is closed.)

output voltage is sensed, it is referred to as voltage feedback. Obviously, current feedback involves the sensing of the current at the output and feeding back a voltage proportional to that current. Compound feedback involves a circuit using both voltage and current feedback.

Feedback can also be classified as to how it is applied. Series feedback, as the name implies, is applied in series with the input signal. It then follows that parallel feedback is applied in parallel with the input. The different types of feedback and different methods of application lead to circuits with differing characteristics. The various attributes are important in the many distinctive audio applications.

THE FEEDBACK EQUATION

Let us start by defining two voltages, e_s and e_{in}. Choose the convention where e_s is the input signal to an amplifying system. The signal may feed passive components at the input to the amplifier. On the other hand, e_{in} is the signal at the input to the amplifier proper, after the signal has passed through the passive components (see Fig. 10-1). It will include e_s and the effect of passive components as well as in all other signals mixed with or added to e_s. If there are no other signals besides e_s feeding the amplifying system, and there are no passive components between e_s feeding the amplfying system, and there are no passive components between e_s and the input to the amplifier, then $e_{in} = e_s$. In this case, the voltage gain, A_v, of an entire amplifier circuit is:

$$A_v = \frac{e_{out}}{e_s} = \frac{e_{out}}{e_{in}} \qquad (10\text{-}1)$$

where e_{out} is the voltage at the output of the amplifying system.

Let us now take a fraction, B, of the output voltage, e_{out}, and feed it, $B\,e_{out}$, back so that it is out of phase with the input signal, e_s (See Fig. 10-2). The difference between these two signals is now feeding the input to the amplifier to establish e_{in}. In this case e_{in} is no longer equal to e_s, but because of Be_{out} it is:

$$e_{in} = e_s + Be_{out} \qquad (10\text{-}2)$$

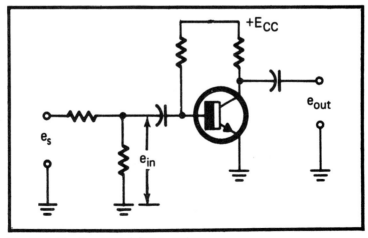

Fig. 10-1. Circuit used to define e_s and e_{in}.

Substituting this into Equation 10-1, the voltage gain of the entire circuit with feedback becomes:

$$A_{vf} = \frac{e_{out}}{e_{in} - Be_{out}}$$ (10-3)

Divide the numerator and denominator by e_{in} and let the ratio e_{out}/e_{in} = A_v. Equation 10-1 becomes:

$$A_{vf} = \frac{A_v}{1 - BA_v}$$ (10-4)

This is the standard often quoted feedback equation.

For negative feedback, BA_v is negative, so the feedback factor, $1-BA_v$, is greater than 1. This implies a 180° phase shift between the input and output. Should there be 0° phase shift, BA_v is positive. When BA_v is equal to +1, the denominator is zero and the gain is infinite—an oscillating condition. This can occur at very high frequencies, just above the audio spectrum.

MARGIN OF STABILITY

It is obviously undesirable that an amplifier be unstable at any frequency or band of frequencies, even if the resulting oscillation is outside the audible band. High-frequency oscillation has been known to burn out the tweeters of loudspeaker systems. Power used to produce such oscillaton is wasteful and can be put to more useful purposes. Oscillation at high frequncies can also cause the reproduced program material over the entire band to sound distorted.

The tendency of an amplifier to oscillate can be determined in several different ways. An analysis can involve a Nyquist plot. This is a graph of the real against the imaginary components of the BA_v factor in Equation 10-4. This curve is plotted at all frequencies that can be amplified, even if they are outside the audio band. Should the resulting curve touch or encircle the point -1, $+ j0$ on the graph, the amplifier will be unstable and oscillate. This method, while accurate, requires quite a bit of calculation.

A simple method, best applied experimentally, can be explained using the voltage feedback circuit in Fig. 10-3A as an example and the revision of the circuit in Fig. 10-3B. In the revised circuit the feedback loop is opened. Two types of feedback are used in the circuit in Fig. 10-3A. Disregarding the connection between R_F and the emitter of Q1, the first stage of amplification has an unbypassed resistor, R_{E1}, in the emitter. The signal current flowing through this resistor develops a signal voltage across R_{E1}. This

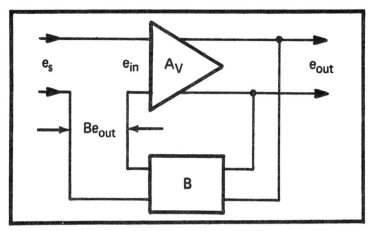

Fig. 10-2. Block diagram of a voltage feedback amplifier.

voltage, e_{RE1} opposes e_s so that the signal feeding the amplifier, e_{in}, is $e_s - e_{RE1}$. Since the current flowing through the resistor determines the voltage developed across it, this is an example of current feedback.

The signal at R_{C1} is amplified by Q2. The output voltage is fed back through R_F. A portion of this output voltage is developed across R_{E1} due to the voltage divider action of resistors R_F and R_{E1}. The voltage developed across R_{E1} due to this network depends upon the size and type of output voltage. This, the second type of feedback in the circuit, is a voltage feedback arrangement. B for this circuit is R_{E1}/R_F. Since the gain in the forward circuit is usually large, the voltage gain with feedback is approximately R_F/R_{E1}.

The procedure used to experimentally check the stability of an amplifier starts with the disabling of the voltage feedback circuit. The connection between R_F and R_{E1} is broken. A resistor, R_{EF}, equal to R_{E1} is connected from R_F to ground so that the output circuit is not upset. This is shown in Fig. 10-3B.

The voltage fed back to the input is e_f. A curve (Fig. 10-3C) is drawn to show how this voltage varies in dB with frequency, when the input signal is maintained constant. To derive this curve, start by connecting an audio sine wave signal generator at e_s in Fig. 10-3B. Keep e_s constant while varying the frequency of the signal. The output is measured across e_f. Twenty log (e_f/e_s) is the ratio in dB of the voltage gain at a specific frequency. Note this ratio at all frequencies. Using the highest number as a 0 dB reference, plot the

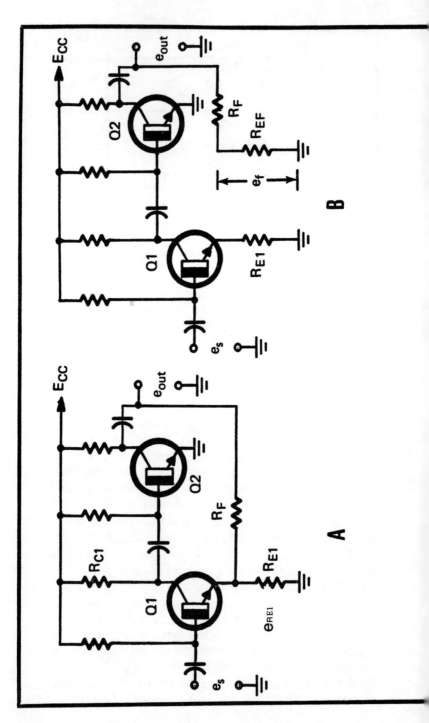

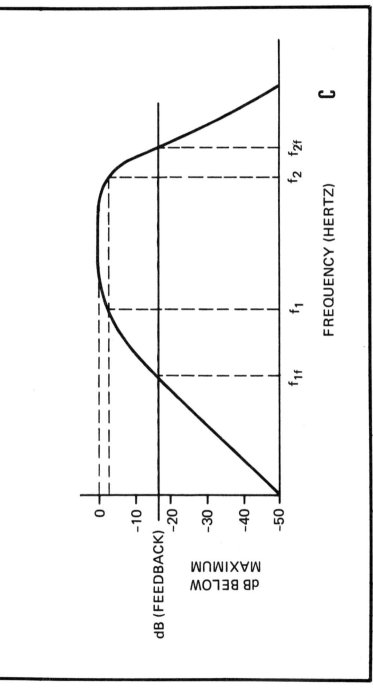

Fig. 10-3. Procedure to make a frequency response plot of a forward amplifier circuit. Circuit A is a two-stage amplifier with feedback. Circuit B has been modified to enable you to measure the response curve of the forward circuit. C is the response curve of the forward circuit of the amplifier.

245

number of dB the output varies below the 0 dB point over the frequency range of the amplifier. You should get a curve similar to that shown in Fig. 10-3C.

Now determine the amount of voltage feedback present in the circuit. Feed a fixed signal at e_s. The frequency used must have 0 dB attenuation as plotted in Fig. 10-3C. Place a meter at e_{out} for the circuit in Fig. 10-3B. The voltage at e_{out} should be relatively clean. Call this output voltage e_{out1}. Then reconstruct the circuit as in Fig. 10-3A and read e_{out}, referring to this latter reading as e_{out2}. The voltage feedback in dB can be determined from the equation dB (feedback) $= (20) \log (e_{out1}/e_{out2})$.

Using the dB (feedback) figure, draw a line in Fig. 10-3C at this number of dB below the 0 dB level. Note where this line crosses the curve previously drawn. If the rolloff of the curve is slower than at the rate of 12 dB/octave at these points, the amplifier will be stable. It is most desirable that the design be for a slower rolloff than 9 dB/octave to provide a reasonable margin of stability for the overall circuit.

The curve and feedback can, of course, be calculated from the circuit, but this can be a very tedious and approximate operation. Some factors affecting the curve may not be considered in the analysis or are so complex as to make paper calculations difficult if not impossible.

One of the major factors that must be accounted for when calculating the frequency response curve, is stray lead capacity. Another factor, most important when dealing with large power transistors, is the beta cutoff frequency, written $f_{\alpha e}$ or f_{β}. At this frequency, the beta is 3 dB less (about 0.7 of the size) than it is at the low frequency normally specified on data sheets. Beta rolls off at the rate of 6 dB/octave, following the high-frequency rolloff curves discussed in Chapter 9 with reference to capacitive and inductive filters. It is drawn as Fig. 10-4 to show the beta variations.

Another important frequency on the curve is f_T, the frequency at which beta is equal to 1 (beta has rolled off to 0 dB). This is approximately equal to the alpha cutoff frequency, written f_{hbo}, $f_{\alpha b}$, or f_{α}, at which alpha has rolled off 3 dB from its low-frequency value. Similar to the beta curve, the curve plotting alpha against the frequency exhibits the 6 dB per octave characteristic shown in Fig. 10-4 for the beta variations.

Several interesting relationships can be evolved. On the rolloff portion of the beta curve, the product of the frequency and the beta at any frequency remains constant. Hence, f_T can be found by simply

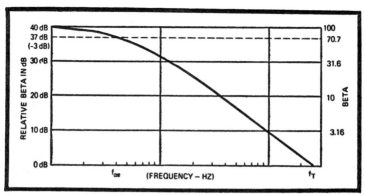

Fig. 10-4. Curve showing the variation of beta with frequency. For this particular transistor, it is assumed that beta is equal to 100 at low frequencies.

setting the beta equal to 1 and equating f_T to the product of the beta and frequency at a known point on the curve. There is an approximate relationship between f_α and f_β, namely $f_\alpha = \beta_0 f_\beta$ where β_0 is the beta specified at a low frequency.

As for the JFET, there are input and output capacities. Here, as for the bipolar device, the Miller effect can be important. Basically, the Miller effect states that the input capacity of a device is the actual input capacitance added to the product of the output capacity and the voltage gain of the device. For the JFET, the input capacity is $C_{iss} + A_v C_{rss}$, where C_{iss} is the sum of the gate-to-source capacitance, C_{gs}, and the gate-to-drain capacitance, C_{gd}. C_{rss} is approximately equal to C_{gd}. These are discussed in Chapters 5 and 6.

As for the bipolar device the input capacitance resulting from the Miller effect is $C_{b'e} + A_v C_{b'c}$. In this relationship, b represents a point inside the transistor that is not accessible by a lead or probe. $C_{b'e}$ is the capacitance from that point to the emitter lead and $C_{b'c}$ is the capacitance from that point to the collector. Using more easily recognizable symbols, the input capacitance is approximately equal to $C_{ob} A_v + 1/6.28 \, r_e f_\alpha$. Here, C_{ob} is the collector-to-base capacitance in the common-base equivalent circuit and r_e is the AC emitter resistance.

However analyzed, feedback has two glaring disadvantages. There, is, of course, a loss in gain. There is also the tendency towards instability. However, the many benefits far outshine these drawbacks.

CHARACTERISTICS OF CIRCUITS USING VOLTAGE FEEDBACK

There are several consequences of voltage feedback when placed around an audio circuit. Should the feedback be applied in series with the input signal, the input impedance increases to:

$$Z_{if} = Z_i (1 - BA_v) \qquad (10\text{-}5)$$

where Z_i is the input impedance without feedback and Z_{if} is the input impedance with feedback. In Fig. 10-3A, the portion of the output voltage developed across R_{E1} due to the voltage divider action of R_F and R_{E1}, when placed in series with e_s, is an example of series voltage feedback. Here, a portion of the output is fed back across R_{E1} and subtracted from e_s.

In all voltage feedback circuits, the output impedance with feedback, Z_{of}, is less than without feedback, Z_o. They are related by the equation:

$$Z_{of} = Z_o/(1 - BA_v) \qquad (10\text{-}6)$$

Another consequence of feedback is the extension of the bandwidth of the overall circuit. This can be illustrated with the help of Fig. 10-3C. Without feedback, the bandwidth is from f_1 to f_2. Feedback extends this bandwidth so that it is from f_{1f} to f_{2f}, where the dB (feedback) line crosses the plot of the frequency response curve of the amplifier's forward circuit. The frequency f_{1f} can be determined from the equation:

$$f_{1f} = f_1/(1 - BA_v) \qquad (10\text{-}7)$$

while the upper frequency of the band, f_{2f}, can be found from:

$$f_{2f} = f_2 (1 - BA_v) \qquad (10\text{-}8)$$

The voltage gain of an amplifier varies with the various parameters and components. This variation is reduced considerably when feedback is applied. The amount the gain changes with feedback, ΔA_{vf}, is related to the amount the gain changes when there is no feedback, ΔA_v, by the equation:

$$\frac{\Delta A_{vf}}{\Delta A_v} = \frac{A_f}{A_v} \left(\frac{1}{1 - BA_v} \right) \qquad (10\text{-}9)$$

Distortion is similarly reduced by a factor of $1/(1\text{-}BA_v)$. Noise is reduced by the same factor only if it is repetitive and the feedback loop encompasses the source of the noise.

CHARACTERISTICS OF CURRENT FEEDBACK

The circuit in Fig. 10-5 is that of a single-ended audio amplifier feeding a loudspeaker. A small resistor, R_F, is placed in series with the speaker. The current that flows through the speaker (i_L) also flows through R_F. A voltage is developed across R_F due to the current flowing through the resistor. The voltage is proportional to

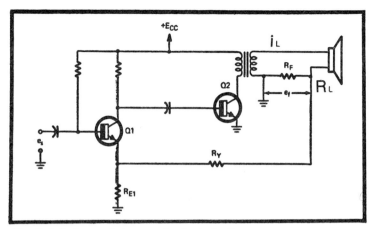

Fig. 10-5. Series-applied current feedback circuit.

the output current. A portion of this voltage is applied through a resistor to R_{E1}. This voltage bucks e_s, reducing the voltage gain of the overall circuit. The gain is thus related to the output current. The voltage fed back is related to the resistors R_F, R_Y and R_{E1}, and the load resistance of the loudspeaker, R_L. The voltage gain with feedback is:

$$A_{vf} = \frac{A_v}{1 - \gamma A_v} \qquad (10\text{-}10)$$

The equation is very similar to that for the voltage feedback. Because R_F is much smaller than R_L , $\gamma = BR_F (R_L + R_F) = BR_F/R_L$, where B is the fraction previously defined for voltage feedback. The ratio R_F/R_L can easily be determined by reconsidering Equation 10-2. Here, e_{in} to the amplifier proper is $e_s + Be_{out}$. But in Fig. 10-5, the sensed signal fed back is not from the output voltage, but is that appearing across R_F. If this voltage is e_f, $e_{in} = e_s + Be_f$. Since $e_f = R_F(i_L) = (e_{out})R_F/R_L$, $e_{in} = e_s + Be_{out}(R_F/R_L)$. The $B(R_F/R_L)$ in the relationship is the γ in Equation 10-10 and the rest of the equation reverts to the form of Equation 10-4. B is, of course, $R_{E1}/(R_Y + R_{E1})$, which is approximately equal to R_{E1}/R_Y.

Another example of a series-applied current feedback circuit is shown in Fig. 10-6. The output current is sensed across R_E. The voltage developed across R_E bucks the input signal, e_s. Here, $\gamma = R_E/R_C$ while the voltage gain with feedback is R_C/R_E when γA_v is very large.

A similar situation exists if a common-emitter resistor is used for several stages of amplification, as shown in Fig. 10-7. Here, $\gamma =$

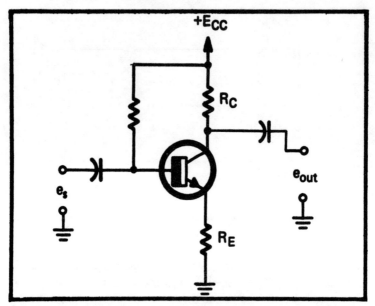

Fig. 10-6. Series-applied current feedback circuit in one stage of amplification.

R_E/R_{C3} and the voltage gain despite the large amount of amplification in the forward loop of the amplifier is R_{C3}/R_E.

The above examples all deal with series-applied current feedback. Shunt-applied current feedback is shown in Fig. 10-8. This circuit can be considered as a voltage feedback **or** current feedback arrangement. As a voltage feedback circuit, the portion of e_{out} fed back to the input is related to the voltage divider formed by R_B with the parallel combination of the input impedance of the transistor, Z_i, and R . This combination, $R_s \| Z_i$, is in series with R_B, so B in Equation 10-4 becomes:

$$\left(\frac{R_s \| Z_i}{R_s \| Z_i + R_B} \right) \qquad (10\text{-}11)$$

This factor has little effect on the voltage gain of the circuit.

On the other hand, the current gain is dependent upon R_C, R_B and $R_s \| Z_i$. The portion of the current fed back from the output is $R_c/[R_B + (R_s \| Z_i)]$. Letting this portion of the output current be B_i, the current gain with feedback becomes:

$$A_{if} = \frac{A_i}{1 - B_iA_i} \qquad (10\text{-}12)$$

where A_{if} is the current gain with feedback and A_i is the current gain without feedback. If R_B is much larger than $(R_s \| Z_i)$, $B_i = R_c/R_B$.

250

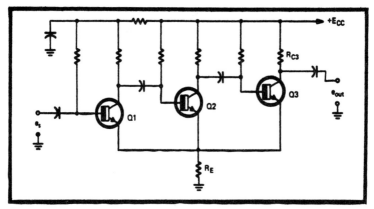

Fig. 10-7. Series-applied current feedback direct-coupled to three stages of amplification.

Using Equation 10-12, the current gain with feedback is R_B/R_C when $B_i A_i$ is very large.

Few of the circuit characteristics due to current feedback differ from those using voltage feedback. In the case of series-applied current feedback, only the output impedance is different. While it is reduced in the case of voltage feedback, it increases by a factor of $(1 - \gamma A_v)$ in current feedback circuits. As for shunt-applied

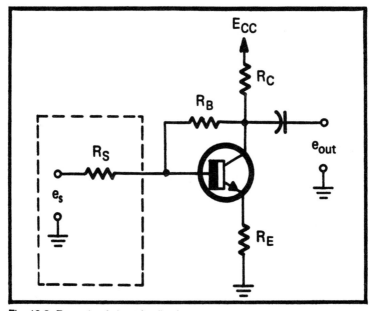

Fig. 10-8. Example of shunt feedback.

251

current feedback, the input impedance is reduced by a factor of $1/(1 - B_iA_i)$ rather than being characterized by the increase inherent in the voltage feedback arrangements.

POSITIVE FEEDBACK

The circuit in Fig. 10-9A is known as a bootstrapped amplifier. It is an example of positive feedback as used around a bipolar transistor circuit. The signal voltage at the emitter is approximately equal to that at the base. One end of resistor R_Y is connected to the emitter through C (or the voltage that is acoss the emitter is fed back to this end of R_Y through C) and the other end of R_Y is connected to the base of the transitor. Since signal voltages at both ends of R_Y are equal (as is the case with any emitter follower), zero volts is across R_Y.

Signal generator e_s sees an input impedance Z_i. Impedances seen by signal sources are equal to the input voltage divided by the input current, or e_s/i_s, where i_s is the input current. The bulk of the input current must flow through R_Y and is equal to the voltage across R_Y divided by the resistor. Since the voltage across R_Y is zero due to feedback capacitor C, then i_s must be $0/R_Y = 0$. Hence, $Z_i = e_s/i_s = e_s/0 = \infty$. It is, of course, not infinite since the voltages at the two ends of the resistor can never be identical.

A similar circuit can be drawn for the JFET to increase its input impedance. This circuit, in Fig. 10-9B, is a bootstrapped amplifier. The bias voltage is developed across R_S and applied through R_G to the gate.

As for the bipolar circuit, the AC portion of Fig. 10-9A can be redrawn as Fig. 10-10. It must be recalled that E_{cc} is at AC ground and that C is an AC short circuit. Because E_{cc} is at AC ground, R_B is across R_X. Since C is an AC short, the parallel combination of R_B and R_X is across R_E in the emitter circuit. R_Y is shorted by the base-emitter junction. In the emitter, R_E, R_X and R_B are all in parallel. When reflected into the base circuit, e_s sees this parallel combination multiplied by the beta of the transistor. This impedance of the circuit is certainly much higher than it would be without the bootstrapped positive feedback components.

The analysis of the JFET circuit is more complex, but it leads to the simple solution that the input impedance is:

$$Z_i = \frac{R_G \left[(1 + g_m (R_S + R_F) \right]}{1 + g_m R_S} \qquad (10\text{-}13)$$

where g_m is the transconductance of the device at the operating point.

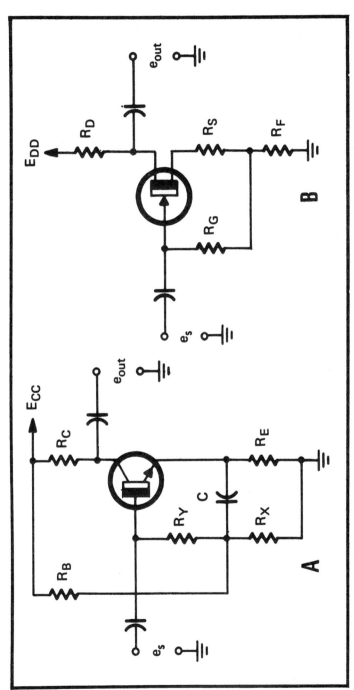

Fig. 10-9. Bootstrapped circuits using positive feedback: bipolar bootstrap circuit (A) and a JFET bootstrap circuit (B).

253

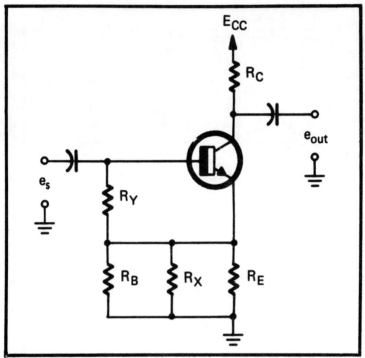

Fig. 10-10. Equivalent of the circuit in Fig. 10-9A used to analyze the effect of bootstrapping.

This bootstrapping concept is important where extremely high impedance is required. In the quasicomplementary output circuit to be discussed in the next chapter, an important application of this concept is detailed.

FEEDBACK EQUALIZATION

Records and tapes are not recorded with a flat frequency response characteristic. Not all frequencies are recorded with equal amplitude. The amplitudes at the upper end of the audio band are recorded with a rising characteristic so that the music can override the noise. Playback curves at this end of the spectrum must exhibit rolloff to compensate for the emphasis in the recording process, while further improving the signal-to-noise ratio.

On the other hand, in the recording process the low frequencies are reduced in amplitude with respect to the mid-frequencies so that the width of the record groove can be maintained within reasonable limits. Therefore, the playback curve must emphasize the low frequencies.

254

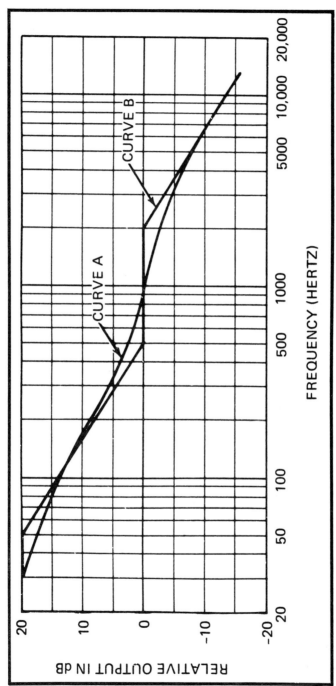

Fig. 10-11. Phonograph playback curves when using magnetic cartridge. The exact frequency response curve is shown at A, and B is a straight line approximation of Curve A.

The final factor affecting the frequency characteristics of the reproduced record or tape is the transducer. The widely used magnetic type cartridge does not have an output with a linear relationship to the amplitude being reproduced. It is a velocity-sensitive device in which the output voltage is proportional to the frequency of the signal when identical amplitudes are being fed to it at all frequencies.

Taking all these factors into account, the phonograph preamplifier section of the playback amplifier must have the frequency characteristic as described by curve A in Fig. 10-11. The overall frequency response of the complete system from record through playback will be linear only if the playback is as shown. A straight line approximation to the curve has been drawn as curve B in Fig. 10-11.

Note that the curve has three distinct sections—two 6 dB/octave rolloffs starting at 50 and 2000 Hz, and a flat response between 500 and 2000 Hz. The latter region can be simulated by a 6dB/octave rise in amplitude beginning at 500 Hz to offset the equivalent rolloff which begins at 50 Hz. The circuit in Fig 10-12 can be used to simulate this curve. It is similar to the circuit in Fig. 10-3A, except that a reactive network is used to replace R_F as the feedback element.

The design procedure can proceed in several logical steps: A minimum of about 40 dB of feedback must be available to be applied around the circuit. This allows for 0 dB of feedback at 30 Hz and for more than the required 36 dB of feedback at 15 kHz with respect to the 30 Hz. Since 40 dB is a voltage ratio of 100:1, the gain of the circuit without feedback must be greater than 100. This is easily accomplished with the two transistors in the figure.

Next, design the R-C networks in the feedback loop. As discussed earlier, the voltage gain, A_{vf}, of the circuit in Fig. 10-3A is about R_F/R, because the forward loop gain is sizable. The impedance network in the feedback circuit of Fig. 10-12 can be substituted for the R_F in the gain ratio. Refer to this impedance as Z_F. As the gain is now Z_F/R_{E1}, the circuit in Fig. 10-12 has a gain approximately equal to:

$$A_{vf} = \frac{Z_F}{R_{E1}} = \frac{1 + j\,6.28f\,R\,(C_1 + C_2)}{j\,6.28f\,C_1 R_{E1}\,[1 + j\,6.28\,f\,C_2\,R]} \qquad (10\text{-}14)$$

This follows from the fact that Z_F is equal to the reactance of C_1 or $1/j6.28fC_1$ in addition to the impedance of the parallel combination of R and C_2 or $R/(1 + j6.28fC_2R)$. In the equation, j indicates a 90° phase shift.

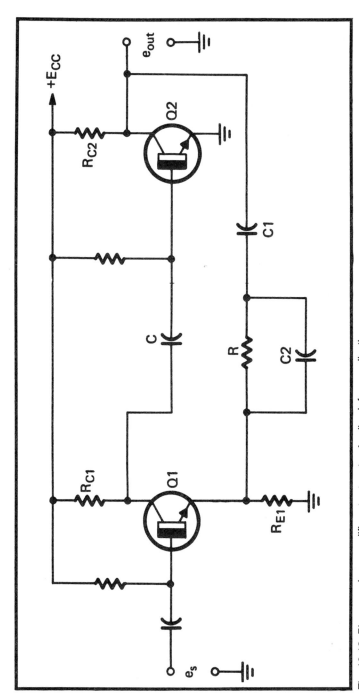

Fig. 10-12. Phonograph preamplifier circuit using feedback for equalization.

257

Equalities in the form of Equation 10-14 can easily be analyzed to determine corner frequencies. All factors in the form of $(1 + jx)$ are set equal to $(1 + j)$. All other factors incorporating a j term are set equal to zero. Thus, for the numerator, $1 + j6.28fR(C_1 + C_2) = 1 + j$, and then:

$$f_{o1} = 1/6.28R (C_1 + C_2) \qquad (10\text{-}15)$$

f_{o1} is one corner frequency. Similarily, the $(1 + j)$ term in the denominator yields the second corner frequency, f_{o2}:

$$f_{o2} = 1/6.28RC_2 \qquad (10\text{-}16)$$

The third corner frequency, f_{o3}, is found by setting the $j6.28C_1R_{E1}$ term equal to zero:

$$f_{o3} = 0 \qquad (10\text{-}17)$$

Now substitute the actual corner frequencies noted in Fig. 10-11 for f_{o1}, f_{o2} and f_{o3}. Curve rolloffs begin at the corner frequencies determined from the factors in the denominator of Equation 10-14, while they rise beginning at frequencies determined from the numerator. Rolloff starts at $f_{o3} = 0$ Hz from Equation 10-17 and continues to 500 Hz as determined from f_{o1} in Equation 10-15. It begins to roll off again at $f_{o2} = 2000$ Hz, which can be calculated from Equation 10-16. The equations can be solved simultaneously to determine the values of the various components.

You may justifiably ask why the rolloff begins at 0 Hz rather than 50 Hz. Simplification in the calculation is afforded by the pendiency of this approximation. Actually, the coupling capacitor between stages in the forward circuit can be adjusted to move the corner frequency from 0 Hz to 50 Hz. A more accurate circuit includes a resistor across C_1 to readjust the corner frequency to its proper location at 50 Hz.

A similar curve may be derived for a tape playback equalized preamplifier. A very rough approximation to the 7½ IPS playback curve is shown in Fig. 10-13. There are two corner frequencies—one at 50 Hz and a second one at 3000 Hz. Once again, a circuit smaller to the one in Fig. 10-12 can be used. Just substitute the series R-C circuit in Fig. 10-14 for the network of C_1, C_2 and R in Fig. 10-12. Let Z_F be the impedance of the R-C circuit or $Z_F = (R + 1)/j6.28fC = (j6.28 fRC + 1)/j6.28 fc$. Since the voltage gain with feedback is approximately Z_F/R_{E1}.

$$A_{vf} = (j6.28fRC+1)/j6.28R_{E1}fC \qquad (10\text{-}18)$$

The rolloff begins at the frequency where the denominator is equal to zero. This is:

$$f_{o1} = 0 \text{ Hz} \qquad (10\text{-}19)$$

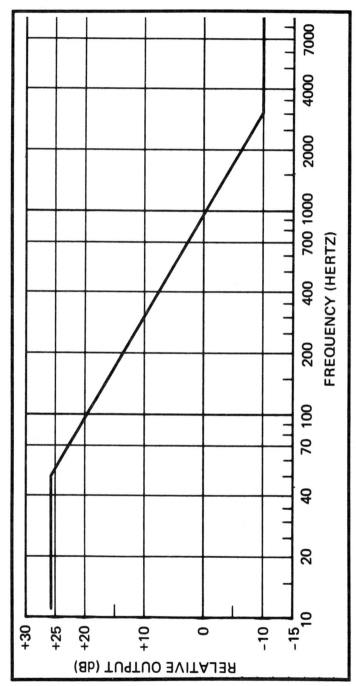

Fig. 10-13. Rough approximation of the 7½ IPS equalization curve for tape reproduction.

259

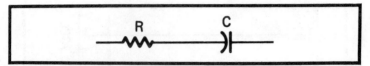

Fig. 10-14. Circuit used in place of R-C1-C2 in Fig. 10-1 to get tape playback equalization.

The rise begins at 3000 Hz or wherever the numerator is equal to j + 1. This frequency is:

$$f_{02} = 3000 \text{ Hz} = 1/6.28RC \qquad (10\text{-}20)$$

Once again, the 50-Hz rolloff point must be treated as in the previous discussion of phono feedback equalization.

Now, the most important step in the design must be pursued. Check the design in the laboratory and adjust the equalization using actual components. Too many stray factors are usually omitted in the paper design for the calculated components to be sufficiently accurate.

Bipolar devices were used in the examples. JFETs can serve equally well in these applications. In both instances, the first stage must be designed for minimum noise while the second transistor circuit must be adjusted so that there is sufficient swing at its output during peaks in the music. A phonograph amplifier with about 3 or 4 millivolts RMS input sensitivity for an average size signal and that will accommodate 60 or 70 millivolts RMS input before the output distorts, is indeed satisfactory. A similar ratio of maximum-to-minimum input signal is required for the tape amplifier, but the minimum input sensitivity in this case should be about 1 millivolt RMS.

OPERATIONAL AMPLIFIER

The operational amplifier, in conjunction with differential amplifier circuitry, is usually associated with computer electronics. Actually, the feedback circuit known as an operational amplifier or anode follower has been in use for many years in tone control circuits in high quality amplifying equipment. Because they are no more expensive or complex than the "losser" type of base and treble boost and cut controls (based on the passive R-C circuits discussed in Chapter 9), the feedback control is used almost exclusively in all good audio equipment. Analysis requires some knowledge of the characteristics of operational amplifiers.

An operational amplifier circuit involving an FET appears in Fig. 10-15. The DC gate bias voltage for this stage is developed across R_S and applied to the gate through R_G. R_G is made as large as practical so as not to affect any other factors in the circuit. It is assumed that **no** AC signal current flows through this resistor.

From the gate through the drain, the stage is an ordinary amplifier where e_{in} will be amplified to produce an output voltage across R_D. However, the actual signal generated, e_s, is applied through R_B to the amplifier. R_F feeds the output signal back to the gate in a feedback circuit. In this circuit, C is considered to be a short circuit for audio signals and is designed into the circuit with the sole purpose of keeping the DC at the collector away from the gate.

The signal current flowing through R_B is $(e_s - e_{in})/R_B$. This current divides between R_G, the gate circuit, and R_ι. Since the currents flowing through R_G are negligible when compared to that flowing through R_F, we can, with reasonable accuracy, conclude that "all" the current flowing through R_B also flows through R_F. The current in R_F is $(e_{out} - e_{in})/R_F$. Equating the current flowing through R_B with that flowing through R_F, we have:

$$(e_s - e_{in})/R_B = (e_{out} - e_{in})/R_F \qquad (10\text{-}21)$$

We can now write a second equation which considers the gain, A_v, of the amplifier stage itself:

$$e_{out} = e_{in} A_v; \quad e_{in} = e_{out}/A_v \qquad (10\text{-}22)$$

Since the gain is usually extremely high (assumed infinite), e_{in} approaches zero. Although e_{in} is **practically** zero, the gate is not at

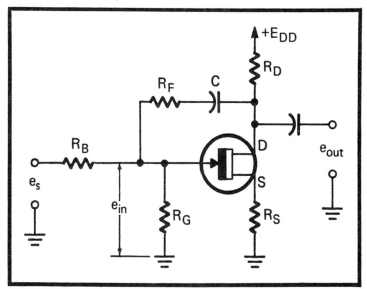

Fig. 10-15. JFET operational amplifier.

ground. This point is referred to as a "virtual ground." Substituting $e_{in} = 0$ into Equation 10-21, we get the well known relationship:

$$e_{out}/e_s = R_F/R_B \qquad (10\text{-}23)$$

The ideal operational amplifier has six primary characteristics:

- ■ Infinite input impedance
- ■ Zero output impedance
- ■ Infinite gain
- ■ Zero offset—zero output signal when the input is zero.
- ■ Zero response time—instant response at the output when the input signal is applied.
- ■ Infinite bandwidth.

Obviously, no amplifier will fully meet any of these requirements. The closer the circuit approaches the ideal, the more accurate the calculations below will be.

FEEDBACK TONE CONTROLS

Let us now analyze a practical feedback tone control which is, in its complete form, known as the Baxendall tone control circuit. Start with the bass control section in Fig. 10-16. C_1 and C_4 are short circuits for the audio signals and are used only to prevent DC from entering the gate circuit. R_1 is made equal to R_3, C_2 is equal to C_3 and R_2 is a linear potentiometer set at the center of rotation.

Compare Fig. 10-16 with Fig. 10-15. R_1 plus the parallel combination of C_2 and the left-hand half of R_2 are the equivalent of the R_B arm in Fig. 10-15, while R_3 plus the parallel combination of C_3 and the right-hand half of R_2 are the equivalent of R_F in Fig. 10-15. Because $R_F = R_B$ at all frequencies (since it has been specified that $R_1 = R_3$, $C_2 = C_3$ and R_2 is linear so that the right-hand half is equal to the left-hand half), the voltage gain of the circuit is $e_{out}/e_s = 1$ (see Equation 10-23) at all frequencies. The curve relating gain to frequency is theoretically flat from 0 Hz to ∞ Hz.

Now move the wiper arm to the extreme left. C_2 is shorted while C_3 is a relative short across R_2. In this position, the R_B arm of Fig. 10-15 becomes R_1 while the R_F arm is effectively R_3 in series with C_3. The impedance of the R_F arm is $R_3 + 1/j6.28fC_3 = (j6.28fC_3R_3 + 1)/j6.28fC_3$. Applying Equation 10-23, the output becomes:

$$e_{out} = e_s \left(\frac{j6.28fC_3R_3 + 1}{j6.28fC_3R_1} \right) \qquad (10\text{-}24)$$

The curve will begin to rise at the frequency f_{oLB} where the numerator is equal to $(j + 1)$ or $f_{oLB} = 1/6.28C_3R_3$. It should level off at the frequency where the denominator is zero or $f = 0$ Hz.

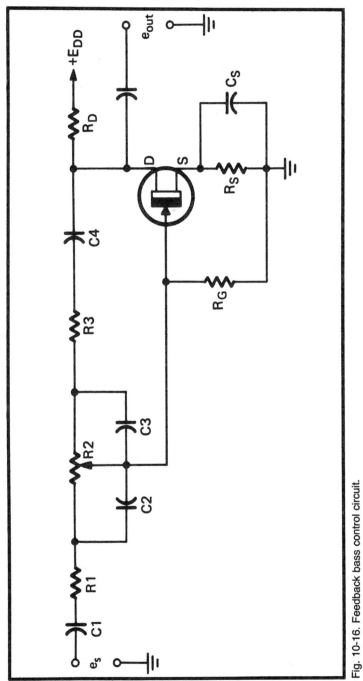

Fig. 10-16. Feedback bass control circuit.

263

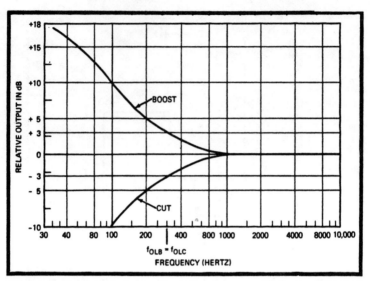

Fig. 10-17. Approximate bass cut and boost curves with the control set at maximum positions.

Equation 10-24 defines the maximum bass boost curve shown in Fig. 10-17.

The maximum bass cut occurs when the wiper arm is at the maximum right-hand setting. Here, R_B of Equation 10-23 becomes $R_1 + 1/j6.28fC_2 = (j6.28fC_2R_1 + 1)/j6.28fC_2$, while R_F is simply R_3. Substituting this into Equation 10-23 yields:

$$e_{out} = e_s \left(\frac{j6.28fC_2R_3}{j6.28fC_2R_1 + 1} \right) \qquad (10\text{-}25)$$

The curve will begin to roll off at the frequency f_{oLC} where the denominator is equal to $j+1$ or $f_{oLC} = 1/6.28\ C_2R_1$Hz. It should level off at $f = 0$ Hz, the frequency when the numerator is equal to zero. This bass cut curve is also illustrated in Fig. 10-17. We can now choose the components for this circuit. It is desirable to make the control as large as practical. A 1-megohm potentiometer was the component originally chosen by the inventor.

We can expect 15 dB of boost and cut at the extreme settings of the control if we overdesign for a maximum cut and boost of 20 dB. 20 dB is an actual voltage ratio of 10:1. Again applying Equation 10-23, $e_{out}/e_s = 10/1 = R_F/R_B$. Since $R_B = R_F/10$, R_1 is made equal to about one-tenth of R_2, or about 100,000 ohms. For symmetry of the boost and cut modes, R_3 is set equal to R_1.

Fifteen dB of boost is required at 50 Hz. Applying the curves discussed previously exhibiting an eventual 6 dB/octave boost or

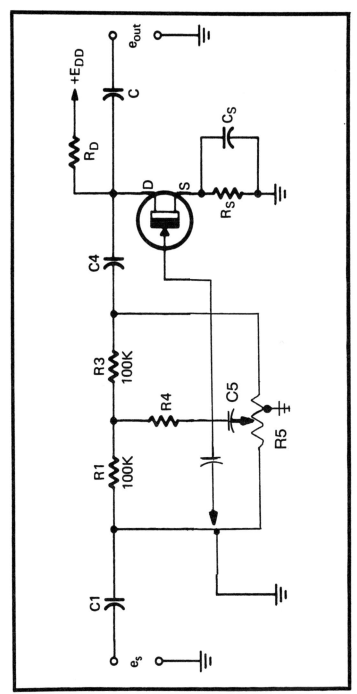

Fig. 10-18. Feedback treble control circuit.

265

rolloff, the corner frequency should be set at about 300 Hz. Substituting 300 Hz for f_{oLB}, C_3 is about 5000 pf. For symmetry reasons, f_{oLC} is also 300 Hz and $C_2 = C_3$.

Intermediate settings of this control will give intermediate amounts of boost and cut. 300 Hz will not be the corner frequency at these settings. The corner frequency will shift closer to the low end of the band when less emphasis or attenuation is required. The high and mid-frequencies will not be affected regardless of the setting of the control.

The treble activating circuit is shown in Fig. 10-18. C1, R1, R3 and C4 are from Fig. 10-16. Bass potentiometer R2 has been drawn as a short circuit and omitted because at the high frequencies involved, C2 and C4 are effective shorts across the bass control. Qualitatively, with R5 at the maximum left-hand setting (maximum treble boost), the control is a shunt across R1 in addition to several other components. Thus, the high frequencies are fed more easily to the gate than are the lower frequencies. This meets the requirements of a treble boost circuit.

Similarly, at the extreme right-hand setting of R5, C5 shunts R3 as well as several other components in the circuit. It feeds the high frequencies back from the output to the gate more readily than it does the lower frequencies. Hence, there is treble cut.

Both the boost and cut circuits are in the operational amplifier circuit and Equation 10-23 does apply. Converting R_1, R_3 and R_4 mathematically from a "tee" to a "delta" configuration to facilitate anaylsis, will yield a corner boost frequency at f_{oHB} and a corner cut frequency at f_{oHC}. They are both equal to $1/6.28C_5 (R_1 + 2R_4)$.

The intermediate settings of the control will yield intermediate amounts of treble boost and cut. As was the case with the bass control, the corner frequency here too is shifted away from the center frequency when less boost or cut than maximum is required at the upper ends of the bands. The setting of the control will not affect the center- or low-frequency regions of the band.

C_5 was originally chosen at about 100 pf so that it will not load the input circuit excessively and yet be large enough not to be affected by stray capacities in the circuit.

f_{oHB} was chosen so that there will be about 16 dB of boost at 10,000 Hz. An approximate curve used to determine the corner frequency is shown in Fig. 10-19. At the maximum setting of the control, $f_{oHC} = f_{oHB} = 1.5$kHz. Since R_1 and C_5 are already known, R_4 can be calculated to be about 500,000 ohms. R_5 must be made as small as practical when compared to the impedance of C_5 at the

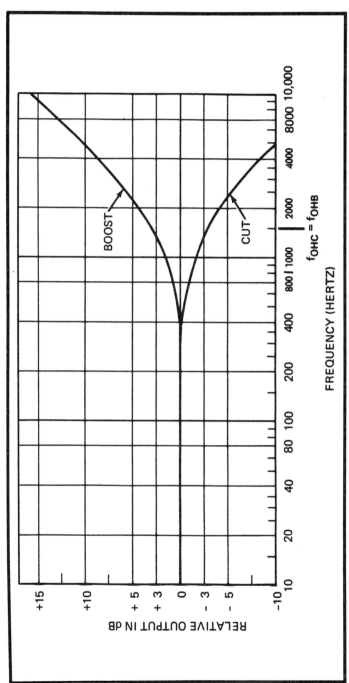

Fig. 10-19. Approximate treble cut and boost curves with the control set at maximum positions.

267

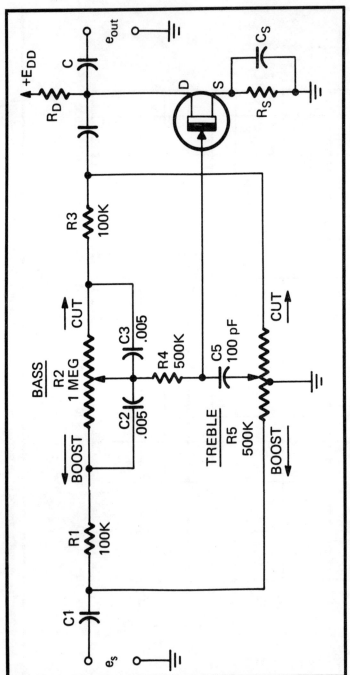

Fig. 10-20. Complete tone control using the operational amplifier feedback circuit.

268

highest audio frequency that must be boosted. A 500,000-ohm linear center-tapped control was found to be satisfactory.

A low-gain amplifier or lower impedance bipolar transistor is frequently used in the feedback tone control circuit. Since these components cause the operational amplifier to differ radically from the ideal, the components must change from the calculated values to effect results similar to those outlined above. The circuit should be designed in the laboratory in this case. Since the function of each component has been detailed, the effects of changing a component is known and the design procedure does not have to be haphazard

The complete tone control circuit in Fig. 10-20 shows the bass and treble controls. The following factors affecting the various functions of the control should be noted. The amount of action of the treble control is affected by R_4 and C_5. Make either component larger if more treble action is required. To a lesser degree, increasing R_1 will increase the amount of treble boost while increasing R_3 will affect the size of the treble cut. As for the basic circuit, C_3 and R_3 must be increased to further emphasize the boost, while C_2 and R_1 must be increased to accentuate the cut.

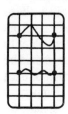

Chapter 11
Output Transformerless
Power Amplifiers

Power amplifiers are discussed in Chapters 7 and 8 on a more or less theoretical and introductory basis. The discussion classifies and details different modes of operation, covers heat sinking considerations, and describes the thermal cycling characteristic. In these circuits output transformers are prescribed as the component used to couple the output transistors to the loudspeaker system.

An output transformer imposes severe limitations on the quality of a design. To overcome its bandwidth restriction, the transformer must be both expensive and bulky. Furthermore, phase shifts at high and low frequencies set boundaries on the amount of feedback that can be placed successfully around a circuit before it becomes unstable.

While practical amplifiers designed for public address applications use output transformers, this component is omitted in just about all pieces of true high fidelity equipment. The loudspeaker is capacitively or direct-coupled to the output devices. The industry uses variations on three basic circuits.

One circuit uses a driver transformer for phase inversion. In this application the transformer is not as taxed as when it is used as an output device. Hence, the size and cost are relatively small. A second arrangement, the quasicomplementary circuit, uses two identical output devices driven by two lower powered complementary transistors arranged to provide the equivalent of phase inversion. The third, the fully complementary amplifier, uses a complementary pair of devices in the output so that phase inversion occurs in the power output transistors themselves, or in the combination of the output transistors and their drivers. The basic characteristics of these three circuits are discussed here.

Any of the circuits described here and in Chapter 7 can be used to drive a full range loudspeaker covering all audio frequencies from 20 to 20,000 hertz (Hz), or at least a good portion of this range. The distortion characteristics and efficiency, to a degree, of any of these systems can be improved through the use of biamplification. Here, the audio signal is split into at least two groups. One group provides signal for reproduction of the low frequency end of the band and the other provides for the high frequencies. This frequency range split takes place just after the preamplifier section of the audio circuit. The high frequencies are then fed to one power amplifier and from there to a high frequency loudspeaker or a tweeter. The low frequencies are fed to a second power amplifier and from there to a low frequency loudspeaker or a woofer. The advantage of doing this is derived from a statistical fact which indicates that more audio output power is needed to reproduce the low frequency end of the band rather than the high frequency end. Hence, a large power amplifier can be used to feed the loudspeaker delivering signal at the low frequencies, and a small power amplifier is used to feed the high frequency loudspeaker. Through the use of this biamplification system, loudspeakers and amplifiers are not overloaded as easily as when using the conventional all range amplifier-loudspeaker system.

Crossover networks similar to those used in loudspeaker systems can be used to split the signal into high and low frequency groups within the amplifier. Each manufacturer uses a different active or passive network to do the job. A simple network provides 6 dB/octave rolloff on each side of the center frequency. One such network is shown in Fig. 11-1. Here, $L = R/2\pi f$ and $C + 1/2\pi fR$, where R is the load resistance presented to the output from the filter and f is the selected crossover frequency. The crossover frequency is usually between 300 and 700 Hz, although other frequencies may be used.

Although biamplification has many advantages, its primary disadvantage is that two power amplifiers are required. Each single

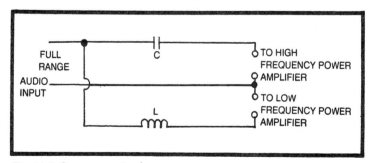

Fig. 11-1. Crossover network.

power amplifiers described here can be used in a biamplification system or in a system to reproduce the entire audio spectrum.

TRANSFORMER PHASE INVERTERS

A circuit using a transformer as the phase inverter is shown in Fig. 11-2. Q1 and Q2 may be considered as a 2-stage voltage amplifier driving power transistors Q3 and Q4 through the driver transformer. To be specific, each transistor stage can be thought of as a power amplifier. Thus, Q1 delivers its minute amount of power to drive a somewhat larger device, Q2, which in turn, must deliver enough power to drive the high-power output transistors, Q3 and Q4. Theoretically, Q3 and Q4 are bigger devices than Q2, which is, in turn, bigger than Q1.

The input signal is capacitively coupled to Q1. Direct coupled to Q2, Q1 receives its bias voltage from the emitter circuit of the latter transistor. Since the DC feedback through R_{B1} from the junction of R_{E2} and R_{EB} is substantial, this circuit is extremely temperature stable. R_{EB} in the emitter circuit is bypassed to ground by C_{EB} to prevent any AC from being fed back from this point along with the DC.

The output from Q2 is fed to a transformer with two identical secondary windings—preferably bifilar wound. The phase relationship between the two windings indicate that these ends are in phase with respect to the unmarked ends.

Should the portion in a cycle be such that the unmarked ends are positive with respect to the ends with the dot, Q3 is forward biased and will conduct while Q4 is reverse biased. In the next portion of the cycle, the opposite polarity will exist at the bases and Q4 will conduct while Q3 will remain idle. The composite signal is reconstituted across R_L.

The impedance ratio of the transformer is based on the goal of presenting an ideal load to the driver transistor. Conventional designs use an impedance ratio of about 9:1. The ratio should be optimized in the laboratory, specifying this ratio for minimum overall distortion.

Assuming adequate transistor capability and heat sinking, the amount of power the circuit can deliver is based upon the size of the supply voltage, E_{CC}, the collector-to-emitter saturation voltage, of transistors Q3 and Q4, and the voltage across emitter resistor R_{E3} or R_{E4}. Power is related to the load at the output by the equations e_{rms}^2/R' and $i_{rms}^2 R_L$. Peak-to-peak voltage for a specific power output is $e_{p-p} = 2.82\, e_{rms}$, while peak-to-peak current is $i_{p-p} = 2.82\, i_{rms}$. The

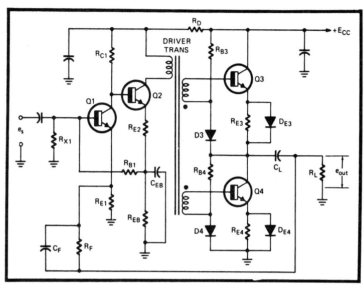

Fig. 11-2. Circuit using a driver transformer for phase inversion.

supply voltage must be capable of swinging the peak-to-peak voltage e_{p-p} across the load in addition to the peak-to-peak voltage across one of the emitter resistors, or $i_{p-p}R_{E3}$.

Collector-to-emitter saturation voltage limits the swing of the voltage across the load. Because two transistors are involved, the sum of both saturation voltages at the peak of the collector current swing must be added to $e_{p-p} + i_{p-p}R_{E3}$ to estimate the minimum supply voltage required if the amplifier is to deliver a specified amount of power. Keeping operation in the linear region requires that the specified saturation voltage be multiplied by a factor of at least three before being added to the other quantities already in the relationship.

Diodes D3 and D4 in the output stage are forward biased and are in the circuit in the interest of stabilizing the quiescent current against variations of V_{BE} with temperature. The actual idling current is established by the voltage developed across the diodes as well as across the other resistors in the DC circuit.

In the emitter circuit, resistors R_{E3} and R_{E4} are used primarily to supply AC and DC feedback and provide some relief for the distortion and DC stability problems inherent in this circuit. As a fringe benefit, it limits somewhat the emitter current to offer some protection to the output devices against over dissipation when the load, R_L is accidentally shorted. In Class-A amplifiers, the design is such that about 0.5 to 1.5 volts is developed across the resistor. Similar voltages are desirable in Class-AB or Class-B circuits during peak current intervals in the cycle.

Diodes D_{E3} and D_{E4} are not absolutely required in this circuit. Should they be used, the emitter resistors can be increased in size to improve the temperature stabilization characteristics. These diodes will bypass large resistors, thus allowing sufficient collector current swings during peaks in the cycle.

The signal at the output transistors is coupled to the load, R_L, through capacitor C_L. The capacitor limits the gain at low frequencies. Use the smallest C_L that will not limit the performance of the overall circuit.

R_F and C_F, in conjunction with R_{E1}, are the primary components of the feedback circuit. C_F is usually adjusted in the laboratory for the most faithful reproduction of square waves.

The output circuit in Fig. 11-2 can, of course, be simplified by omitting all diodes and replacing those in the base circuit with properly sized resistors. This can be done, but at the expense of performance and temperature stability.

Circuits using driver transformers are necessary primarily when germanium output devices are being used. Due to the relatively large leakage currents, complete isolation of the output transistors by the driver transformer is desirable. Although quasi-complementary circuits without transformers have been used with germanium devices, this circuit emerged as the primary arrangement when silicon bipolar transistors became readily and economically available.

QUASI-COMPLEMENTARY POWER AMPLIFIERS

The basic circuit of the quasi-complementary arrangements is shown in Fig. 11-3. It is direct-coupled throughout. The signal is amplified by Q1 and fed to the complementary pair, Q2 and Q3. During the positive portion of the cycle, the bases of the complementary pair are positive with respect to the emitters; the NPN device (Q2) will conduct while the PNP transistor (Q3) is turned off. The reverse is true during the alternate half cycle.

The half cycles are supplied to the output devices, Q4 and Q5, after amplification by the complementary pair. Both portions of the cycle are fed to R_L through C_L and reconstituted across the load resistor. Feedback is accomplished through the parallel combination consisting of C_F and R_F.

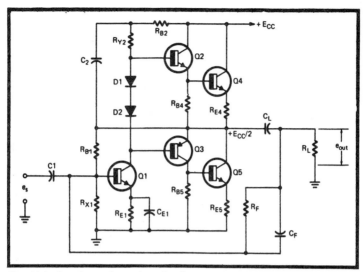

Fig. 11-3. Quasi-complementary circuit.

The DC quiescent conditions are such that half the supply voltage should be present at the point labeled in the drawing as $+E_{CC}/2$. Determined by resistors R_{B1} and R_{X1}, the bias current flowing through Q1 is instrumental in establishing this quiescent condition. The collector load on the transistor consists essentially of $R_{B2} + R_{Y2} + D1 + D2$. The diodes are used to set and maintain the idling current in the output circuit despite temperature fluctuations, and may be replaced by other temperature-sensitive devices. Resistors are often used when compensation for temperature variation is not essential.

There are several inherent problems with this circuit, and all can be solved with the addition of capacitor C2 in a positive feedback bootstrapping arrangement. Note also that the resistors in the base circuit used to bias Q2 have been split into two components, R_{B2} and R_{Y2}, providing a junction to accept C2. On large signals, the bias on the driver transistors tends to shift the operation of Q2 to Class B, producing crossover distortion. To compensate for this, large amounts of feedback must be placed around the circuit. Gain must be large to accommodate all the feedback that is required. Positive feedback supplied by capacitor C2 increases the load impedance the complementary pair presents to Q1, with the consequent increase in gain of the circuit.

Large positive peaks in the signal tend to cut off Q2 by placing the base and emitter of the transistor at $+E_{CC}$. However, there is a

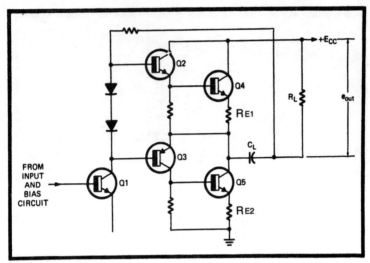

Fig. 11-4. Circuit designed to eliminate the need for a special bootstrap capacitor. C_L doubles as the coupling and bootstrap capacitor. The load is returned to AC ground, $+E_{cc}$.

voltage across C2 due to its being charged while the circuit is idling. This voltage keeps the base at a positive potential with respect to the emitter so that Q2 will continue conducting during all portions of the cycle. Thus, C2 serves two functions. It is instrumental in both increasing the load impedance in the collector circuit of Q1 and in keeping Q2 in a conducting state at all times.

The design of the bootstrap circuit is quite simple. Since R_{B2} and R_{Y2} are essentially across the load through C2, they should be made as large as possible consistent with the current requirements of the base circuit of Q2. Both resistors are usually specified as equal to each other. Under quiescent conditions, $E_{cc}/2$ appears across the series circuit formed by R_{B2} and C2. Since $R_{B2} = R_{Y2}$, the voltage across C2 is one half of $E_{cc}/2$ or is equal to $E_{cc}/4$. Charged to this voltage, C2 maintains a constant current through R_{Y2} and the base-emitter junction of Q2. C2 must be so large as to maintain its charge even when low frequencies are being reproduced.

An alternate bootstrap circuit designed to eliminate the need of capacitor C2 and resistors R_{B2} and R_{Y2} is shown in Fig. 11-4. Instead of these components, a resistor is connected from the junction of C_L and R_L to the base of Q2. C_L doubles as the bootstrap capacitor besides fulfilling its function to couple the signal to the output load resistor or loudspeaker. R_L is connected to $+E_{cc}$, an AC ground. The major drawback of this circuit is that the DC base current for the drivers flows through the load R_L. If this current is very small,

276

it should not affect the operation of the loudspeaker usually used as R_L.

A constant-current source at the bases of the complementary drivers can eliminate the need for the bootstrap capacitor. A drawing of this circuit is in Fig. 11-5. A constant current is supplied to the drivers while a high impedance is presented to the voltage amplifier stage, Q1. The voltage drop between the base of Q6 and +Ecc should be as small as practical so as not to limit the output voltage swing. Hence, low forward-voltage-dropping silicon diodes should be used in the constant-current circuit, rather than the higher voltage zener diodes. Main advantages of this circuit include the improved distortion at low frequencies and more symmetrical clipping of peaks in both halves of the signal.

DIRECT-COUPLED LOAD

In all quasi-complementary circuits discussed thus far, the load was coupled to the output transistors through a large electrolytic capacitor, C_L. Although frequently used, the capacitor has several drawbacks, not the least of which is the inherent nonlinearity of electrolytic coupling devices. Other reasons for eliminating C_L are the low frequency rolloff due to the R_L-C_L high-pass filter, and the corner frequency created by this rolloff which can contribute to instability when feedback is applied around the circuit. Finally, and

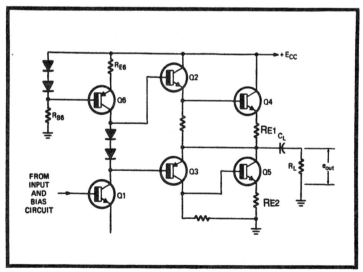

Fig. 11-5. Quasi-complementary circuit using a constant-current source, Q6, to maintain the quiescent current through the output devices at all times.

perhaps the most important drawback is that this capacitor must be charged through the output transistors. If, in the process, the transistor handles more energy (power × time) than it can dissipate, it will destroy itself.

In Fig. 11-3, one end of R_L is connected to ground. When idling, the other end of R_L must be at the same ground potential if there is to be no DC current flowing through the resistor (or loudspeaker) load. This is easily accomplished when a coupling capacitor is used. In the absence of C_L, the junction of Q4 and Q5 must be placed at a zero potential with respect to ground while the circuit is idling. To accomplish this, a positive voltage with respect to ground, $+E_{cc}$, is placed at the collector of Q4 while an identical negative voltage, $-E_{cc}$, is placed at the emitter of Q5, or more exactly at the lower end of resistor R_{E5}. If both transistors, Q4 and Q5, conduct identical currents during the idling period, there is zero voltage at the junction of the two devices to which the load is connected (or at the junction of the collector of Q5 and the lower end of R_{E4}). With a signal applied, the positive-going portion swings the voltage across R_L from zero towards $+E_{cc}$ while the negative portion of the signal swings it from zero towards $-E_{cc}$.

All would be great if the quiescent current can be maintained constant at all times, so that the voltage across R_L will not shift from zero. Unfortunately, Q1 is subject to drift with temperature, as is the case with all transistors. But any change in the amount of collector current flowing through Q1 will upset the balance at the output more than collector current drifts in transistors further advanced in the chain. Drift due to the drivers and outputs is minimized by maintaining the upper and corresponding lower devices at equal temperatures on heat sinks or in free air. In this manner, drift in one half of the driver and output circuit is balanced by the drift in the other half. Q1 has no corresponding transistor with which to overcome or balance collector current changes due to drift. A partner must be added.

Differential amplifier circuits use two transistors. If one is placed in the proximity of the other, or in the same physical case, temperature variations affect both equally. This is especially true if they are matched pairs. A drawing of this type of arrangement is shown in Fig. 11-6. The differential circuit placed before the + and − drives replaces Q1 in the interest of stability.

Q1 and Q2 in Fig. 11-6 are a differential pair driving a second differential pair, Q3 and Q4. A signal at the input to Q1 appears amplified at the collectors of Q1 and Q2. While the input signal is in

278

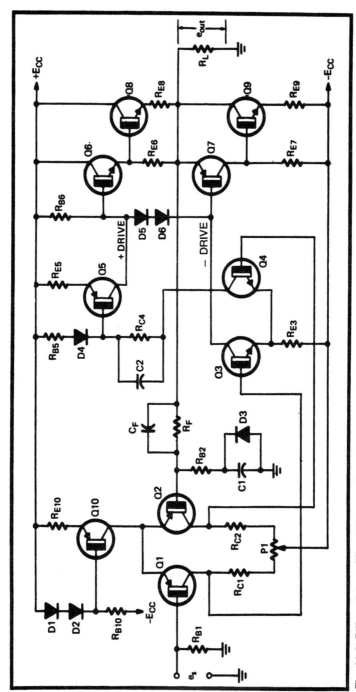

Fig. 11-6. Differential amplifier driving quasi-complementary circuits.

279

phase with the signal appearing at the collector of Q2, it is out of phase with the signal at the collector of Q1. When amplified further by Q3 and Q4, the signal undergoes a 180° phase reversal between the bases and collectors of the respective transistors. The collectors of both transistors are driven to $-E_{cc}$ by the signal. "$-$Drive" is provided at the collector of Q3 to the lower pair of output devices, Q7 and Q9.

From Q4, the signal is fed to the base of Q5, which is arranged as a unity gain amplifier. The phase of the signal is once again reversed. The signal drives the collector of Q5 to $+E_{cc}$, providing the "$+$ drive." The phase reversal in Q5 makes the $+$ drive signal identical in phase with the $-$drive signal at Q3. Two signals with identical phase characteristics are fed to the quasi-complementary output circuit consisting of Q6 through Q9. Proper phase relationships are achieved here to provide the reconstituted amplified output of the input signal. The $+$ drive causes the output of the upper pair of devices to swing to $+E_{cc}$ while the output of the lower pair of devices swings from $-E_{cc}$ due to the $-$ drive. Equal output excursions of both halves of the output circuit to $+E_{cc}$ and $-E_{cc}$ makes bootstrapping unnecessary.

Feedback is applied from the output through R_F and C_F. AC and DC feedback are developed across R_{B2}. It is connected to ground through C1 as a return for the AC feedback and connected to ground through D3 for the DC feedback return.

The circuit shown is raw. It will not operate properly unless it is designed carefully in each aspect. Instability will be prevalent unless the frequency rolloff is carefully controlled at both ends of the audio band. Let us now carefully analyze various sections of the circuit.

Q10, the constant-current amplifier, is designed to establish and maintain the sum of the idling currents through Q1 and Q2. Assuming all silicon devices are used, the voltage across the base-emitter junction of Q10 and across D2 are identical. Hence, the voltage across D1 and R_{E10} are identical and equal to about 0.7 volt, the voltage across a silicon diode. If the sum of the idling currents through Q1 and Q2 are adjusted to, let us say 2 mA, 2mA must flow through R_{E10}. Then the resistor will be 0.7 volt/0.002 ampere $= 350$ ohms. R_{B10} is used to establish a current through, and consequently fix the voltage across, D1 and D2.

The required idling current for Q1 and Q2 can be determined by first noting the maximum current required across the output load at the peak of the signal. It is divided by the product of the current gains of all stages excluding the first. This is the minimum collector current required from each of the two input devices.

If Q3 and Q4 are to be capable of swinging almost to $-E_{CC}$, the voltage across R_{E3} must be small; let us make it 1.5 to 2 volts. This voltage added to V_{BE} of Q3 or Q4 is present at the collectors of Q1 and Q2. Since, during idling, 1 milliampere is to flow through each collector, a simple Ohm's Law calculation will help determine the size of the resistances in the collector circuits. A portion of each collector resistor is taken from R_{C1} and R_{C2} to compose potentiometer P_1. The control is used to balance the relative quiescent current flowing through each transistor and is adjusted for zero volts across R_L when the circuit is idling. The DC feedback is expected to maintain this idling condition.

The + drive must be identical in amplitude to the − drive. To accomplish this, R_{B5} is made equal to R_{E5}. Voltages across D4 and the base-emitter junction are equal. Hence, the currents flowing through R_{B5} and R_{E5} are equal, producing a + drive current in the collector circuit equal to the current flowing through R_{B5}. Since the current flowing through R_{B5} is almost identical to the collector current flowing through Q3 and Q4, the − drive is equal to the + drive. R_{C4} dissipates power available at the collector of Q4 and not required at the base of Q5.

D5 and D6 set the quiescent idling current flowing through the output devices. Should adjustment flexibility be desirable, one of the diodes may be replaced by a potentiometer. For better temperature compensation, the diodes can be replaced with the transistor circuit in Fig. 11-7, and the circuit will still retain the ability to stabilize the current in the circuit.

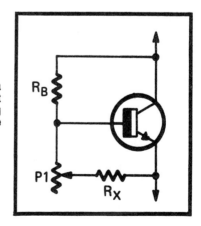

Fig. 11-7. This circuit contains a transistor that enables you to adjust the amplifier's bias while retaining temperature compensation in the unit.

A simplified variation of the circuit of Fig. 11-6 is shown in Fig. 11-8. Here, the differential output is taken from one transistor of the pair, Q1 and Q2. R$_{E1}$ is made large enough so that a constant-current source is not required, eliminating the cost of one transistor. The signal, fed to Q3, is then passed on to the quasi-complementary circuit consisting of Q4 through Q7. C1 is a bootstrap capacitor required here so that the upper transistor, Q4, can swing to saturation. The independent drivers, capable of signal excursions to the limits of the power supply voltage, make the bootstrapping circuit unnecessary for the arrangement in Fig. 11-6.

FULLY COMPLEMENTARY OUTPUT

A close look at the quasi-complementary arrangement reveals that the upper two transistors are a Darlington pair while the lower two form a complementary beta-multiplier pair. Although quite similar, the ultimate quality amplifier is designed with identical pairs. That is either a complementary pair or a Darlington arrangement should be used for both halves of the circuit. The two arrangements are shown in Fig. 11-9.

Either circuit can be substituted directly for the quasi-complementary arrangements. Either circuit can be used to replace transistors Q6 through Q9 in the arrangement discussed with respect to Fig. 11-6. Design requirements are not unlike those described above.

When circuits are designed around VFETs, identical output devices are frequently used in both halves of the push-pull circuit. In addition, properly phased push-pull signals are needed to drive these VFETs. A circuit involving these output devices is shown in Fig. 11-10, being driven from a push-pull driver arrangement. Potentiometer R is adjusted so that there will be zero DC voltage across R$_L$ when no signal is at the input to the output transistors. It is interesting to note that $-E_{GG}$ is usually larger than $+E_{DD}$ and $-E_{DD}$ and that there is more signal voltage required at the input to the VFETs than is available at their outputs. However, the power available at the output is much higher than at the inputs to these devices, so that they serve well in their chosen tasks as power amplifying devices.

Complementary VFET amplifiers are also available. In this type of circuit, one N-channel and one P-channel device is used. The two devices are fed in-phase signals. The inversion required for proper push-pull operation takes place in the output devices themselves. This is shown in Fig. 11-11. In conjunction with $-E_{GG}$, R$_1$ is used to

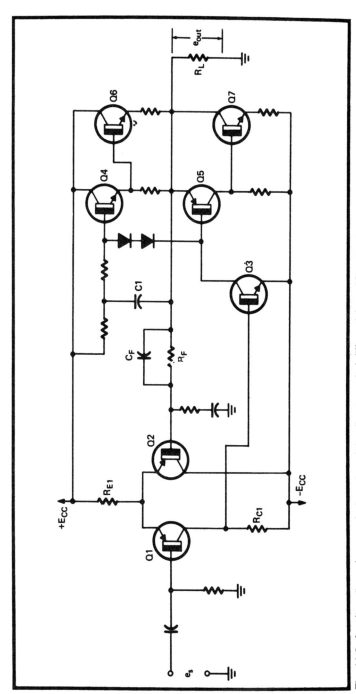

Fig. 11-8. An alternate and economical version of the direct coupled differential amplifier circuit.

283

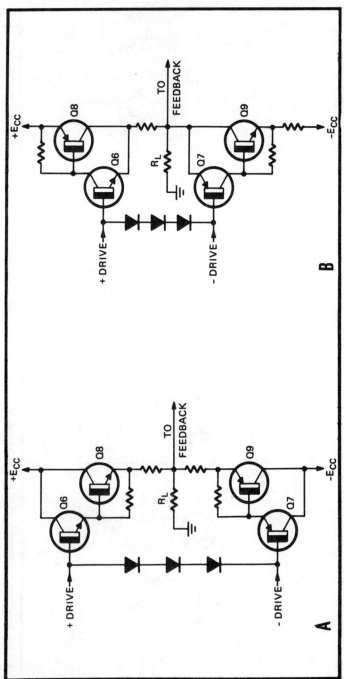

Fig. 11-9. Two output circuits used to replace the transistor counterparts in Fig.11-6—a dual Darlington (A) and a dual beta multiplier (B).

set the bias voltage for the N-channel transistor Q6 and in conjunction with $+E_{GG}$, R_2 is used for setting the bias for the P-channel device, Q7. Note that the polarities of the two bias voltage sources differ from that of the two drain supply voltages for the transistors. As before, zero volt DC is required across R_L when no input signal is applied to the circuit. Potentiometers R_1 and R_2 are adjusted to achieve this goal.

The complementary circuit can also be used in a class D arrangement, usually involving bipolar output transistors. Pulses from the circuit in Fig. 7-22 can be used to drive devices in just about any of the output circuits. This type of circuit adds the pulses at its output to reform the original sinusoidal or music signal. In Fig. 11-12, the integrating circuit composed of inductor L in conjunction with the load, R_L, serves to smooth the output for a clean signal. An R-C network can be used instead of the L-R_L circuit to perform the same function. The R-C network is implemented by replacing L in Fig. 11-12 with a resistor and adding a capacitor to shunt the load, R_L.

Class G fully complementary output stages are based essentially on the circuit in Fig. 11-13. Supplies $+E_{CCA}$ and $-E_{CCA}$ are identical in magnitude, but opposite in polarity, as are supplies $+E_{CCB}$ and

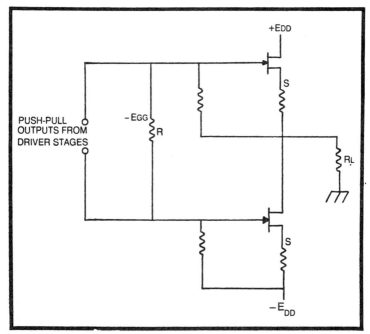

Fig. 11-10. VFET output stages driven by push-pull input signal.

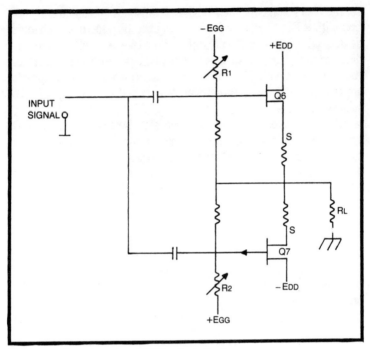

Fig. 11-11. Complementary VFET output circuit.

$-E_{CCB}$. However, the E_{CCB} supplies are considerably larger than the E_{CCA} supplies—up to twice the voltage.

Only Q8 and Q9 are turned on by the input signal when the magnitude of that signal is relatively low. Now, the audio loudspeaker current for R_L flows only through these transistors Q10 and Q11, the higher voltage supplies take over and load current flows through transistors Q10 and Q11 as well as through Q8 and Q9. Diodes D5 and D6 prevent current originating at $+E_{CCB}$ and at $-E_{CCB}$ from flowing into the lower voltage power supplies, when transistors Q10 and Q11 are turned on. Diodes D2 and D3 are placed in the bases of transistors Q8 and Q9 so that transistors Q10 and Q11 start conducting before transistors Q8 and Q9 go into saturation. Diodes D1 and D4 serve to limit the base-emitter leakage current of Q10 and Q11 when the reverse voltages across these junctions are high.

In the simplified class H circuit in Fig. 11-14, low voltages $+E_{CCA}$ and $-E_{CCA}$ are supplied to the output transistors Q8 and Q9 through diodes D1 and D2. When the signal increases across the load, R_L, this information is fed to the *vari-proportional logic circuits*.

286

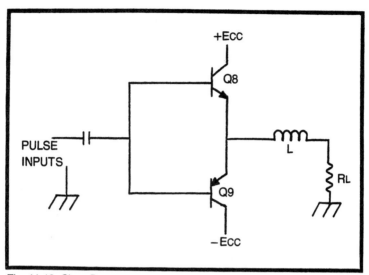

Fig. 11-12. Class D output circuit using L-R$_L$ as the integrating network.

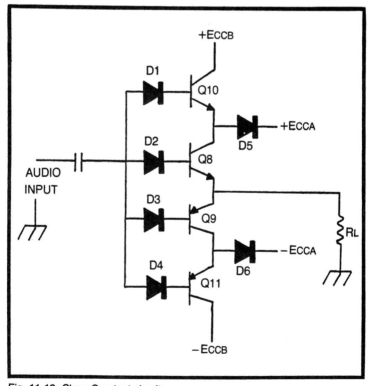

Fig. 11-13. Class G output circuit.

Should the signal exceed a predetermined level, the output voltage from the logic control circuit turns on transistors Q10 and Q11. Now paths are completed between the high voltage supplies +E$_{CCB}$ and −E$_{CCB}$ to output transistors Q8 and Q9, respectively. Because of these higher voltages, more power can be delivered to R$_L$ before the signal is clipped than was possible when only the lower voltages were available to the output transistors. The logic circuit assures that the higher voltages are applied before the clipping level is reached due the low voltages powering the output devices. In the original class H amplifier produced by Soundcraftsman, E$_{CCB}$ is 50% larger than E$_{CCA}$.

Rudimentary circuits used in the various classes of operation are shown here. In the actual hi-fi equipment, the circuits are considerably more complex and involve many essential refinements. In Chapter 13, we define some digital logic applicable to the operation of these circuits.

PROTECTING THE OUTPUT DEVICES

The output transistors are in a vulnerable position in all of the circuits. The load plays havoc with the amount of power the device is forced to dissipate. Under normal load conditions, the chances of destroying a transistor are negligible. But consider what happens when the load is accidentally reduced in size from the norm, or shorted. More current can flow through the output devices than is normally possible or required with proper size load resistors.

Should a capacitive load be placed across the nominal rated load or voice coil of a loudspeaker, the amplifier may become unstable and break into oscillation. Transistors can break down as a result of overdissipation when the circuit is oscillating. A situation of this type may occur when an electrostatic tweeter is placed at the output of the power amplifier.

Capacitor Loads

Electrostatic tweeters are not simple capacitors. Equivalent circuit diagrams involve more than a capacitor. However, a capacitor of 2000 to 3000 pf may be considered as an adequate representation of this type of high-frequency speaker for most experimental work.

The amplifier can be tested for stability or marginal stability by simply placing a capacitor across the normal load resistor at the output. The circuit should be checked with capacitors ranging from 500 pf to 1 mfd. Any instability or signs of instability indicates the

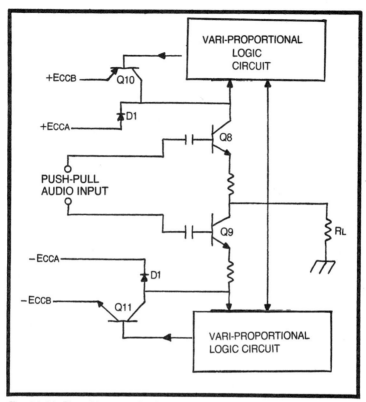

Fig. 11-14. Class H output circuit.

design requires some additional experimental work to correct the condition.

The test for marginal instability involves feeding a 10-kHz or 20-kHz square wave through the amplifier. Next, place various values of capacitors across the load resistor. This may, or probably will, distort the square wave by rounding the leading edge. Ringing may also be observed on the horizontal portion of the square wave when some sizes of capacitors are placed across the output load resistor. The rounding of the leading edge can be ignored, but the ringing usually cannot be neglected. If there is ringing, the amplifier is marginally stable. However, if the ringing decays rather than increases as the square wave progresses through the cycle, it need be of no concern to the designer.

A small capacitor placed across a base-collector junction at the output, or between some other judiciously and experimentally chosen points in the amplifier, may remove any signs of instability. A

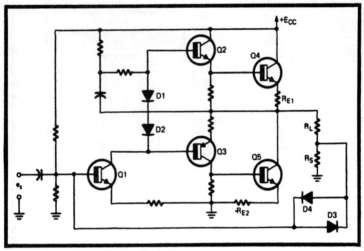

Fig. 11-15. Quasi-complementary circuit in which the output is sensed across Rs and fed back to the input through D3 and D4 when the input voltage is larger than the threshold voltage of the diodes.

series R-C network across the output load or loudspeaker may at times also be required. A small 2 or 3 microhenry RF choke made from 18 to 20 gauge wire, placed in series with the load, will frequently negate any tendency towards oscillation. The choke is usually shunted by a small resistor; ten ohms or somewhat less will do. Complete elimination of the undesirable oscillation requires a considerable amount of trial-and-error type of experimentation on the wired circuit.

Current Limiting

By far, the primary cause of transistor failure is excess emitter and collector current due to a short circuit across the output load or loudspeaker. Circuits have been devised to sense the output current. At some predetermined output current, a device of some sort is turned on to shunt drive signal away from the power amplifiers. Limiting the drive will curtail the amount of current flowing through the output devices.

The most straight-forward circuit uses a small resistor, R_s, in series with the load, R_L, as shown in Figs. 11-15 and 11-16. This resistor should be made as small as practical so as not to substantially affect the damping of the circuit. Never make it larger than one-fourth the impedance of the speaker so that the damping factor will never be more than its minimum acceptable value of 4.

In Fig. 11-15, the output current flows through R_s as well as through the output load resistor, R_L. A voltage is developed across R_s by the output current. The resistor value is chosen so that the portion of the output voltage developed across it will bias diodes D3 and D4 in a conducting mode when more than the permissible amount of current flows through the output circuit. When the peaks of this voltage are sufficiently large so as to turn on either or both diodes, D3 and/or D4, a negative feedback loop is completed through the diodes to the input circuit, reducing the gain of the overall circuit. Consequently, the output is limited by a reduced drive until the cause of the excess current is eliminated.

The output current in Fig. 11-16 is likewise sensed as a voltage across resistor R_s. This time R_s is placed between the load, R_L, and the amplifier. R_s is adjusted so that the voltage developed across it when excess current flows through the output circuit is sufficient to turn on transistors Q5 and Q6. In turn, these transistors shunt signal or drive current away from the output circuit, limiting the output current to predetermined safe levels.

A similar circuit is used in the fully complementary arrangement in Fig. 11-17. Here, the current flowing through the output devices develops voltages across the individual emitter resistors, R_{E1} and R_{E2}. As in Fig. 11-16, this voltage is applied to transistors Q5 and Q6. When the voltage is high due to excessive emitter current, Q5 and Q6 are turned on and consequently shunt signal away from the output circuit. Diodes D3 and D4 are provided so that

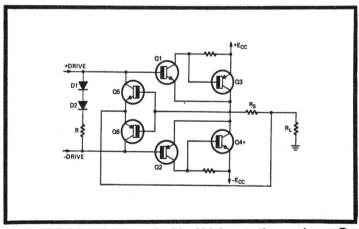

Fig. 11-16. Fully complementary circuit in which the output is sensed across Rs. Here, the signal is used to turn on Q5 and Q6 which shunt the drive signal away from the output transistors.

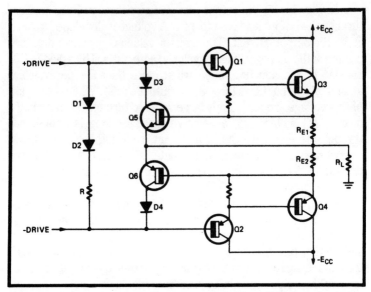

Fig. 11-17. Fully complementary circuit with protection devices similar to the circuit in Fig. 11-16. Here, however, the current is sensed across individual emitter resistors in each output pair of transistors.

the signal will not forward bias the collector-base junction of transistors Q1 and Q2. Forward bias on these junctions would cause the output signal to distort.

There is nothing tricky and unusual in the circuits described thus far. The output is sensed. Information is then fed back to an earlier stage which limits the drive and consequently controls the amount of output current that can flow.

Simpler methods have been devised to do the job; some are more effective while others are not quite as good. The simplest method is to use excessively large output devices which can easily dissipate and deliver all the power they must, even when the output load is shorted. A second circuit limits the supply voltage to the drivers so that the output transistors cannot be overdriven. A variation of this is the built- in poor regulation in the power supply of the amplifier in order to limit the maximum power available to the output devices.

A third method incorporates fuses in series with the load or in series with each emitter of the output devices (replacing R_{E1} and R_{E2} in Fig. 11-4). The fuses are theoretically supposed to blow before the transistors. Actually, they race the transistors to oblivion. Instead of fuses, small bulbs have been used in place of the emitter

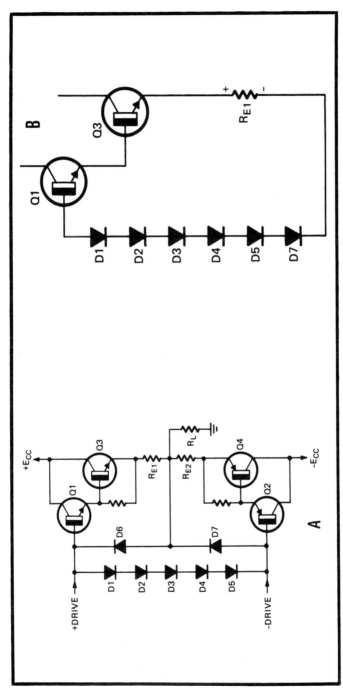

Fig. 11-18. Schematic A is a fully complementary circuit in which diodes D1 through D7, in conjunction with R_{E1} and R_{E2}, limit the drive to the output devices. Schematic B is an equivalent circuit of the diodes across R_{E1}.

resistors in the output circuit. Based on the premise that the bulb resistance will increase when the current is large, it is theoretically a practical measure which can be used to limit current peaks. Unfortunately, bulbs have a thermal time lag. The output transistors are thus not protected during instantaneous bursts of output signal current.

The circuits in Figs. 11-18 A and 11-19 are quite effective and simpler than those just discussed. However, their capabilities to limit the output current peaks are not as obvious. In both circuits, the bias is maintained by diodes D1 through D5. In the positive portion of the cycle, transistors Q1 and Q3 conduct. A voltage is developed across R_{E1}. If the voltage across R_{E1} is sufficiently large, the diodes connected across the series circuit consisting of R_{E1} and the Q1 and Q3 base-emitter junctions, also conduct. In Fig. 11-16A, these diodes consist of D7 in series with D1 through D5. As is obvious from Fig. 11-18B, the series combination of diodes is in parallel with the series circuit consisting of R_{E1} and the base-emitter junctions of Q1 and Q3. Consequently, the sum of the base-emitter junction voltages and the voltage across R_{E1} are equal to the voltage across the combination of·diodes D1 through D5 and D7.

For this discussion, assume the voltage across each conducting junction and diode is 0.7 volt. When conducting, the maximum voltage across the series combination of diodes D1 through D5 and D7 is 6 × 0.7 volt = 4.2 volts. This is also the maximum voltage across the series combination of R_{E1} and the junctions of Q1 and Q3. When conducting, the voltage across two of the diodes is equal to the voltage across the junctions of Q1 and Q3. Under normal conditions, the maximum voltage across R_{E1} is identical to that across the remaining four diodes in the circuit, or 4 × 0.7 volt = 2.8 volts. The voltage remaining for the the junctions of Q1 and Q3 is 4.2 volts - 2.8 volts = 1.4 volts.

Now assume the current flowing through Q3 and, hence, through R_{E1} is so large that more than 2.8 volts is developed across the resistor. Since the voltage at the base of Q1 is maintained at 4.2 volts maximum by the series diode circuit, less than 1.4 volts will then be across the two base-emitter junctions. Therefore, transistor current will tend to be reduced. R_{E1} is selected so that transistor current will be limited to safe values.

In the negative portion of the cycle, Q2 and Q4 conduct. Should the voltage across R_{E2} be sufficiently large, D6 will be turned on and complete a current path through diodes D1 through D5. An equivalent limiting sequence to that detailed above will then apply to the bottom portion of the transistor circuit.

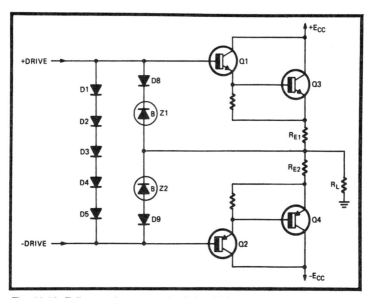

Fig. 11-19. Fully complementary circuit in which zener diodes shunt excess drive away from the respective bases to which they are connected through diodes D8 and D9.

Should it be that large magnitudes of voltage are required across R_{E1} and R_{E2}, diodes D6 and D7 in Fig. 11-18 can be replaced by zener diodes Z1 and Z2, in series with conventional diodes D8 and D9, as shown in Fig. 11-19. The voltage across D8 is identical to that of the base-emitter junction of Q1. Should the sum of the base-emitter voltage at Q3 and the voltage across R_{E1} exceed the breakdown voltage of Z_1, it will conduct. The drive current reaching the base of Q1 will be reduced. A similar course of events will occur in the lower portion of the circuit involving D9, Z2, R_{E2}, Q2 and Q4. R_{E1} and R_{E2} are adjusted so that Z1 and Z2, respectively, will conduct when more than the maximum allowable current passes through the output device. D8 prevents negative signals from being shunted through Z1, while D9 serves the same function with respect to Z2. D1 through D5 set the bias of the output devices and stabilizes it against temperature variations.

Adding Protection

The current-limiting systems are good. However, more protection can be provided by sensing not only the current flowing through a device, but also the power dissipated by the device at every instant in the cycle. Since the power is the product of voltage

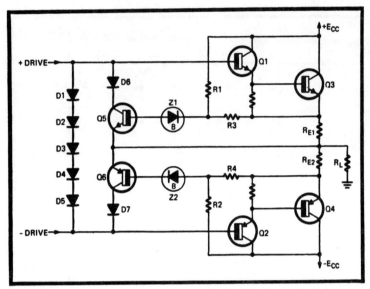

Fig. 11-20. Fully complementary circuit in which dissipation is limited.

and current, the input to the power amplifiers can be reduced or completely turned off when the two factors exceed a specific combined level. A circuit of this type is shown in Fig. 11-20.

As far as the upper portion of the push-pull circuit is concerned, the instantaneous current is sensed across R_{E1} and fed through R3 to the cathode end of zener diode, Z1. Meanwhile, resistors R1 and R3 form a voltage divider. The voltage fed to this divider is the instantaneous voltage across transistor Q3. A portion of the sensed voltage is fed to the cathode end of zener diode Z1, along with the sensed current. The information about the current and voltage are added together at the cathode of Z1. If the resulting voltage is large enough, it will cause Z1 to break down and thus turn on Q5. This transistor will shunt excess drive away from the base of Q1 and from Q3. Diode D6 prevents normal signals from being shunted through the collector-base junction of Q5. An identical description can be used to detail the operation of the lower portion of the circuit using Q6 as the key transistor in the protection arrangement.

Circuits can be designed to sense the value of the load resistor. The drive signal can be reduced considerably or entirely eliminated when the output is shorted. A circuit of this type has been drawn in Fig. 11-21. Assume first that the junction of R3 and R4 is connected to the emitters of Q5 and Q6, rather than to ground. The circuit will then revert to that shown in Fig. 11-17 with the exception that the voltage developed across emitter resistor R_{E1} is divided by resistors R1 and R3 before being applied to Q5, and the voltage developed across R_{E2} is divided by R2 and R4 before being applied to Q6. Hence, the circuit will limit the current.

Next, change the connection so that the circuit becomes the one shown in Fig. 11-21. The base-emitter junction of Q5 is connected across the series resistor combination of R3 and R_L. In addition to the voltage across R3, (which is related to the collector current of Q3), the voltage across R_L is a factor in the amount of voltage that appears at the base-emitter junction of Q5. The voltages across R3 and R_L are out of phase and thus buck each other. Obviously, when R_L is large, more signal voltage will be developed across the resistor by the output current than when R_L is small. Therefore, when R_L is large, more signal voltage is required across resistor R_{E1} (and in turn across R3) to turn on shunting transistor Q5, than when R_L is small. This is due to the fact that the large voltage developed across R_L bucks the voltage across R3.

Should R_L be shorted, no voltage is available to buck that developed across R3. A relatively small amount of signal voltage across R_{E1} (and hence across R3) will turn on shunting transistor Q5. Since the voltage across R_{E1} is due to the amount of current flowing through Q3, less current can flow through the output devices under shorted load conditions than under normal load conditions before the shunting transistors are activated. Dissipation can

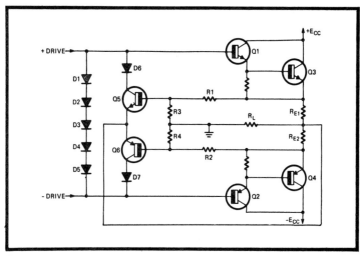

Fig. 11-21. Fully complementary circuit in which the output is a function of the value of load resistor R_L.

be limited to safe values by simply adjusting the size of the resistors in the circuit. A similar description can be evolved for the lower half of the push-pull arrangement.

Unfortunately, high-frequency operation is adversely affected by this circuit. To overcome this drawback, a portion of the circuit should be modified to that shown in Fig. 11-22. Here, resistors R3 and R4 of Fig. 11-21 are shunted to ground through diodes D8 and D9, while a 5000-ohm or 10,000-ohm resistor, R5, is placed between the diodes.

The final circuit to be discussed here is used in the 700-watt Phase Linear Company amplifier. The protection arrangement is an integrated circuit computer. Unfortunately, the circuit is a closely guarded secret, but the description is nevertheless interesting and informative. The following is an excerpt from a letter from Mr. Robert Carver, with permission to publish the information.

"The operation of this energy-limiting computer, henceforth known as the limiter, is as follows: Information is fed into the input of the limiter, consisting of the instantaneous current, voltage, time rate of voltage change, and time rate of current change supported by the output transistors. In addition, a "clock pulse" is generated at the zero-axis crossing which serves as a pulse to reset the **integrator**, a circuit internal to the limiter. The output of the integrator, which is an analog voltage proportional to the energy absorbed by the transistor silicon chip, is applied to a summing junction.

"Another section of the limiter, the **common-mode detector**, generates a voltage which is again an analog voltage and which represents the amount of current being carried simultaneously by the output transistors. The common-mode detector generates its voltage indirectly by measuring di/dt and dv/dt (author's note: di/dt is a change in current with respect to time and dv/dt is a change in voltage with respect to time) and performing an appropriate computation. It is not possible to simply act on common-mode current directly unless some sort of frequency-selective process is used, because the ability of the amplifier to drive a low-frequency, high hysteresis load would be limited.

"The **comparator** is self explanatory. The analog outputs are summed at the summing junction, and if this sum (which represents the stress level the output transistors are sustaining) is of sufficient amplitude, the A-D converter, normally in a 0 state, switches to a 1 state, and turns on the **enable**. This causes the disconnect diode to be forward biased and pulls down the drive current at the base of the driver transistors.

298

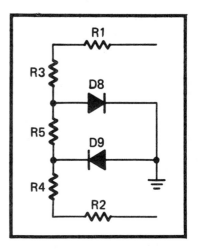

Fig. 11-22. Modification of the circuit in Fig. 11-15 to permit good operation at high frequencies.

"Note that the protective circuit is either **on** or **off**. This insures that right up to the threshold of limiting, normal operation of the amplifier is not in any way affected."

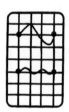

Chapter 12
Power
Supplies

The forward and reverse characteristics of the diode are discussed in Chapter 1, where it is indicated that the diode will conduct when the anode or P-type semiconductor material is made positive with respect to the N slab, the cathode. The diode will not conduct when the voltages are applied in the opposite direction. Due to these unique characteristics, the diode can be used effectively in power supplies.

BASIC POWER SUPPLIES

An audio amplifier uses many different types of power supplies to convert the AC line supply into useful DC power at the required voltage and current levels. They are all based upon the simple half-wave supply shown in Fig. 12-1.

The 120 volts derived from house power is reduced to usable levels by means of power transformer, T. The voltage ratio of the primary to the secondary is, of course, proportional to the turns ratio of the two windings of the transformer.

The secondary voltage is applied across the load, R_L, through diode D1. There is current flowing through the circuit when terminal 1 of the transformer secondary is positive with respect to terminal 2. Only then is the anode of the diode positive with respect to its cathode, thus biasing the diode in its forward-conducting mode. The output across R_L is in positive half cycle pulses. On alternate portions of the cycle, the diode is reversed biased and it does not conduct.

The average voltage across the load is almost V_p/π while the RMS voltage of this half cycle is just about $0.5\,V_p$. The pulsating DC across the load has a large amount of ripple. As it stands, the circuit has little value as a practical power supply for an audio amplifier. It has too much ripple. But a large capacitor placed across the load will

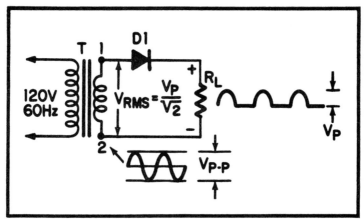

Fig. 12-1. Simple half-wave power supply circuit.

reduce this ripple so that the supply is usable as a smooth source of DC power. The capacitor is charged through the rectifier during the conducting half of the cycle and is only somewhat discharged through the load during the portion of the cycle when the diode does not conduct. It maintains the voltage across itself and the paralleled load at a relatively clean and constant DC.

The DC voltage across the load, V_{RL}, depends upon several factors, namely:

- ■ The line frequency, f.
- ■ The load resistance, R_L.
- ■ The sum of the resistance, R_T, of the transformer with all other resistors, R_s, in series with the rectifier, as well as the resistance of the rectifier, r_{ac}. (r_{ac}, the forward AC resistance of the rectifier is 26/I, where I is the average or DC current flowing through the rectifier and expressed in milliamperes.)
- ■ The size of the filter capacitor.

A series of curves relating these factors is shown in Fig. 12-2.

To use this plot, the initial requirement is to determine the particular curve applicable to the circuit in question. To do this, determine $(R_T + R_s)/R_L$. Use the curve which most nearly approximates this ratio. If you like, you can interpolate between two curves. Next, calculate the product $6.28fR_LC$ for your circuit. Mark this point on the curve you selected and note the ratio V_{RL}/V_P at the vertical axis. V_P is the peak voltage at the secondary of the transformer, or the RMS voltage multiplied by $\sqrt{2}$. Then calculate V_{RL}, the DC voltage across the load, from the information derived.

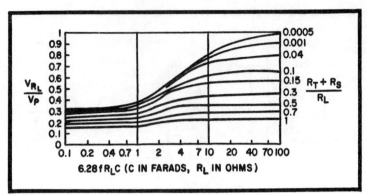

Fig. 12-2. Plot for a half-wave power supply, showing the VRL/Vp to 6.28fRLC relationship for various values of (Rs + RT) /RL.

The amount of ripple that can be allowed to ride on the filtered DC depends upon the section of the audio amplifier to which the rectified and filtered voltage is applied. Increasing the size of capacitor C will reduce the ripple. Fig. 12-2 can be used to recalculate the output voltages as related to different Cs. It should be noted that the output remains relatively constant as the product 6.28fRLC is increased above 100.

A full-wave rectifier system, shown in Fig. 12-3, will reduce ripple and ease the filtering problem. However, in this circuit the ripple is of the more objectionable 120-Hz type rather than the 60-Hz variety in the half-wave supply. (This, of course, assumes a 60-Hz power supply.)

In the full-wave supply, two diodes are used; each conducts on alternate half cycles. The missing half cycle pulse at the output of the half-wave supply in Fig. 12-1 is filled in here. The unfiltered average DC voltage across the load is $2V_p/\pi$ while the RMS voltage is .707 Vp. Should a capacitor be placed across the load, the ripple will be less than in the half-wave supply because the capacitor is not required to hold the charge as long as was previously necessary. The capacitor is recharged each half cycle rather than waiting for a full cycle for the next pulse, as is the case with the half-wave supply. The curves in Fig. 12-4 illustrate the various relationships for the full-wave supply. Here, Vp refers to the voltage across half the secondary of the transformer.

PRACTICAL POWER SUPPLIES

The power amplifier using a capacitor to couple the output transitors to the loudspeaker system (see Fig. 11-2) requires a

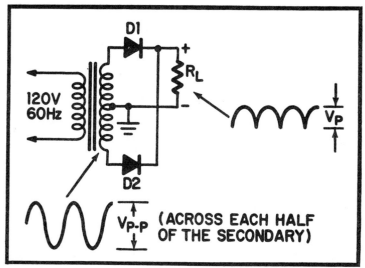

Fig. 12-3. Full-wave power supply circuit.

single simple power supply. Only one voltage source is needed with respect to ground. The standard full-wave supply in Fig. 12-3, using a centertapped secondary winding, is commonly used in such cases.

The bridge circuit shown in Fig. 12-5 can also be used. It is not as costly to build as the one with the centertapped secondary on the transformer. For the identical amount of DC output current, less RMS current passes through the transformer in the bridge circuit than in the previously encountered arrangement. Hence the transformer used in the bridge circuit is the cheaper of the two. The major drawback with the bridge circuit is that four diodes are

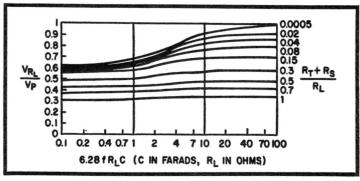

Fig. 12-4. Plot for a full-wave power supply showing the V_{RL}/V_P to $6.28fR_LC$ relationship for various values of $(R_S + R_T)/R_L$. (V_P is the peak voltage across half the secondary winding of the power transformer).

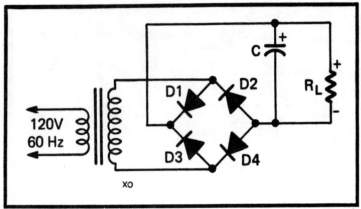

Fig. 12-5. A bridge circuit supplies a full-wave rectified output more economically than does the conventional half-wave center-tapped transformer circuit.

required. However, each diode is rated at the peak voltage across the secondary winding or 1.41 multiplied by the RMS voltage. In the center-tapped arrangement, the PIV of each diode is double this, or 2.82 V_{RMS}. Here, each diode will probably be more expensive than those required for the bridge supply.

The operation of the circuit is self-evident. During the half cycle when the upper leg of the winding is positive with respect to the lower end, electron current flows opposite to the arrows in the diode symbol, through D4, R_L and D1. The polarity of the voltage across R_L is as shown. In the next half of the cycle, when the polarity of the voltage across the transformer is reversed, the electron current flows through D2, R_L and D3. Once again the polarity of the voltage developed across R_L is as shown. Current flows in the same direction through the resistor during both halves of the cycle. Full-wave rectification has been accomplished. The curves in Fig. 12-4 can be used to determine the output voltages with the particular filter capacitor used. Since the circuit is "floating" either end of the load resistor can be grounded.

Power amplifier circuits which do **not** use a capacitor to couple the output devices to the loudspeaker system (see Fig. 11-6), require two identical supplies. One must be positive with respect to ground and the other must be negative. The positive voltage is applied to one half of the output stage while the negative voltage is applied to the other half. A circuit which can provide this is shown in Fig. 12-6. It resembles the bridge, but is actually analyzed as two full-wave supplies wired across one center-tapped transformer winding.

The DC power supplied to the output stages may contain a considerable amount of ripple, but hum will nevertheless remain inaudible. Voltage amplifiers preceding the power stage require relatively smooth supplies. Ripple in these portions of the amplifier is magnified by all succeeding stages. A ripple-free supply is most critical when considering phono or tape preamplifiers. Here, the power source must be virtually free of any trace or ripple. One function of the R-C decoupling network in Fig. 12-7 is to accomplish this goal.

Relatively poorly filtered voltage is used as the supply for the output transistors at A. The drivers are supplied power from point B in the decoupling network. The ripple present at A is filtered by the R1.C1 network to provide power with a better ripple factor for the drivers than is supplied to the output devices. Ripple is further reduced before being applied to amplifier stages connected to points C and D by two additional R-C filter sections. The various resistors in the decoupling circuit serve a dual function—as components in the filter network and as components in voltage dividers to establish the proper voltages across the capacitors for the different sections

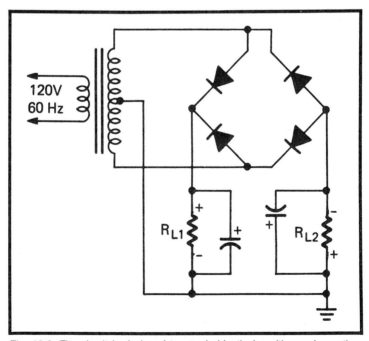

Fig. 12-6. The circuit is designed to supply identical positive and negative voltages to an amplifier.

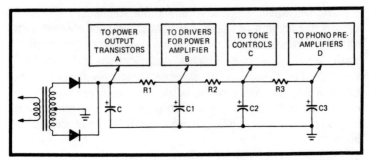

Fig. 12-7. This filter circuit provides the correct operating voltages to each section of the amplifier and prevents unwanted interstage coupling.

of the amplifier. Once the resistors have been chosen, the capacitors can be determined experimentally. Just observe the contribution of hum by each stage as different capacitors are substituted into the network. Use the smallest capacitor that will do the job.

Decoupling circuits serve another very important function. Each power supply has a specific impedance. Amplifier stages can be inadvertently coupled to each other through the supply. Coupling of this type can cause the amplifier to oscillate at a low frequency. This type of oscillation is known as motorboating. This can be cleared up by separating stages from each other. It is accomplished by connecting them across different capacitors in the decoupling circuit. It is best not to connect more than two transistors to any one point in the filter network or decoupling chain.

Some amplifiers are unstable unless the supply voltage presents a low impedance. This characteristic can be achieved by placing a transistor in a power supply circuit, as shown in Fig. 12-8. The resistors in the circuit are chosen to establish the bias voltage needed to put Q1 in the active region. The capacitors are ripple filters. Voltages at the output across C2 are equal to the input voltage less the few volts dropped across Q1. The stage must be capable of passing all current required at the output. Q1 must not be in saturation. It is not in saturation if the voltage measured between the collector and emitter is greater than the saturation voltage of the device. The power the transistor dissipates is equal to the product of the current flowing through Q1 and the voltage across it.

Should the audio amplifier be combined with a tuner in one circuit, the resulting receiver derives its total power from one supply. The low-impedance power supply is usually not adequate to provide the near perfect and constant DC voltage needed at the tuner section. Voltage supplied to the tuner (and even to the preamplifier section) frequently must be regulated. This is due to the fact that the supply used for the tuner is simply a filtered extension of the supply providing power to the output transistors. Power transistors draw a considerable amount of current. The current varies with the portion of the signal cycle being amplified. Therefore, this current variation produces cyclic voltage fluctuations in an unregulated supply. When used as a power source for a tuner or preamplifier, the supply with large voltage fluctuations can cause the tuner to perform poorly.

Zener diodes may be used in a circuit to provide the simplest form of voltage regulation. The circuit in Fig. 12-9 can be used as a basic arrangement to help describe a design procedure. Zener diodes are devices in which the reverse breakdown voltage is controlled. Once it breaks down, the voltage across the diode, and across any load in parallel with the diode, is maintained fairly constant despite some changes in the amount of current flowing through the zener device.

In designing the circuit, determine the voltage required across the load, R_L, and the current, I_L, that must flow through it. Choose a zener diode with the breakdown voltage, V_{BR}, equal to the voltage required across R_L. The average zener current, I_z, can be assumed to be 25% of that flowing through R_L. The power the zener must be capable of dissipating is $I_z V_{BR}$ plus a 25% safety factor. If the minimum unregulated voltage supplied to the circuit is $V_{sdc}(min)$, the maximum size R_B can be is $(V_{sdc}(min) - V_{BR})/(I_L + I_z)$, by Ohm's

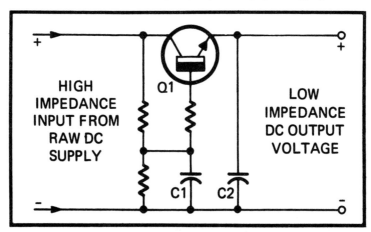

Fig. 12-8. A high input impedance DC voltage is reduced to a low impedance output voltage by this circuit.

Law. The power R_B must be capable of dissipating is $(V_{sdc}(max) - V_{BR})^2/R_B$, where $V_{sdc}(max)$ is the maximum unregulated voltage.

Better regulation than can be provided by the zener circuit in Fig. 12-9, is at times required to feed various stages of the amplifier and receiver. A transistor feedback circuit such as the one shown in Fig. 12-10 may be used. Here, the output voltage is sensed and fed back to the base of Q2. This transistor is an important factor in controlling the current flowing into the base and subsequently out of the emitter of Q1. Variations in the current flowing into the base of Q1 corrects the emitter current in such a manner as to maintain it, and the subsequent output voltage developed across the load resistor, at a constant value.

Q1 passes DC current in an emitter-follower circuit. The base current of Q1 is determined by R_c and the collector current of Q2, because R_c limits the total current that can flow from the base of Q1 and collector of Q2. For example, suppose that the DC input voltage increases with a consequent increase in voltage across R_L. The voltage at V_J, the junction of resistor R_B and R_x, is likewise increased. Since the voltage across the zener diode, D, and hence at the emitter of Q2, is constant, the base-emitter voltage is increased. The current flowing through the base-emitter junction of Q2 is likewise increased, as are the emitter and collector currents flowing through this transistor. Q2 now demands a larger portion of the current that can flow through R_c. Less current now remains for the base of Q1, reducing its emitter current as well as the load current flowing through and the voltage developed across the load. The voltage across R_L is restored to the level it was before the input voltage shifted. Should the supply voltage be reduced rather than increased, a sequence similar to that outlined above would result. The feedback circuit has been established in a type of operational amplifier arrangement.

In the design procedure, the minimum unregulated DC voltage, $V_{sdc}(min)$, must be determined when a maximum current, $I_{sdc}(max)$, is flowing at the unregulated input of the supply. Likewise, the DC voltage at the input will be at a maximum, $V_{sdc}(max)$, when the minimum current, $I_{sdc}(min)$, is flowing. The input impedance of the unregulated supply is, from Ohm's Law,

$$R_S = \frac{V_{sdc}(max) - V_{sdc}(min)}{I_{sdc}(max) - I_{sdc}(min)} \qquad (12\text{-}1)$$

The desired regulated voltage, V_{REG}, must then be specified.

The breakdown voltage of the zener diode in the circuit should be somewhere between $V_{REG}/4$ and $3V_{REG}/4$. Diodes with break-

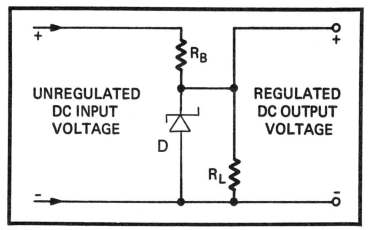

Fig. 12-9. Zener diode regulating circuit.

down voltages about midway between these two values are most desirable.

Current flowing through R_c should be about 1/20 the current flowing through R_L. Regulated current, I_{REG}, is equal to V_{REG}/R_L (if R_L is a constant the current as well as the voltage are regulated) so that the current flowing through R_c is approximately $V_{REG}/20R_L = I_c$.

Ideally, the beta of Q1 should be more than 500. Base current for Q1 will then be about $I_{REG}/500$. About 1/25 of the current that flows through R_c will thus flow into the base of Q1. However, transistors with betas in the range of 500 are hard to get unless they are of the small-signal type. These are seldom useful as the current pass transistor, Q1, in regulated supply circuits due to their limited current and power capabilities. Q1 can be replaced with two or more devices in a Darlington arrangement as shown in Fig. 9-31 or in a complementary circuit arrangement (Fig. 9-34). The product of the betas of all devices used should be greater than 500.

I_{REG} must flow through R_s and develop a voltage across it. $V_{sdc}(min) - I_{REG}R_s$ is the minimum voltage appearing at the junction of R_c, R_E and the collector of Q1. Since the voltage at the base of Q1 is the regulated voltage plus the approximate 0.7 volt between the base and emitter junction of that transistor, the maximum size R_c can be is:

$$R_c = \frac{V_{sdc}(min) - I_{REG}R_s - (V_{REG} + 0.7)}{V_{REG}/20R_L} \qquad (12\text{-}2)$$

309

if it is assumed that $I_c = V_{REG}/20R_L$. Note that if more than one transistor is used in place of Q1, the 0.7 in the equation must be multiplied by the number of devices involved.

The maximum current, $I_c(max)$, flowing through R_c, flows when the unregulated voltage of the supply is at its maximum, $V_{sdc}(max)$:

$$I_c(max) = \frac{V_{sdc}(max) - I_{REG}R_s - (V_{REG} + 0.7)}{R_c} \quad (12\text{-}3)$$

This is somewhat more than the current flowing through Q2 and D. A decent safety factor dictates that the power Q2 should be capable of dissipating is $I_c(max)$ $(V_{REG} + 0.7 - V_{BR})$.

Current flowing through the zener diode must be sufficient to maintain the device in its constant voltage breakdown region at all times. If it is insufficient, additional diode current can be funneled off the power supply through R_E. The power dissipated by D, the zener diode, is equal to its breakdown voltage multiplied by the sum of $I_c(max)$ and the current flowing through R_E. A substantial safety factor is built into this calculation.

The maximum voltage across Q1 is $V_{sdc}(max) - I_{REG}R_s - V_{REG}$. Multiply this by I_{REG} to determine the power Q1 must be capable of dissipating.

The sum of resistors R_B and R_X is about 100 times the size of R_L. Individual components should be be chosen so that V_j is about equal to $V_{BR} + 0.7$. Trimming of the two resistors for the precise regulated voltage desired should be done in the laboratory.

Specifying Components

Three components in any power supply can cause serious problems and must be carefully specified. These are the power transformer, the silicon rectifiers and the input filter capacitor.

Two primary factors which determine the rectifier to be used in any circuit are the DC forward current it must pass and the DC reverse voltage it must block. The current that flows through the load is V_{RL}, the voltage across the load divided by R_L, the load resistance. In the case of the half-wave circuit, the rectifier must carry all this current. In the full-wave circuit, the load current is divided equally between the diodes.

Since a 0.7 forward voltage drop exists across the diode simultaneously with the forward current flow, I_F, the power dissipated by the diode is the product of the RMS current and RMS voltage averaged over the complete cycle. This power generates heat

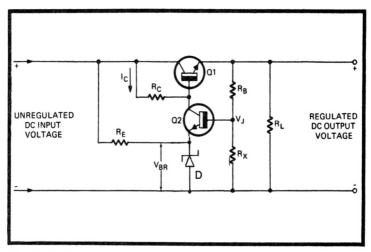

Fig. 12-10. Feedback regulator circuit.

which must frequently be drawn away from the junction by heat sinks. Large rectifiers are mounted in metal cases which can be clamped to a chassis or other mass of metal for this purpose. Small units, rated up to about 3 amperes, use thick leads for conducting heat away from the junction. This latter structure is either a glass or plastic case. The plastic case is more desirable for better heat dissipation, while the glass envelope is used where an absolute hermetic seal is required.

So as a start, specify the average forward DC current. Use maximum figures if the load and diode current vary. Give yourself plenty of leeway; multiply the calculated or measured current by two.

Next, the forward surge current must be considered. Normally, the load current is at its average I_F. However, the filter capacitor across the load is a short circuit at the instant DC is supplied, and it is a partial short until the capacitor is fully charged. During this time, the only resistance in the circuit is the sum of the transformer and diode resistance. The load resistor is shorted by the filter capacitor. A surge current exists initially due to this low circuit resistance. It is approximately the peak voltage V_p (see Figs. 12-1 and 12-3) divided by the sum of all the resistance remaining in the circuit that is not shorted by the filter capacitor.

Diode surge capabilities are denoted by the peak current permitted to flow for one half cycle or for a full cycle. The duration of a cycle of 60-Hz current is 1/60 or .0167 second. Half cycle time is

311

obviously half that figure or 0.0083 second. For 50-Hz lines, this becomes 0.02 and 0.01 for full and half cycle time, respectively. It doubles for the 25-Hz line.

The time constant of the power supply circuit is the product of the filter capacitor in microfarads with the sum of the AC resistance of the rectifier ($26/I_F$ with I_F expressed in milliamperes) and the DC resistance of the transformer winding. This product must be less than 0.0167 for a permissible surge current when the diode is rated for a 1-cycle surge and less than 0.0083 for an allowed surge current when the diode is rated for a ½-cycle surge. This, of course, assumes 60 Hz is the base frequency.

Another consideration is the peak inverse voltage rating of the rectifier. The reverse voltage, V_R, the rectifiers must withstand is equal to twice V_p. Frequently, however, there are peaks and pulses in the power line which can exceed the calculated V_R by a large factor. It is wise to use rectifiers with V_R (or V_{BR} or PIV) ratings exceeding the calculated value by two.

The various shapes the reverse breakdown curve can take are shown in Fig. 12-11. Two different types of diode characteristics, A and B, are shown. Both diodes have the same breakdown voltage, V_{BR}. Diode A has a lower AC and DC resistance after breakdown than does diode B. A large current and voltage pulse is more likely to overheat the junction of B than that of A. A diode with the breakdown characteristics of A is more desirable. These are referred to as controlled avalanche breakdown rectifiers.

The power transformer can be specified with the help of the curves in Figs. 12-2 and 12-4. In addition, temperature rise is an important part of the transformer's specifications. Actually, it is desirable to limit the final transformer temperature to 95° C, since the insulation is normally guaranteed to about 105° C. Considering that the transformer should, at worst, operate in a 55° C ambient, the temperature rise should be limited to 95°—55° = 40° Celsius.

The resistance of the copper wire used in the transformer changes with temperature. It is information of this change which is used in a method of determining the maximum temperature at which the transformer is operating. To determine the temperature rise using this change-of-resistance method, the transformer is first permitted to stay in a room with no power being applied to it. The temperature of the room as well as the resistance of the 110-volt or 120-volt primary winding is noted. Refer to this temperature as T_A and to the resistance of the winding at room temperature as R_A.

Now run the equipment with its normal load for about six hours. The best way to do this with a power amplifier is to place an

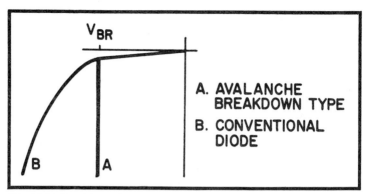

Fig. 12-11. Breakdown characteristic curves for two different types of diodes: avalanche breakdown type (A) and conventional type of diode (B).

8-ohm load resistor with an adequate wattage rating at the output and feed a music signal to the amplifier's input. Increase the level of the amplifier so that the peaks in the music just begin to clip, as observed on a scope connected across the 8-ohm load resistor. Keep the amplifier enclosed in its cabinet. After six hours, disconnect the amplifier from the power source and quickly measure the resistance of the primary winding. Refer to this "hot" resistance as R_H. The temperature rise, T_R, above the ambient is close to:

$$T_R = \frac{R_H - R_A}{R_A\ (.00393)} \qquad (12\text{-}4)$$

Add T_R to T_A and you have the total temperature of the windings. The more accurate your readings of R_H and R_A are, the more accurate will be your determination of the temperature rise, T_R.

The third critical component in the power supply is the first or input filter capacitor. Much of the ripple current passes through this capacitor. Ripple current flowing through the capacitor when it is used in a half-wave circuit is:

$$I_R = 6.28fCE_R \qquad (12\text{-}5)$$

where f is the line frequency in Hz, C is the capacity in farads, and E_R is the RMS ripple voltage in volts. For full-wave circuits, I_R is double that noted in Equation 12-5.

Capacitors are designed to pass specific amounts of ripple current. Capacitors in large cans or cases can pass more current before overheating than those in smaller enclosures. For a specific size of case, the ripple capability of a capacitor is proportional to $C^{1/2}$. If the capacitor is subjected to excess current, it will lose a portion of its initial capacity and, consequently, lose its ability to operate properly in the circuit. Once the value of the desired capacitor has been established and the ripple current requirements have been determined, the manufacturer of the capacitor should be consulted to determine if his device will function properly. Due to economic considerations, a capacitor with less than adequate ability to pass ripple current will frequently be used. This will, of course, limit the life of the component.

As an exercise, assume you need a power supply to deliver 30 volts at 1 ampere. You want low ripple voltage so you select the full-wave circuit with a shunt filter capacitor. The load resistance is R_L = 30 volts/1 ampere = 30 ohms. For reasonable regulation (variation of output voltage with the change in load current) the resistance of the transformer, R_T, should be low. Assume all is satisfactory if the ratio of $(R_s + R_T)/R_L$ is 0.08. Since r_{AC} (forward AC resistance of the rectifier) is the only factor comprising R_s (all resistance in series with the rectifier including the forward AC resistance of the rectifier itself) and assuming r_{AC} is negligible compared to R_T, R_T must be $0.08R_L$ or 2.4 ohms.

It can be shown that the ripple voltage is fairly low if $6.28fR_LC$ is made equal to or made greater than 5. Substituting f = 60 and R_L = 30 into the equality yields a filter capacitor requirement of at least 443 mfd. Feed this information into the curve in Fig. 12-4.

The ratio of the output voltage, V_{RL}, to the peak supply voltage, V_p, for half the transformer is about 0.73. Since V_{RL} is 30, then V_p = 30/0.73 = 43 volts. The RMS voltage across each half of the transformer is $V_p/\sqrt{2}$ = 43/1.41 = 30.4 volts. From the calculations, you find you need a transformer with a 60.8-volt center-tapped secondary and a maximum effective total winding resistance of 2 × 2.4 ohms = 4.8 ohms.

The continuous DC forward current rating of the silicon rectifiers can be 1 ampere. The surge current in the circuit is V_p/R_T = 43/2.4 = 18 amperes. The RC time constant is (2.4) (443 × 10⁻⁶) = 1060 × 10⁻⁶ = 0.0016 seconds. Since this is less than the time for one-half cycle, a diode with a surge current rating of more than 18 amperes for ½ cycle is satisfactory.

The peak inverse voltage rating for the rectifiers must be greater than $2V_p$ = 86 volts. A 100-volt rectifier will be satisfactory if there are no instantaneous surge voltage peaks in the line. To account for these surges, you can double your voltage specification for the rectifier and/or use a device with a sharp avalanche breakdown characteristic.

Layout and Wiring Considerations

All the derivations and discussions here and above describe decisions essential to design an audio amplifier. Once the paper design has been completed, and even after the basic laboratory experimentation has been done, the amplifier may be a "dud." The actual physical layout and wiring of the various elements of the circuit when built into a unified physical device requires much forethought and consideration.

For example, the power transformer can wreak havoc with hum. It can radiate so badly as to establish hum current in sensitive circuits and in the chassis proper. Amplify the hum inadvertently and you have a useless audio amplifier. The flux density of a transformer is the determining factor of just how much of a field it will radiate. You can specify that it be limited to 60,000 or 70,000 gauss, but how are you going to measure it?

In the late 1950s, one transformer manufacturer wound a coil for me consisting of 9200 turns of wire on an American Molded Bobbin 206A form. It may or may not have been a standard throughout the industry. This coil was to be placed against each side of the transformer in turn, when only the primary or 120-volt AC winding was connected. None of the other windings were to be connected and were thus left floating. I did find that if the voltage developed across the leads of the "search coil" was about 1 volt, the radiation of the transformer was within reason for audio applica-

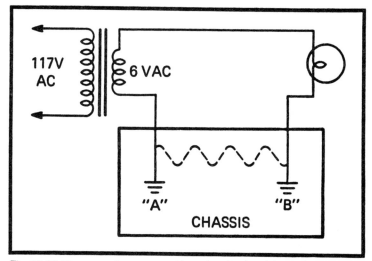

Fig. 12-12. Hum currents are present in a chassis when it is used as part of a pilot-lamp circuit.

tions. Thereafter, I specified that the search coil voltage of all transformers used in audio equipment was to be within 1 volt. If you cannot get the exact coil I have, perhaps you can get another one and calibrate it against the hum voltage induced into it by a known good transformer.

Hum current similar to that generated by the transformer can also be established by improper connections of pilot light bulbs in the amplifier. In Fig. 12-12, the 6-volt winding is grounded to point A on the chassis while the bulb is connected to remote point B on the chassis. AC hum current flows between these two points, establishing a ripple current in this area of the chassis. Voltage is developed across the chassis resistance A—B.

Now suppose that a transistor base circuit is connected to the chassis at points C and D, located somewhere between A and B, as shown in Fig. 12-13. A portion of the hum or ripple voltage across A—B is developed across chassis resistance C—D. Being in the base-emitter circuit of the transistor, the hum is amplified by the transistor along with the input signal, e_{in}. Hum voltage developed across A—C is in series with e_{in} and is also amplified. The voltage developed across D—B at the output may be insufficient to interfere with the much larger output signal.

In practical amplifiers, the power transformer is placed closest to the output stages. Mounted remote from the input circuit, the transformer's contribution to hum is minimized.

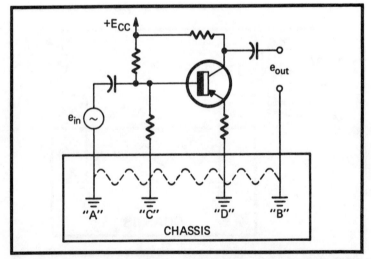

Fig. 12-13. If a transistor circuit is connected with ground returns made to the chassis, the resulting hum currents will be amplified by the transistor.

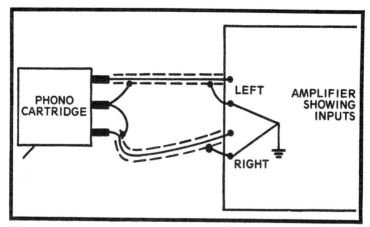

Fig. 12-14. Ground loops can be formed outside the chassis due to an improper method of connecting the signal source to the amplifier. The drawing shows an improper method of connecting an amplifier to a phono cartridge.

The circuit should be wired so that ground loops such as those illustrated in Fig. 12-12 and 12-13 cannot be formed. In Fig. 12-12, connect the 6-volt winding to the bulb with a wire and not through the chassis. The circuit may be grounded at only **one** point on the chassis. In Fig. 12-13, connect A, C and D together with wires and then bring one lead from the floating wires to the chassis.

As a general rule, solder all connections from each individual stage to one floating point or lug. Then connect the individual stages (except the output) together, in sequence from the output to the input. Normally, there will be one chassis ground for the output stages and one for all other stages near the input transistor. In stereo amplifiers, there will be two such sequences of connections.

At times it will be desirable to connect all grounds to one long lug with one end riveted or bolted to the chassis. In this case, the stages should be connected along the length of the lug, in the sequence just outlined. The power stage should be connected to a point on the lug closest to the chassis, and all other stages connected in sequence until the input stage is connected to the top of the lug, farthest from the chassis.

Avoid ground loops when connecting phonograph cartridges or tuners to a stereo amplifier. On some tuners and cartridges, one common ground is used at the outputs of both stereo channels. Two shielded leads, grounded at both the source and amplifier, conduct the stereo signals. Because the grounded shields form a complete circuit and can conduct induced current from nearby power lines,

317

hum will appear at the input of the amplifier. This can be illustrated with the help of Fig. 12-14.

A cartridge is shown with one common terminal for both the left and the right channels. Two shielded leads are used to connect the outputs from the cartridge to the inputs on the amplifier. Both shields are grounded at the cartridge as well as at the amplifier, forming a complete circuit. Hum can be readily induced in the shield.

Proper interconnecting wiring practices dictate that one of the shield connections at the cartridge be opened, so that both shields will be grounded only at the amplifier. The closed-circuit loop will no longer exist. Similar tactics can be used when connecting any other equipment to the amplifier, as well as for the connection of stages and wires within the amplifier proper.

Chapter 13
Digital Techniques
In Audio Circuits

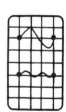

Conventional audio circuits are built ideally around linear amplifiers. A signal is applied to the input of the circuit. Each individual stage in the amplifying chain should magnify the signal without changing its shape in any way. A highly amplified version of the input signal appears at the output of the audio circuit. If the output stages are capable, they deliver power to a loudspeaker.

But this technique is experiencing changes. The input audio signal may be converted to pulses. Pulses can be recorded on tape, retrieved, amplified and reconverted to audio signals. The reconstituted audio signals are usually highly amplified versions of the original audio intelligence before it was changed into the pulse form. This conversion and reconversion uses digital techniques. A type of conversion to and from a pulse system, along with the pulse system itself, was discussed in Chapter 7 under the heading of class D amplifiers.

Digital logic can be used in the class G and H circuits described in Chapter 11 where transistors are turned on, or the voltages applied to the output stages are altered with the level of the applied signal. Similarly, the last output stage protection circuit, described in a quote in Chapter 11, uses digital techniques.

Unfortunately, many of the circuits used are guarded secrets by the various manufacturers. In this Chapter we present a review of digital techniques. Many of these can be applied readily to audio amplifier circuits. With insight into the techniques, we can either deduce what some of the secrets in these circuits are, or develop equivalent (or even superior) circuits to perform the required tasks.

ON-OR-OFF

When an audio signal is applied to a transistor amplifier circuit, the current or voltage at the output of the circuit is proportional in some fashion to the amplitude of the input. This is not so in digital applications. Here the input either turns on the circuit or turns it off. The output from a digital logic circuit is either at a high level, usually referred to as a 1 (one), or at a low level, usually referred to as a 0 (zero). Similar to the output, the input also consists either of a 1 or a 0.

Numbers in what is referred to as the binary system consists of a group of these 1s and 0s. While 10 digits from 0 to 9 are in our decimal system, only two digits (or bits) are in the binary system—a 0 and a 1. The significance of the 1 depends upon its placement in the entire number. This is similar to the idea where in our decimal system a number like 56 is equal to $(5 \times 10) + (6 \times 1)$. Here the number at the right, the least significant digit (LSD), is multiplied by 1 when evaluating the complete number. The number at the left, the most significant digit (MSD), is multiplied by 10. If there were a digit to the left of the 5, such as a 7, to compose the number *756*, the 7 now becomes the MSD for it is the digit furthest to the left in the number. Because it is the third digit from the right, it is multiplied by 100. Now the number is $(7 \times 100) + (5 \times 10) + (6 \times 1) = 756$.

In the binary system, the bits have different significances. The least significant bit (LSB) is the one at the extreme right. To determine its significance in the final number, multiply it by 1. The next more significant bit is written to the left of the LSB and that one is to be multiplied by 2. The next bit to the left of this one is to be multiplied by 4. If you have a four bit number, the bit at the extreme left is the most significant bit (MSB) and it is to be multiplied by 8. Taking this one step further, if the number has five bits, the MSB at the extreme left is to be multiplied by 16. Let us try a few examples using binary numbers. These binary numbers are also referred to as *words*.

- ■ $1 = (1 \times 1) = 1.$
- ■ $0 = (0 \times 1) = 0.$
- ■ $10 = (1 \times 2) + (0 \times 1) = 2.$
- ■ $11 = (1 \times 2) + (1 \times 1) = 3.$
- ■ $101 = (1 \times 4) + (0 \times 2) + (1 \times 1) = 5.$
- ■ $1111 = (1 \times 8) + (1 \times 4) + (1 \times 2) + (1 \times 1) = 15.$
- ■ $11101 = (1 \times 16) + (1 \times 8) + (1 \times 4) + (0 \times 2) + (1 \times 1) = 29.$

Thirty-two binary numbers ranging from 0 to 31, can be written using five bits. They are listed in Table 13-1 with the decimal equivalents to the left of each number. It is obvious that all 0s to the left of the most significant 1 in each number can be omitted without changing the number. Four bit words have been assigned the

Table 13-1. Binary Numbers and their decimal equivalents.

Decimal	Binary					Decimal	Binary				
0	0	0	0	0	0	16	1	0	0	0	0
1	0	0	0	0	1	17	1	0	0	0	1
2	0	0	0	1	0	18	1	0	0	1	0
3	0	0	0	1	1	19	1	0	0	1	1
4	0	0	1	0	0	20	1	0	1	0	0
5	0	0	1	0	1	21	1	0	1	0	1
6	0	0	1	1	0	22	1	0	1	1	0
7	0	0	1	1	1	23	1	0	1	1	1
8	0	1	0	0	0	24	1	1	0	0	0
9	0	1	0	0	1	25	1	1	0	0	1
10	0	1	0	1	0	26	1	1	0	1	0
11	0	1	0	1	1	27	1	1	0	1	1
12	0	1	1	0	0	28	1	1	1	0	0
13	0	1	1	0	1	29	1	1	1	0	1
14	0	1	1	1	0	30	1	1	1	1	0
15	0	1	1	1	1	31	1	1	1	1	1

special name of *nibble*. If the word is expanded to eight bits (here the MSB is to be multiplied by 128, the next bit is to be multiplied by 64, and the sixth bit is to be multiplied by 32), it has the special name of *byte*.

In audio recording systems, up to 16 bit numbers are used. In this case, the most significant bit is to be multiplied by 32,768 to determine its numerical value in the decimal system. The remaining bits are to be multiplied by the following numbers in sequence down to the least significant bit: 16,384, 8,192, 4,096, 2,048, 1,024, 512, 256, 128, 64, 32, 16, 8, 4, 2, 1.

A very useful code using four bit numbers is the binary coded decimal system (BCD). In this system, the binary equivalent of each decimal digit is used to form the number. Using decimal number 318046 as an example, the BCD equivalent number is:

■ Decimal number: 3   1   8   0   4   6
■ BCD equivalent: 0011 0001 1000 0000 0100 0110.

The BCD system is frequently used to provide information for decimal readouts from digital numbers originally supplied to the circuit.

GATES

Two or more pulses can be fed to the input of a digital circuit, or *gate*, at the same time. The various circuits behave in different manners even if the applied pulses at their inputs are the same. Assume for the moment that a particular gate or *digital logic circuit*

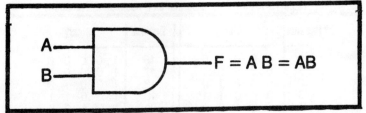

Fig. 13-1. Two input AND gate.

has two inputs, A and B. For the gate under discussion, A *and* B must both be 1, if it is to deliver a 1 to its output. If either A or B is 0 the output is 0. This type of logic circuit has been assigned the name of AND gate. The symbol for a two input AND gate is in Fig. 13-1 along with its *truth table*. If the AND gate has four inputs, the symbol and truth table in Fig. 13-2 can be used. These drawings deserve some more detailed descriptions.

Start with the output in Fig. 13-1, F = AB. If the letters representing the two inputs are placed next to each other, or if a dot is placed between them (A•B), it is in indication of the AND operation. Both A and B must have been fed through some sort of "ANDING" circuit. In Fig. 13-2, the symbol ABCD indicates that all four inputs must have been ANDed.

As for the truth table, it shows you what the output, F, is when different combinations of pulses are fed to the inputs of the gate. In Fig. 13-1, if both A *and* B are 0, F = 0; if A = 0 and B = 1, F = 0; if A = 1 and B = 0, F = 0; but if both A *and* B are 1, F = 1. (This is also shown in Table 13-2.) For all combinations of A, B, C and D in Fig. 13-2, see Table 13-3. F = only if *all* inputs to this AND gate are 1.

Compare the combinations in the A and B columns in the truth table in Table 13-2 with the first four binary numbers, 0 through 3, in Table 13-3. They are identical in sequence. Similarly, when comparing the combinations of ABCD in the truth table in Table 13-3 with the first 16 binary numbers, 0 through 15, in Table 13-1, it can be seen that the number sequences here, too, are identical. To cover all variations, the truth table states all binary numbers starting with 0 and ending with the binary word ·where all bits are

A	B	F
0	0	0
0	1	0
1	0	0
1	1	1

Table 13-2. Truth table for Fig. 13-1.

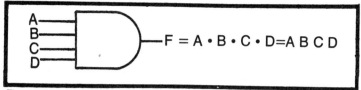

Fig. 13-2. Four input AND gate.

1s. Thus if there are two inputs to a gate, four numbers—00, 01, 10 and 11—are required for the truth table. If there are five inputs to a gate, 32 numbers—0000, 0001, 00010, 00011 and so on to 11111—are required for the truth table. Let us apply this to an OR gate.

When inputs were applied to an AND gate, all inputs had to be 1 if the output was to be a 1. The OR gate differs from this in that at least one of the inputs must be high or at 1 if the output is to be a 1. Should this OR gate have three inputs, A, B and C, the output is noted as $A + B + C = F$. Here the "+" symbol indicates the OR logic. It is read that F is equal to A or B or C meaning that F is 1 if A or B or C is 1. The symbol for the three input OR gate is in Fig. 13-3. The truth table is Table 13-4.

If a 1 output from either gate is fed through an inverter before being fed to the balance of the logic circuit, the output from the inverter is a 0 rather than a 1. This can be noted by a bar over the letter indicating the input or the output. Thus if $F = 1, \overline{F} = 0$. It can also be reversed, for if $F = 0, \overline{F} = 1$. The inverter is referred to as a NOT gate and the circuit symbol for this is a circle at the output of the gate or a circle at the output of a triangle drawn before or after

Table 13-3. Truth table for Fig. 13-2.

A	B	C	D	F
0	0	0	0	0
0	0	0	1	0
0	0	1	0	0
0	0	1	1	0
0	1	0	0	0
0	1	0	1	0
0	1	1	0	0
0	1	1	1	0
1	0	0	0	0
1	0	0	1	0
1	0	1	0	0
1	0	1	1	0
1	1	0	0	0
1	1	0	1	0
1	1	1	0	0
1	1	1	1	1

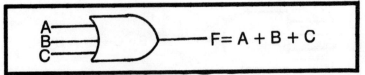

Fig. 13-3. Three input OR gate.

the F output. The two representations of this are shown in Figs. 13-4A and 13-4B for a three input AND and OR gate. The AND gate with a not circuit as its output turns it into a NAND gate and the OR gate with a not circuit at its output, turns it into a NOR gate. This is so in both cases because the output is 0 where it would have been a 1 without the added NOT circuit.

Similarly, an input can be inverted before being fed to the gate. Then the appropriate NOT symbol is at the input to the gate rather than at the output. An example of this is shown in Fig. 13-4C.

The complete description of the output can be determined from a truth table. Terms in an equation derived from the truth table are only those that have a 1 in the F column. Rows that have 0 in the F column have no significance in the final relationship. In order to demonstrate this, let us write an equation for F from the terms in the truth table in Table 13-4. When A, B and C are 0, F = 0, so the information on this line is not in our equation. As F=1 on all other lines, each of the other lines in the table provide us with a factor for the equation. (In the practical procedure used to write the equation, each line where F = 1 supplies us with one term for the equations and each line is ignored where F = 0.) Hence for Table 13-4 listing information in each line in sequence,

$$F = \overline{A}\,\overline{B}\,C + \overline{A}\,B\,\overline{C} + \overline{A}\,B\,C + A\,\overline{B}\,\overline{C} + A\,\overline{B}\,C$$
$$+ A\,B\,\overline{C} + A\,B\,C \qquad \text{13-1)}$$

The first term, $\overline{A}\,\overline{B}\,C$ is from the line in the truth table where $A = 0 = \overline{A}$, $B = 0 = \overline{B}$ and $C = 1 = C$; the second term $\overline{A}\,B\,\overline{C}$ is derived from the next line where $A = 0 = \overline{A}$, $B = 1 = B$ and $C = 0 = \overline{C}$. The third term $\overline{A}\,B\,C$ is from the succeeding line where $A = 0 = \overline{A}$, $B = 1$

A	B	C	F
0	0	0	0
0	0	1	1
0	1	0	1
0	1	1	1
1	0	0	1
1	0	1	1
1	1	0	1
1	1	1	1

Table 13-4. Truth table for Fig. 13-3.

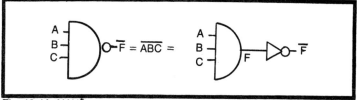

Fig. 13-4A. NAND gate.

$=B$ and $C = 1 = C$ and so on down to the term A B C, representing the last line in the truth table, where $A = 1 = A$, $B = 1 = B$ and $C = 1 = C$. Thus F=1 when any one of the terms in the equation are 1. Using Boolean algebra, this equation can be reduced to the one in the figure, where $F = A + B + C$.

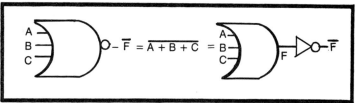

Fig. 13-4B. NOR gate.

BOOLEAN ALGEBRA

The algebraic manipulations required for our work can be summed up in several simple rules.

1. The sequence of the inputs as stated in an equation has no significance, so that $ABC = CAB = BAC$ and so on.

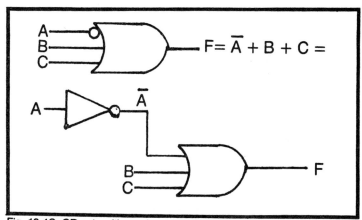

Fig. 13-4C. OR gate with one input NANDed.

Similarly, $A + B + C = C + B + A = B + A + C$ along with other variations. These are known as commutative laws.

2. As in ordinary algebra, $A(B + C) = AB + AC$. Using a similar idea by interchanging the AND and OR symbols, $A + (BC) = (A + B)(A + C)$.

3. In order to get a 1 at the output of an AND circuit, all inputs must be 1. If one of the inputs is held at 1 and the other input, A, can be either a 1 or a 0, the output is the same as whatever the A input is. Written mathematically, $A \cdot 1 = A$. Using similar logic for the OR gate, only one input of a two input gate must be 1 if the output is to be 1. If the second input is held at 0, the output of the OR gate is the same as the state of the first input. Written mathematically, $A + 0 = A$.

4. If you extend the thoughts in rule three to the case where identical signals are fed to both inputs of a two input gate, the output is the same as the inputs. Thus $A \cdot A = A$ and $A + A = A$. Should one of the inputs to the gate be NOTed, the output becomes $A \cdot \overline{A} = 0$ for either A or $\overline{A}$. One must be a 0 in this situation and the other must be a 1. Similarly, $A + \overline{A} = 1$ for either A or $\overline{A}$. One factor must be a 1 while the other factor must be a 0.

5. Taking law four one step step further $A \cdot 0 = 0$ and $A + 1 = 1$.

6. Using laws two and five, we can determine the following identity: $A + AB = A(1 + B) = A(1) = A$. Thus $A + AB = A$.

7. Using laws two and four, we can determine the following identity: $A + \overline{A}B = (A + \overline{A})(A + B) = 1(A + B) = A + B$. Thus $A + \overline{A}B = A + B$.

8. DeMorgan's theorem is very useful. You can prove this theorem for yourself by setting up truth tables for the equations, $\overline{A \cdot B} = \overline{A} + \overline{B}$ and $\overline{A + B} = \overline{A} \cdot \overline{B}$. It is used to remove the NOT symbol that may exist over a group of inputs. The law is implemented by changing the individual symbols over all inputs originally covered by an overall NOT symbol, as well as changing the + to an $\cdot$ and the $\cdot$ to an +. Thus $\overline{A \cdot B} = \overline{\overline{A} + \overline{B}} = \overline{\overline{A} \cdot \overline{B}} = A \cdot B$; or $\overline{A + B} = \overline{\overline{A} \cdot \overline{B}} = AB$.

Getting back to Equation 13-1, we can use Boolean algebra to prove that is the same as the three input OR gate, $F = A + B + C$. Let us start by factoring out quantities in the equation.

$$F = \overline{A}\,\overline{B}\,C + \overline{A}\,B\,\overline{C} + \overline{A}\,B\,C + A\,\overline{B}\,\overline{C} + A\,\overline{B}\,C + A\,B\,\overline{C} + A\,B\,C$$
$$F = C(\overline{A}\overline{B} + \overline{A}B) + B(\overline{A}\overline{C} + A\overline{C}) + A(\overline{B}\overline{C} + \overline{B}C) + ABC$$

Continue by factoring quantities in each of the parentheses.

$$F = C[\overline{A}\,(\overline{B} + B)] + B[\overline{C}(\overline{A} + A)] + A[\overline{B}(\overline{C} + C)] + ABC$$

Because from law four, $\overline{B} + B = 1$, $\overline{A} + A = 1$ and $\overline{C} + C = 1$, the equation reduces to:

$$F = C\overline{A} + B\overline{C} + A\overline{B} + ABC$$

Combining the last two terms

$$F = C\overline{A} + B\overline{C} + A(\overline{B} + BC)$$

Using law two to expand the quantity in the parentheses and then letting $\overline{B} + B = 1$ due to law four,

$$F = C\overline{A} + B\overline{C} + A\left[(\overline{B} + B)\,(\overline{B} + C)\right]$$
$$F = C\overline{A} + B\overline{C} + A\overline{B} + AC$$

By factoring the first and last terms in the resulting equation and letting $\overline{A} + A = 1$,

$$F = C(\overline{A} + A) + B\overline{C} + A\overline{B}$$
$$= C + B\overline{C} + A\overline{B}$$

Expanding the first two terms with the help of law two, and letting $C + \overline{C} = 1$,

$$F = (C + B)\,(C + \overline{C}) + A\overline{B}$$
$$F = C + B + A\overline{B}$$

Similarly expanding the last two terms,

$$F = C + (B + A)\,(B + \overline{B}) = C + B + A$$

which is the quantity we wanted to prove equal to Equation 13-1 when we first started to describe Boolean algebraic procedures.

MORE GATES

With some Boolean algebra under our belts, we can now consider two more commonly used gates. One is the EXCLUSIVE OR gate. This is like the OR gate with one exception. The output from a two input EXCLUSIVE OR gate is 1 only if one of the inputs is 1 and the other is 0. If both inputs are 1s or 0s the output is a 0. The

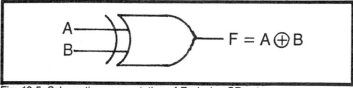

Fig. 13-5. Schematic representation of Exclusive OR gate.

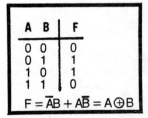

A	B	F
0	0	0
0	1	1
1	0	1
1	1	0

$F = \overline{A}B + A\overline{B} = A \oplus B$

Table 13-5. Truth table for EXCLUSIVE OR circuit.

mathematical symbol for an EXCLUSIVE OR gate is a + in a circle, or plus. The schematic representation is Fig. 13-5. Table 13-5 is the truth table.

A second useful arrangement is the EQUIVALENCE gate. For the output of this gate to be 1, the two inputs of a two input gate must be the same, or A = B as shown in Table 13-6. The mathematical symbol is an equal sign between two angle symbols, or $< = >$.

Both the EXCLUSIVE OR and the EQUIVALENCE gates can be fabricated from ordinary AND and OR gates, if we use the identities shown in Tables 13-5 and 13-6. The circuits are shown in Fig. 13-6. EXCLUSIVE OR and EQUIVALENCE gates are quite easy to implement and complex mathematical manipulations are not required in order to arrive at the simplest arrangement to do the job.

FLIP-FLOPS

Logic gates can be combined to perform different functions. As such, they can do the jobs required of them in various audio amplifiers. Different gates can be arranged in a flip-flop circuit. In this type of arrangement, the state of the output from the circuit is dependent both upon the information being applied to an input as well as upon the previous state of the circuit. A flip-flop arrangement using two NAND gates along with its truth table, (Table 13-7) is shown in Fig. 13-7. R_n, S_n and Q_n show the states of the inputs and upper flip-flop output terminal, before the circuit is triggered. Q_{n+1} shows the state of the upper output terminal after the inputs to the flip-flop have been changed to those shown in the figure. For any flip-flop, the lower output terminal is opposite in state to that of the

A	B	F
0	0	1
0	1	0
1	0	0
1	1	1

$F = \overline{A}\overline{B} + AB = A < = > B$

Table 13-6. Truth table for EQUIVALENCE circuit.

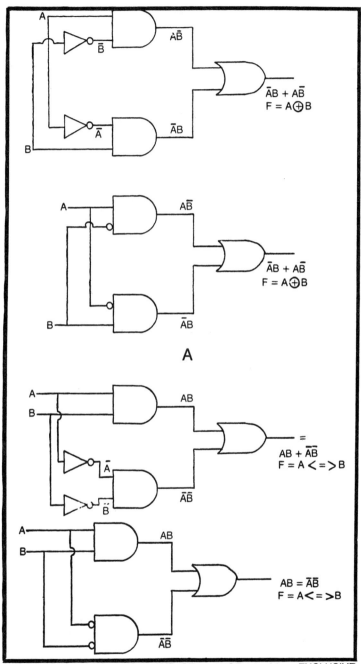

Fig. 13-6. Circuits fabricated from AND, OR, and NOT gate. A is an EXCLUSIVE OR circuit and B is an EQUIVALENCE circuit.

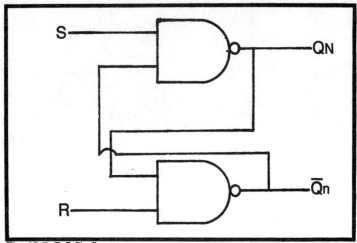
Fig. 13-7. R-S flip-flop.

upper terminal. If the states of the upper terminal are denoted by Q_n and Q_{n+1}, the coincident states of the lower terminal are denoted by $\bar{Q}_n$ and $\bar{Q}_{n+1}$.

From the truth table, it is obvious that if $R_n = 0$, a 1 must be applied to S_n if the output is to be a 0. Should $R_n = 1$, S_n must be made into a 0 if the final output is to be a 1. If S_n were made a 1 while $R = 1$, the output Q_{n+1} would not change from its previous state Q_n. R_n and S_n may not be simultaneously set at 0 when NAND gates are used as flip-flop components. The "?" denotes that the output is indeterminate under this situation. Circuitry can be added to the basic flip-flop so that it will not be tripped until after a pulse has been applied. This is referred to as clocking. Flip-flops can be arranged to change states either on the rising or on the falling portion of the applied pulse.

A special *toggle* (or T-type) circuit using clocking can be designed using the R-S flip-flop (FF). A clocking input may be added to the standard R-S flip-flop. Here, the output changes states each time a pulse hits. Several of these flip-flops can be connected into a circuit to form a ripple counter, as shown in Fig. 13-8. Here, FF3 is

R_n	S_n	Q_{n+1}
0	0	?
0	1	0
1	0	1
1	1	Q_n

Table 13-7. Truth table for Fig. 13-7.

330

tripped on the rising or falling portion of each clock pulse (depending upon the circuit). Consequently, the pulses at Q of FF3 are at one-half the frequency of those at T of FF3. Similarly, the frequency of the pulses at the output of any of the flip-flops in the circuit are at one-half the frequency of the pulses at their respective inputs.

The Q outputs from the various flip-flops in the circuit can be used to count the number of pulses fed to the circuit at T of FF3. Because the last flip-flop to get the information about the input is FF1, it experiences the smallest number of changes of states when compared to the other flip-flops in the circuit. Consequently, the pulses at this output represent the most significant bit (MSB) when counting clock pulses. The significance of the bits represented by the pulses at the Q outputs of the other flip-flops are reduced as we progress from the flip-flop at the right to the flip-flop at the left. By considering all bits or pulses at the various Qs in proper proportion and sequence, starting with the MSB at Q of FF1 and ending at the LSB at Q of FF3, the resulting binary number is the number of pulses originally applied at T of the first flip-flop, FF3.

However useful the R-S flip-flop has been proven to be, its versatility has been surpassed by a similar and more complex device, the clocked J-K flip-flop. The schematic representation is shown in Fig. 13-9 and the truth table is Table 13-8. Unlike the R-S flip-flop, the J-K flip flop can be used in any of the four possible states. There is no indeterminate state.

A circuit to perform the toggle function can be implemented very easily using the J-K flip-flop. From the truth table, it can be seen that Q_{n+1} is $\bar{Q}_n$ when both J and K are 1s. This indicates that when this situation exists, and $J = K = 1$, the flip-flop will change states as each clock pulse strikes. By placing 1s at the J and K

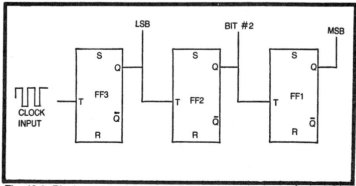

Fig. 13-8. Ripple counter using three R-S flip-flops.

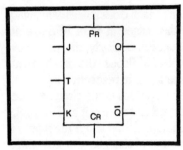

Fig. 13-9. J-K flip-flop.

inputs, the J-K flip flop can be used in a counter similar to the one in Fig. 13-8.

Another mode of operation is achieved when after a clock pulse, the Q output assumes the state of either the J or K input. When a flip-flop does this, it is referred to as a D-type (or delay type), flip-flop. From the truth table, when $J = 0$ and $K = 1$, $Q_{n+1} = 0$. When $J = 1$ and $K = 0$, $Q_{n+1} = 1$. Thus the Q output assumes the same state as is at the J input, or is opposite to the state of the K input, when J and K are in different states. A NAND circuit placed between the J and K inputs can be used to implement the opposite state requirement for the D-type circuit arrangement. The T-type flip-flop and the two variations of D-type flip-flops, are shown in Fig. 13-10.

Two of the inputs on the J-K flip-flop have not been mentioned as yet. These are the C_r and P_r terminals. C_r is an abbreviation for "clear" and P_r is an abbreviation for "preset." C_r and P_r inputs take preference over all other inputs. Both terminals must be at 1 if the clock pulse is to have an effect. When both terminals are 0, the flip-flop will not change states. Letting $C_r = 1$ and $P_r = 0$, $Q = 1$. Setting up the states of the two terminals as noted, an initial setting of flip-flop states can be made before a clock pulse is applied. After the initial setting, P_r and C_r can be set at 1 and the J-K flip-flop will

Relative Amplitude		
Point Sampled	Decimal Representation	Binary Representaton
0	0	0 0 0 0
1	14	1 1 1 0
2	10	1 0 1 0
3	3	0 0 1 1
4	6	0 1 1 0
5	0	0 0 0 0

Table 13-8. Truth table for 13-9.

332

behave as if these terminals do not exist. In fact, these terminals do not exist on various microcircuit versions of flip-flops supplied by different manufacturers.

DECIMAL NUMBERS FROM SEVEN SEGMENT ARRAYS

A digital to analog (D/A) converter is used to change a binary word into a voltage or current reading in the analog world. Here, a binary number is fed to the input of the converter. The output voltage or current from the D/A converter is proportional to the size of that input number.

Similarily, an analog to digital (A/D) converter can be used to change data about voltages or current into a binary number proportional to the magnitude of these electrical factors. Because both D/A and A/D converters are readily available as integrated circuits (ICs), the electronic circuit discussion of just how these devices do their jobs will not be pursued here.

The outputs from A/D converters are in binary number form. Decoders (also available as ICs) are used to convert these binary numbers into four bit BCD numbrs. In turn, the BCD numbers are decoded to form decimal digits for use on seven segment arrays. Integrated circuits are also available to do this job. A seven segment array is used to form individual digits used in the decimal system, as shown in Fig. 13-11. Each segment lights up as required, when different BCD numbers are applied to the decoder, to form the

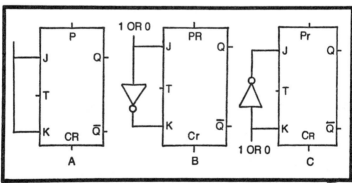

Fig. 13-10. Variation on the J-K flip-flop. A is the T-type. $J = K = 1$. $Q_{n+1} = \overline{Q}_n$ or the output at Q changes with each clock pulse at T. B is the D-type where $Q_{n+1} = J$ when $J = 0$ and $K = 1$ or $J = 1$ and $K = 0$. The output at Q is the same as the state at the J input. C is the D-type where $Q_{n+1} = \overline{K}$ when $K = 1$ and $J = 0$ or $K = 0$ and $J = 1$. The output at Q is opposite of the state of the K input. Note that a 1 must be fed to the J and K inputs at all times in the T-type circuit and only the appropriate state, 0 or 1, must be fed to one input in the D-type circuit for here the second input gets its information through an inverting gate.

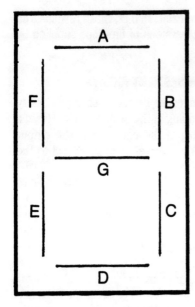

Fig. 13-11. Seven segment array used to form the 10 decimal digits.

appropriate digit. Thus, to form a zero, segments A, B, C, D, E and F light up. Only B and C light up for a 1. Segments light as follows to form the balance of the decimal digits:

- to form a 2: A, B, G, E and D light.
- to form a 3: A, B, G, C and D light,
- to form a 4: F, G, B an C light,
- to form a 5: A, F, G, C and D light;
- to form a 6: A, F, G, E, C and D light;
- to form a 7: A, B and C light;
- to form an 8; A, B, C, D, E, F and G light;
- to form a 9: A, F, B, G, C and D light.

APPLYING DIGITAL TECHNIQUES TO AUDIO CIRCUITS

The arrangement for the class D circuit in Fig. 7-22 can be considered as an AND circuit. Looking first at Fig. 7-21, note that the sawtooth waveform varies from a minimum zero-volt to a peak, V_{MAX}. The half cycle of the sine wave superimposed on the sawtooth works along with the sawtooth to turn on the circuit in Fig. 7-22. When both the sawtooth and sinewave are greater than zero, or are both 1s, current flows through Rc. As both signals must be 1s to turn on Q2, the circuit is in an AND arrangement.

In Fig. 11-14, logic circuits are used to turn on transistors Q10 and Q11 when high voltage is required at the collectors of Q8 and Q9.

I do not know how this is done commercially, but we can easily figure out some logic circuit which should do the job. Considering the upper logic circuit in the figure, a fixed low voltage is applied to it from the $+E_{CCA}$ source. Signal voltage across R_L is also applied to the logic circuit. Voltages are trimmed so that they can be applied safely and reliably. When the voltage across R_L approaches $+E_{CCA}$, the voltages in the logic circuit are so adjusted as to turn on an AND gate. When the output from the gate becomes a 1, its voltage is applied to base of Q10. The higher supply voltage, $+E_{CCB}$, is then applied to the collector of Q8 through Q10. Once the voltage across R_L is reduced somewhat below $+E_{CCA}$, the AND gate in the logic control box is turned off and $+E_{CCA}$ resumes its original function. A similar sequence can be expected to occur in the logic control box at Q11 and Q9.

Two items should be noted. First, the voltage across R_L may vary too quickly to turn Q10 and Q11 on and off with reasonable speed and without unwarranted transients. The voltage across R_L may first be rectified and filtered by a large capacitor before being applied to the logic circuit, to add some undesirable time delay in the action. The second item worthy of note is the use of diodes D1 and D2. The lower supply voltages are applied to the circuit through these diodes. The higher supply voltages are applied to the same points in the circuit. Without these diodes, if $+E_{CCA}$ were connected to the collector of Q10 and $-E_{CCA}$ were connected to the collector of Q11, low voltages would be connected across the higher supply voltages. However, in the circuit shown, when the voltage at Q10 (or Q11) is higher than that of $+E_{CCA}$ (or $-E_{CCA}$), the diodes are reverse biased, cutting off the $+E_{CCA}$ and $-E_{CCA}$ voltages from the balance of the circuit. Only the higher voltages are now applied through Q10 and Q11 to the output transistors.

Time Delay System

Audio Pulse, Inc., is producing a time delay system using digital techniques. It is based on the premise that live music, when played in the concert hall, contains reflections from the floors, walls and ceiling in the hall in which it is being played. In order to recreate this effect, four channel systems have been developed. Here, supposedly reflected sound is reproduced by speakers placed at the rear of the listener in the privacy of his own home. The Audio Pulse system handles this situation or illusion somewhat differently. It reproduces the reflected sound by first encoding the audio signal into pulses of one form or another. These pulses are fed through a time delay circuit such as a shift register. This is essentially a circuit consisting of a series of flip-flops in which the output of one flip-flop is connected to the input of the next one. A number of flip-flops are connected in this fashion. There is a time delay from the moment the pulse enters the first flip-flop until it appears at the output of the last flip-flop. The delayed pulses at the output from the last flip-flop are then reconverted into an audio signal for reproduction.

Recording Sounds on Tape

Digital techniques are also being applied to recording audio sounds on tape. Here, the relative amplitudes of the audio signal are being sampled between 32,000 and 55,000 times each second. The frequency of the sampling depends upon the particular system used by a specific corporation. The relative amplitudes are converted to binary numbers using 1s and 0s. As an example, use the music signal (not sinusoidal) in Fig. 13-12A and Table 13-9. Here, the signal is sampled five times. The signal is placed above a zero level. Now assume the fundamental frequency of the signal is 10,000 Hz and it is being sampled five times so that the sampling frequency is 50,000 Hz. Let us assume that the relative amplitudes are to be sampled in steps which are denoted by four bit numbers. Then only 16 steps are possible. If we let the highest amplitude be represented by a 15, lower amplitudes are represented by numbers between 0 and 14. Table 13-9 shows the digital numbers representing each sampling point in Fig. 13-12A. Each order bit in the binary number (or each column in the binary number) is recorded on a different track of the tape, in the sequence sampled. Thus the digital information for the system can be recorded on a four track tape, starting with point 0 and going to point 5.

This information is usable but not really the ultimate. Actually, the amplitude of the audio signal should be divided into many more

Table 13-10. Relative amplitude for Fig. 13-12B.

Point Sampled	Decimal Representation	Binary Representation
0	44,000	1010101111100000
1	60,000	1110101111100000
2	50,000	1100010101000100
3	24,000	0101111010001000
4	31,500	0111101100001100
5	44,000	1010101111100000

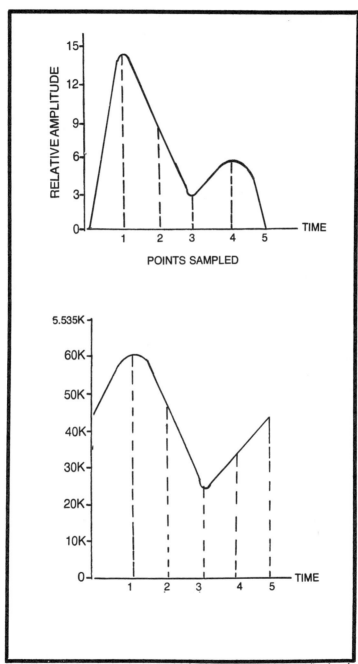

Fig. 13-12A and 13-12B. Sampling methods for conversion from audio signals to digital pulses.

337

than only 15 parts. Various manufacturers divide the amplitude into more pieces using binary numbers with anything between 12 and 16 bits. A sample of a signal can be more accurately defined digitally. The information about the amplitude variations are recorded in sampled sequences, as pulses on 16 tracks of tape. If a digital stereo recording is to be made using this system, 32 tracks are required—16 for each channel.

Regardless of the tape encoding standard used, equal amplitude pulses are recorded on tape. The pulses are retrieved, converted into amplitude gyrations and smoothed to recreate the original audio signal fed to the system.

There are numerous advantages to digital audio recording. Because all pulses are of equal magnitude, they are recorded well above the tape's residual noise level. The pulse can thus easily be retrieved. They are also recorded below the tape saturation level, for the amplitude of the recorded pulses does not limit the dynamic range of the signal. The dynamic range is enhanced by sampling the signal at many amplitude levels (such as at 65,536 levels in Fig. 13-12B) using the largest number of tracks possible (also see Table 13-10). The tape and tape head do not limit the audible frequency range in this system, nor do they produce distortion at the output. These factors are determined by the number of pulses available on the tape, and no other factors. Similarly, audible noise becomes a secondary factor. It is well below the level accepted when using conventional recording techniques. Print-through from one layer of tape to the next layer is unimportant as the signal because print-through is low and the reproducing mechanism will only sample signals that are above a specified amplitude.

Chapter 14
Build It
Yourself

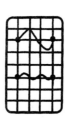

With the daily changes prevalent in electronics, many devices which perform the same function can be made from different types of components. Discrete semiconductors, resistors and capacitors can be used to form audio-applicable circuits. On the other hand, microcircuits can be used. These are aggregates of unseverable electronic components. Microcircuits can take different forms.

Originally, microcircuits were composed of discrete components wired between two parallel-oriented circuit boards. Leads were brought out from this *micromodule* and the package itself was potted. Later on, *hybrid microcircuits* were manufactured. Here, passive components were formed on an insulated foundation while discrete capacitors, transistors and diodes were wired to the assembly. Depending upon the techniques used to form the circuits and chips as well as the final product, these microcircuits were referred to by names such as *multichip*, *thick film* and *thin film*. The final step in the development of the integrated circuit (IC) is the *monolithic IC* where both active and passive components are formed on a semiconductor slab. Whatever microcircuit is used, the manufacturer's ratings and limits must be observed. Heat sinking assemblies, similar to those used when conventional power transistors are applied, should also be utilized for ICs.

Different practical circuits are described below using ICs, discrete devices or combinations of both. Parts to build these circuits are available at large distributors such as Radio Shack, Lafayette Radio, Electronic City, Burstein Applebee, Newark Electronics and so on. Other suppliers of components can be located through ads in the popular electronics magazines. Some difficult to attain semiconductors may be listed for a particular circuit. It should be no problem to the builder to get readily available equivalents under the Motorola HEP label, the RCA SK label, the Sylvania ECG label and so on.

All circuits can be built on ordinary perforated boards which are stocked at many radio parts stores. Power devices should be mounted on heat sinks. Flat metal heat sinks or specially designed devices with fins can be used. In either case, the sink should be mounted vertically. If the heat sink has fins, the fins should be vertical. The orientation should allow for the circulation of air, considering that heat rises. Air should be available to both sides of the sink.

PROJECT ONE: REGULATED VARIABLE-VOLTAGE POWER SUPPLY

Diodes D1 and D2 are in a full wave power supply circuit developing a positive voltage, with respect to ground, across the 1000 uf filter capacitor, C1 (Fig. 14-1). In a similar arrangement, a negative voltage is developed across C2 due to current flowing through D3 and D4. The negative voltage is applied through R2 to germanium diodes D5 and D6, turning them on. It is also applied through R3 to turn on the zener diode, D7. While diodes D5 and D6 keep the emitter of Q3 at a fixed voltage (about $-0.5V$ with respect to ground), the zener diode keeps the voltage at its anode fixed at about -10 volts.

Positive voltage across capacitor C1 is applied to the collectors of Q1 and Q2. It is filtered further and also applied to the collector of Q3 and the base of Q2 through resistors R6 and R7. Current flows through the Q1– Q2 Darlington pair due to the current applied to the base of Q2 through R6 and R7. Current from Q1 is also at the regulated DC output terminals. It flows through a load connected across these terminals. A voltage is developed across this load. This voltage is also applied across the series circuit consisting of potentiometer R8, resistor R9 and zener diode D7. Base current of Q3 is varied by changing the setting of R8. The collector current of Q3 varies along with its base current, adjusting the base current left to flow into Q2. The regulated output voltage varies with the base current available for Q2. Once R8 is set, base voltage at Q3 (and hence at Q2), change only as the regulated voltage changes. This change can be due to either line voltage variations, load variations or both. These minute base current changes cause the output voltage to readjust to the desired fixed value. Output voltage can be measured through use of the circuit consisting of the 1 mA meter movement and the 30,000 ohm, 1% resistor.

When building this power supply, all parts should be mounted on an ordinary perforated board, with the exception of Q1. Q1 should be mounted on a flat metal surface, 14 inches square or larger. A heat sink with O_{SA} of 7.5 or less can be used instead.

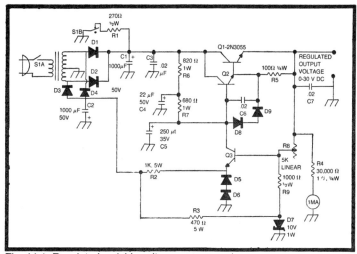

Fig. 14-1. Regulated variable-voltage power supply.

A DPST on-off power switch, S1A-S1B, is shown in Fig. 14-1. Section S1B is used to discharge capacitor C1 so that no voltage will be at the output when the power is switched off. If this feature is not required, resistor R1 and section S1B of the switch can be omitted.

As for the transistors, the equivalent of RCA types 2N3055 and TIP-29 can be used for Q1 and Q2, respectively. The equivalent of GE 2N3393 can be used for Q3. Diodes D1, D2, D3 and D4 are 1A, 200 PIV (or more) silicon rectifiers, such as the 1N4003, while D5 and D6 are germanium junction devices similar to the newer type of 1N-34. Diodes D8 and D9 are low-voltage silicon devices. Here, low-voltage, low-current diodes such as the 1N914 can be used, although devices in the 1N4000 series will serve as well. The transformer should have a 54 or 60 volt center-tapped secondary winding rated at at least 0.5 amperes. The Stancor type P8198 can be used. Just ignore the 6.3 volt winding. All .02 capacitors can be of the 500-volt disc ceramic variety. These components are included in the circuit in the interest of maintaining stability.

PROJECT TWO: 9-VOLT REGULATED POWER SUPPLY

The function of this circuit is similar in many respects to the one in Fig. 14-1, except here the regulated output voltage is fixed at 9 volts (Fig. 14-2). The 10K trimmer pot across the output terminals is used to permanently set this voltage to the desired 9 volts. Stancor's P-8395, 24 volt, 200 mA transformer with a center-tapped secondary can be used to supply the proper voltage to operate this supply. Transistor TIP-29 is used to extend the current

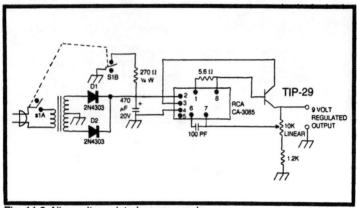

Fig. 14-2. Nine-volt regulated power supply.

capabilities of the IC to that of the transformer. The transistor should be mounted on at least a 10 inch square metal surface to optimize the thermal resistance of the physical arrangement. The balance of the circuit can be built on an ordinary perforated board.

PROJECT THREE: PREAMPLIFIER
FOR USE WITH A DYNAMIC MICROPHONE

Using two low noise transistors, the preamplifier shown in Fig. 14-3 can be fed from a microphone using a dynamic cartridge. The output can be applied to an auxiliary input on a hi-fi or PA amplifier. Q1 is a high gain preamplifier stage while Q2 is a low output impedance emitter follower. The circuit should be powered either from a 9-volt battery or from a low ripple power supply. Gain can be varied by increasing or decreasing the 150 ohm resistor in the emitter of Q1, as required.

PROJECT FOUR: PREAMPLIFIER
FOR USE WITH A CERAMIC MICROPHONE

The microphone preamplifier in Fig. 14-4 looks very much like the one in Fig. 14-3. Here, however, an N-channel FET is used as the input stage. This presents a high impedance to the microphone. This high impedance must be presented to a microphone using the conventional crystal or ceramic cartridge, if low frequencies are not to be lost due to the low capacity of the cartridge itself, coupled to a low impedance input circuit.

As for the JFET, the 2N4303 is shown. Motorola HEP type 801 or 802 can be used instead. And HEP type 726 can be a substitute for the 2N3391A.

342

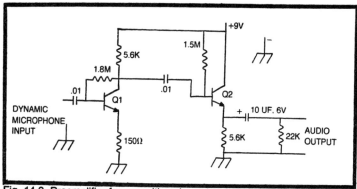

Fig. 14-3. Preamplifier for use with a dynamic microphone.

All preamplifiers—the one here as well as the one in Fig. 14-3—are subject to hum pickup. All leads connecting to and from the preamplifier should be short and preferably shielded. Keep the preamplifier away from a power source supplying AC currents and voltages. If possible, the preamplifiers should be mounted in a metal shielded container.

PROJECT FIVE:
IC POWER AMPLIFIER WITH ABOUT 0.5 WATTS OUTPUT

The power amplifier in Fig. 14-5 is easy to build. It does not require a heat sink due to the low power that both the chip dissipates (up to about 0.5 watt) and the circuit can deliver. Despite its simplicity, the output from the circuit is clean.

The output transformer should be specified and selected carefully. The full primary should present about 130 ohms to the chip at

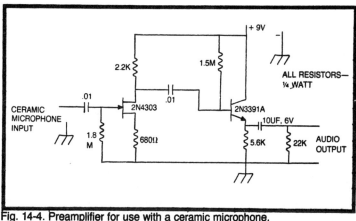

Fig. 14-4. Preamplifier for use with a ceramic microphone.

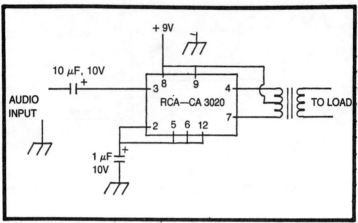

Fig. 14-5. IC power amplifier with about 0.5 watts output.

its output terminals, 4 and 7. If an 8-ohm load is to be used, the impedance ratio of the primary to the secondary winding of the transformer should be about 130 ohms to 8 ohms. Should a 4-ohm load be used, the impedance ratio is obviously 130 ohms to 4 ohms. In either case, the primary should be center-tapped. Transformers such as the Stancor TA-42 or Triad TY-45X can be used. They have a 500 ohm center-tapped primary winding with 4, 8 and 16 ohm secondaries. The impedance ratio of this transformer, 500:16, is about the same as the required, 130:4, for a 4 ohm load. Should an 8 ohm load be used, the 150:12 impedance ratio Stancor transformer TA-39 or Triad transformer TY-48X, can be used. With the 100 ohm to 8 ohm ratio (150:12 = 100:8), these transformers are as close as we can get to the required 130 ohm:8 ohm ratio with a readily available component. The output load of this amplifier can be a loudspeaker.

PROJECT SIX: HIGH POWER AUDIO AMPLIFIER

Should a good quality high output power amplifier be required, the circuit in Fig. 14-6 can be used. This is a practical version of the circuit shown in Fig. 11-8. The output transistors must be mounted on a heat sink with a thermal resistance of less than 3°C/watt. This means that a sink similar to the Wakefield 623A or K should do the job. As an alternate, a ⅛ inch thick aluminum plate can be used with an area of about 100 inches squared on each side. The 2N5320 and 2N5322 driver transistors also require some type of heat sinking. The Wakefield 296-4 can be clipped to each of these transistors to perform this function. Drivers as well as the balance of the circuit

344

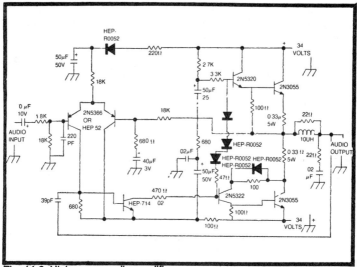

Fig. 14-6. High power audio amplifier.

can be mounted on ordinary perforated boards. The output signal can be used to drive a 4 or 8 ohm loudspeaker with up to 40 watts.

PROJECTS SEVEN AND EIGHT:
TONE CONTROL AND PHONO PREAMPLIFIER WITH EQUALIZATION

A practical Baxendall Tone Control circuit is drawn in Fig. 14-7 while two amplifying circuits that can be used to compensate for the phono cartridge and record equalization are in Figs. 14-8A and 14-8B. Each circuit with the exception of the one operational

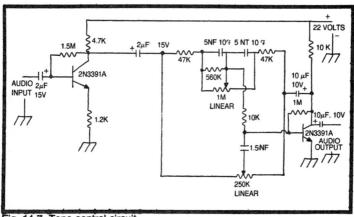

Fig. 14-7. Tone control circuit.

amplifier IC has been described in the text. Each circuit should be mounted on a perforated board. Confine the parts to a small area, and possibly within a shielded box, so the chances of picking up stray signals and hum interference will be minimized. As for the integrated circuit, an ordinary operational amplifier is used with RIAA compensated feedback. In each circuit, all resistors are ¼ watt (5%) and the capacitors in the feedback loop should be 10% components.

PROJECT NINE: GENERAL PURPOSE AUDIO VOLTAGE AMPLIFIER

The circuit in Fig. 14-9 is a straightforward audio amplifier built around an operational amplifier. The 1 megohm potentiometer can

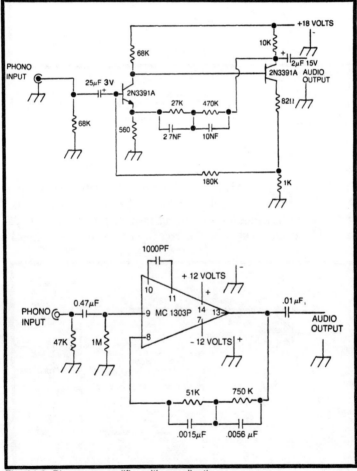

Fig. 14-8. Phono preamplifier with equalization.

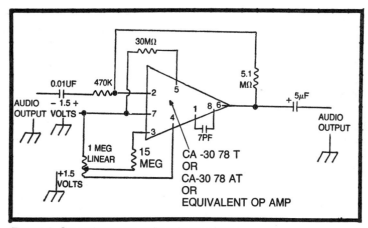

Fig. 14-9. General purpose audio voltage amplifier.

be used to adjust for any deviation from zero DC volts between pin #6 and ground, when no signal is applied to the audio input. This circuit is quite versatile. It can be used as is, or with tone control, phono, tape, loudness or any other type of frequency compensating network.

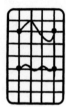

Index